SIR WINSTON CHURCHILL HIGH SCHOOL

Scandium	Sc	21	45.0
Selenium	Se	34	79.0
Silicon	Si	14	28.1
Silver	Ag	47	107.9
Sodium	Na	11	23.0
Strontium	Sr	38	87.6
Sulfur	S	16	32.1
Tantalum	Ta	73	180.9
Technetium	Tc	43	(97)
Tellurium	Te	52	127.6
Terbium	Tb	65	158.9
Thallium	Tl	81	204.4
Thorium	Th	90	232.0
Thulium	Tm	69	168.9
Tin	Sn	50	118.7
Titanium	Ti	22	47.9
Tungsten (Wolfram)	W	74	183.8
Uranium	U	92	238.0
Vanadium	V	23	50.9
Xenon	Xe	54	131.3
Ytterbium	Yb	70	173.0
Yttrium	Y	39	88.9
Zinc	Zn	30	65.4
Zirconium	Zr	40	91.2
Unnilquadium	Unq	104**	(260)
Unnilpentium	Unp	105	(262)
Unnilhexium	Unh	106	
Unnilseptium	Uns	107	

*The names and symbols of elements 104 and 105 have not yet been agreed upon internationally.

Erbium	Er	68	167.3
Europium	Eu	63	152.0
Fermium	Fm	100	(253)
Fluorine	F	9	19.0
Francium	Fr	87	(223)
Gadolinium	Gd	64	157.2
Gallium	Ga	31	69.7
Germanium	Ge	32	72.6
Gold	Au	79	197.0
Hafnium	Hf	72	178.5
Helium	He	2	4.00
Holmium	Ho	67	164.9
Hydrogen	H	1	1.008
Indium	In	49	114.8
Iodine	I	53	126.9
Iridium	Ir	77	192.2
Iron	Fe	26	55.8
Krypton	Kr	36	83.8
Lanthanum	La	57	138.9
Lawrencium	Lr	103	(256)
Lead	Pb	82	207.2
Lithium	Li	3	6.94
Lutetium	Lu	71	175.0
Magnesium	Mg	12	24.3
Manganese	Mn	25	54.9
Mendelevium	Md	101	(257)
Mercury	Hg	80	200.6

*A value given in parentheses denotes the mass of the isotope with the longest known half-life

CHEMISTRY TODAY

SECOND EDITION

CHEMISTRY TODAY, Second Edition

Components: **Student Text**
Laboratory Manual
Teacher's Guide

R.L. Whitman
Vice-Principal, Queen Elizabeth High School

E.E. Zinck
Dean of Science, Acadia University

R.A. Nalepa
Head of Science Department, Halifax West High School

CHEMISTRY TODAY

SECOND EDITION

PRENTICE-HALL CANADA INC., Scarborough, Ontario

To our wives: Gwen, Chérie, Lin.

Canadian Cataloguing in Publication Data

Whitman, R.L. (Ronald Laurie), 1944-
Chemistry today

For use in secondary schools.
Includes index.

ISBN 0-13-129544-6

1. Chemistry.   I. Zinck, E. E., 1938-
II. Nalepa, R. A. (Robert Allan), 1948-
III. Title.

QD31.2.W57 1982   540   C81-095018-9

Supplementary Material: Laboratory Manual and Teacher's Guide

Prentice-Hall, Inc., Englewood Cliffs, New Jersey
Prentice-Hall International, Inc., London
Prentice-Hall of Australia, Pty., Ltd., Sydney
Prentice-Hall of India Pvt., Ltd., New Delhi
Prentice-Hall of Japan, Inc., Tokyo
Prentice-Hall of Southeast Asia (PTE) Ltd., Singapore

ISBN 0-13-129544-6

 Metric Commission Canada has granted use of the National Symbol
for Metric Conversion.

Design: Julian Cleva
Production Editor: Olga V. Domján

Printed and bound in Canada by Bryant Press
Typesetting by Alpha Graphics Limited

Cover Photograph: Strathcona Refinery (Photo courtesy of
Imperial Oil Limited)

Contents

Acknowledgements

We would like to begin by thanking our publishers, Prentice-Hall Canada Inc., many of whose staff members have helped us since the inception of CHEMISTRY TODAY. These staff members include John Perigoe, Rob Greenaway, Rand Paterson, Veronica Orocio, Steve Lane, Ken Kosow, Sharon Lindala, and Olga Domján. We especially thank Olga for her valuable assistance during the final crucial months preceding publication of the Second Edition.

It is an impossible task for us to completely acknowledge our debt to all those who aided us in one way or another in the revision of CHEMISTRY TODAY. Many teachers and students gave us valuable comments and suggestions based on their experiences with the first edition, as did the helpful staff at Prentice-Hall. We thank them all for their contributions, and we accept responsibility for any flaws that still remain. We also thank Ada Crosby for her assistance in checking the galley proofs and Ralph Kolewe for his help in preparing the glossary.

Finally, we give special thanks to our wives. Their patience and long-suffering, during our many absences from home for the two and a half years it took us to complete this book, were indispensable. Without their support we would have been unable to complete our task.

R. L. Whitman
E. E. Zinck
R. A. Nalepa
Wolfville, N.S.

Preface

CHEMISTRY TODAY is a program for the first year of chemistry in Canadian high schools. CHEMISTRY TODAY has two basic aims: to introduce students to the fundamental principles of chemistry, and to show them how chemistry affects their lives. It is an introduction to the principles and applications of chemistry for students who will pursue further studies in chemistry as well as for those who will take only one chemistry course.

For students who will study chemistry again, CHEMISTRY TODAY is designed to provide a basic foundation for future studies in secondary and post-secondary institutions. For other students, this book may be their first and last look at chemistry. Nevertheless, we hope that they will gain an understanding and appreciation of the nature of chemistry and the methods by which chemical knowledge is acquired.

Our goal in writing this text has been to be clear and concise and yet to include all necessary topics in sufficient detail to explain them clearly. CHEMISTRY TODAY develops an understanding of basic principles and continues to build on these in a logical manner.

The text begins with a general description of science and the scientific method. The second chapter provides an introduction to measuring and problem-solving in chemistry. The factor-label method is introduced here and is used consistently throughout the book as a means of solving problems.

Chapters 3 to 10 follow a relatively traditional pattern of developing such chemical concepts as matter, atomic theory, the periodic table, chemical bonding, chemical nomenclature, the liquid phase and chemical reactions. Chapters 11 and 12 are comprehensive chapters of descriptive chemistry. The former deals with hydrogen, oxygen and water, and the latter covers the chemistry of the alkali metals and the halogens.

Most of the mathematical topics are contained in Chapters 13 to 15. Chapter 13 illustrates the use of the mole concept in chemistry while Chapter 14 introduces the gas laws. Finally, Chapter 15 extends the mole concept to situations in which gases are involved as reactants or products.

Chapters 16 to 19 (Organic Chemistry, Biochemistry, Chemistry and Industry, and Nuclear Chemistry) deal with chemical topics which are useful, interesting and relevant to today's students.

A detailed discusssion of all the chapters can be found in the *Teacher's Guide*.

Although CHEMISTRY TODAY was written with a one-year course in mind, it is not intended that all chapters be covered. There is more than enough material here for an introductory chemistry course. There are also certain topics that have been included in order to challenge the more capable students. We have included all of this material in order to make the text suitable for the needs of teachers with varying teaching styles and ways of organizing courses as well as students of different abilities, goals and interests.

The subject matter is presented in a logical manner. However, the presentation is flexible enough to enable teachers to use alternative chapter orders and to omit certain chapters altogether. For example, Chapters 13 to 15 explore the more mathematical topics of the mole and gases. These chapters could easily be omitted by those desiring a less rigorously mathematical approach. Other teachers may prefer a less descriptive approach and omit such sections as Chapters 11 and 12 or 16 to 19. A more complete description of how to utilize this text can be found in the Teacher's Guide. We hope that CHEMISTRY TODAY will be a book that teachers can use without feeling restricted by a limited choice of topics.

The authors believe that an extremely important part of a student's study of chemistry is laboratory work. Chemistry is an experimental science and thus, to understand chemistry fully, students must be involved in actual investigation. To this end, the Laboratory Manual contains approximately 50 class-tested experiments related to the student text. These labs are an integral part of the program and are designed to provide students with practical experience in a laboratory as well as to teach them skills in observation, inquiry and analysis of concepts.

Before beginning work on this revision, the authors and publishers asked many teachers and students for suggestions about how CHEMISTRY TODAY could be improved. Based on the response, the Second Edition was prepared with the same fundamental goals as the First Edition. Thus, this revision retains the approach, style and organization of the original.

A comparison of the text with the earlier edition shows that CHEMISTRY TODAY has been almost completely rewritten. There are five new chapters:
—Measurement in Chemistry (Ch. 2)
—Bonding in the Solid Phase (Ch. 7)
—Two Elements and a Compound: Hydrogen, Oxygen and Water (Ch. 11)
—Two Chemical Families: The Alkali Metals and the Halogens (Ch. 12)
—Chemistry and Industry (Ch. 18)
Several internal revisions have also been made in the text:
—The introductory chapter has been rewritten to place more emphasis on the reasons for studying chemistry.
—Chapter 3, Matter, contains new sections on changes in the states of matter, the Law of Multiple Proportions, and the discovery of the elements.
—Chapters 4 and 5 have been completely revised so that atomic theory and periodic law can be studied in terms of either energy levels or the more modern wave mechanical model. A knowledge of atomic orbital theory is not required for an understanding of the rest of the book.
—Chapter 6, Chemical Bonding, has been reorganized and rewritten. Some new material has been added on VSEPR theory and coordinate bonding.
—Chapter 9, The Liquid Phase and Solutions, features an expanded treatment of liquids. In addition, water pollution is treated as an application of the liquid phase and solutions.
—Chapter 10, Chemical Reactions, has been extensively rewritten.
—Chapter 13, The Mole and Its Use, includes new sections in limiting reagents and concentration.

—Chapter 14, Gases, features new material on the behaviour of real gases, as well on environmental pollution in the atmosphere.

—There is also much new material in Chapters 16, 17 and 19.

The following are some of the other changes featured in the Second Edition of CHEMISTRY TODAY:

—In addition to the 5 new chapters, the revision features a more comprehensive treatment of major topics.

—*Real World Examples*: Wherever possible, the new edition relates the principles of chemistry to the everyday world.

—*Practice and Reinforcement*: Improved and increased assignment material is provided:

    i) questions—additional end-of-chapter questions have been added to challenge the more capable students.

    ii) problems—more problems have been added.

—*Readability:* The reading level has been carefully controlled in the revision, keeping the needs of students in mind. Attention has been paid to vocabulary and sentence length.

—*Improved Format*: The new edition features a format designed to make the material more readable. A more open, single-column format permits effective use of the margins for illustrations. In addition, there is generous use of the new second colour (blue). Furthermore, many more line drawings and photographs appear in the second edition than in the first.

—*Topic Development*: Lengthy sections have been broken down into subheadings to help students follow the topic development more easily.

—*Reinforcements of New Terms and Concepts*: New terms are now printed in blue when they are first introduced and defined. A list of key terms appears at the end of each chapter, along with a summary of major concepts. As well, a glossary is provided at the end of the text, before the index.

—*Key Objectives*: The student learning objectives at the beginning of each chapter now highlight only the major goals in order to enable students to focus on the most important objectives of the chapter.

—*Reference Appendices*: The number of appendices has been greatly expanded.

—*Laboratory Manual*: The lab manual has undergone a number of changes in the new edition. Some new experiments have been added and many of those that have been retained have been rewritten to allow concepts to be investigated more effectively. In addition, greater emphasis has been placed on safety in the laboratory.

A number of additional features have been employed in the text to increase reader comprehension. These are listed on page xiv.

It is our feeling that an introductory chemistry course can be a valuable, interesting, and enjoyable part of anyone's educational experience, and we hope that CHEMISTRY TODAY helps students enjoy their introduction to chemistry.

R.L.W.
E.E.Z.
R.A.N.

Prentice-Hall Canada Inc., Educational Book Division, and the authors of CHEMISTRY TODAY, Second Edition are committed to the publication of instructional materials that are as bias-free as possible. This text was evaluated for bias prior to publication.

The authors and publisher of this book also recognize the importance of appropriate reading levels and have therefore made every effort to ensure the highest possible degree of readability in the text. The content has been selected, organized, and written at a level suitable to the intended audience. Standard readability tests have been applied at several stages in the text's preparation to ensure an appropriate reading level.

Readability tests, however, can provide only a rough indication of a book's reading level. Research indicates that readability is affected by much more than word or sentence length; factors such as presentation, format and design, none of which are considered in the usual readability tests, also greatly influence the ease with which students read a book.

One other important factor affecting readability is the extent to which the text is motivational for students. Thus, the following features were incorporated into this book to further increase reader comprehension. (Page references are given to provide examples of most features.)

— *Real World Examples*: Wherever possible, the text relates the theory to the everyday world, motivating students and making the content more meaningful by showing that applications of chemistry are everywhere. In addition, some applications of chemistry are developed in major sections or entire chapters. Examples include water pollution (Chapter 9), air pollution (Chapter 14), organic chemistry (Chapter 16), biochemistry (Chapter 17), industrial chemistry (Chapter 18), and nuclear chemistry (Chapter 19).

— *Questions and Problems*: The text offers abundant questions and problems. End-of-chapter questions and problems are designed for review, extension and application. Step-by-step solutions to sample problems are integrated into relevant chapters (e.g., p. 65, pp. 320-321). Simple drill and practice problems follow the sample problems for immediate reinforcement (e.g., pp. 94-95). Answers are provided for these problems as study aids for students.

— *Attractive Format*: An attractive format will appeal to students and encourage the use of the book. The text features an uncluttered single-column format. In addition, generous use is made of second colour.

— *Numerous Illustrations*: Over 250 line drawings and photographs provide visual reinforcement of the printed word.

— *Topic Development*: Chapters are divided into clearly-marked major sections. Lengthy sections are further broken down into subsections to help students to follow the development of a particular topic more easily.

— *New Terms*: Terms are printed in blue and defined in context when introduced.

— *Chapter Openings*: Each chapter opens with an introduction which arouses student interest and describes the topics to be developed (e.g., p. 70, p. 414).

— *Student Learning Aims*: A list of major student learning aims follows the introduction. These are designed to enable students to focus on the key ideas of the chapter (e.g., p. 16, p. 198).

— *Chapter Conclusions*: Each chapter ends with a brief overview of the major parts of the chapter, a list of the key terms, and questions and problems (e.g., pp. 66-69, pp. 253-255).

— *End of Text*: The book concludes with a number of useful appendices, a glossary of terms, and a comprehensive index.

— *Biographies*: Brief biographies of important chemists are located throughout the text to help show students that chemistry is a human pursuit (e.g. p. 76, p. 469).

1

The Science Called Chemistry

Thousands of Canadians earn a living working with the science called chemistry. They work for industry, for government, and for schools, colleges, and universities. Some of them try to increase the amount of chemical knowledge. Others use their knowledge of chemistry to make items for industries. Still others try to pass their knowledge of chemistry on to their students. These people are scientists, engineers, and educators.

What is science? What is the science called chemistry? Why do so many people enjoy working with chemistry? What are these people like? Are they different from the rest of us? What skills do they need? What methods do they use? Most important of all, is a study of chemistry worth the effort?

We attempt to answer these questions in this chapter. Of course, the answers that we can give in this introductory chapter only scratch the surface. Better answers to these questions come while you actually work with and study chemistry yourself. In the first section we attempt to answer the question, Is a study of chemistry worth the effort?

Key Objectives

When you have finished studying this chapter, you should be able to
1. name and describe the type of knowledge upon which science is based.
2. describe the general nature of chemistry and its place among the sciences.
3. list the steps in the traditional scientific method, and explain why methods other than the traditional scientific method are appropriate for the investigation of nature.
4. list and explain three requirements of scientific observation.
5. explain the difference between a law, a theory, and a model, and identify examples of each.

1-1 Why Study Chemistry?

Fig. 1-1 Chemical Complex at Redwater, Alberta. (Photo courtesy of Imperial Oil Limited)

When students are asked why they take a chemistry course, they usually give reasons that are chosen from a fairly short list. A few students take a chemistry

Fig. 1-2 A University Chemistry Laboratory

course because they already know something about chemistry, and they enjoy it. Other students study chemistry because they generally do well in science courses, and they expect to succeed in chemistry also.

However, the most common reason is, ''I need the course.'' Chemistry is a necessary course for many areas of study such as nursing, medicine, engineering, and some other sciences. Chemistry is also necessary for some programs given at technical schools. A few students need another course to round out their high school program, and they take chemistry because they do not like the other available courses.

However, even if you do not need chemistry, we think there are some good reasons for taking a chemistry course. In the following subsections, we present some of these reasons.

Chemistry Affects Our Lives

To live in the modern world is to be surrounded by the products of chemistry. We all make use of these products. Synthetic fibres such as nylon and polyesters are used to make clothing, carpeting, and many other useful items. Plastics seem to be used all around us. Grooming products such as deodorants, soaps, and hair sprays are products of chemistry. In fact, the list of chemicals found in our homes seems endless.

Some chemicals are useful; however, care must be taken when they are used. Sodium nitrite is added to cured meats such as hot dogs and ham to improve colour and to stop the growth of the bacterium which causes a dangerous type of food poisoning (botulism). However, sodium nitrite reacts with other substances in our bodies to produce products which could be harmful.

Thus, its use as a food additive must be closely watched. Hexachlorophene is a useful germicide (a substance used to destroy germs) which is used in hospitals and is included in some deodorants, mouthwashes, and cosmetics. However, hexachlorophene can be absorbed through healthy human skin, and it causes brain damage in rats and monkeys. Thus, hexachlorophene must be used with care. Drain cleaners are necessary in our homes to clear clogs in pipes. However, most drain cleaners contain a very corrosive substance, sodium hydroxide. We must be careful in our own use of drain cleaners and keep them away from children.

Occasionally, a basic knowledge of chemistry could have prevented people from making a tragic mistake. Families have died because they used a charcoal barbecue inside their homes. They did not know that burning charcoal gives off the odourless poisonous gas, carbon monoxide. Charcoal barbecues should not be used indoors. Farmers have died from breathing too much of the foul gas coming from pig manure. Its characteristic rotten-egg odour was caused by the extremely poisonous gas, hydrogen sulfide. People have been injured when they mixed bleach with acid-containing substances such as toilet bowl cleaners. They thought that the bleach and the cleaner would do twice as good a cleaning job. They did not know that bleach reacts with acids to produce toxic, irritating chlorine gas.

A knowledge of chemistry will probably not alter the course of your life, but it may help you to avoid making a bad mistake. At the very least, a knowledge of chemistry will teach you to be cautious when you use any of the chemical products available to you.

Chemistry and Our Environment

For centuries, we have attempted to alter our environment to improve our quality of life. Will we be able to continue to modify the natural environment to suit ourselves? It appears that many of the things we have been doing to improve our lives are starting to threaten us.

Products of chemistry such as medicines, pesticides, and plastics have allowed us to live better and longer lives. However, this has not been done without cost. Many of the chemical plants that make these important products have been guilty of poisoning the surrounding environment. As a society, we are overusing drugs such as tranquilizers and alcohol. The use of pesticides (substances used to destroy such pests as troublesome insects or plants) has improved the productivity of our farms. However, some pesticides are proving to be more dangerous than we would like them to be. The insecticide D.D.T. enabled India to begin its "green revolution" (an attempt to vastly increase food production), but it caused the near-extinction of several species of birds before it was banned. The increased use of plastics has placed a further strain on our decreasing supply of fossil fuels from which plastics are made.

Chemistry is a study for those people who want a deeper knowledge of their environment than most people possess. The environmental problems facing us are numerous. Chemistry is an excellent training ground for the type of person we will need if we are to solve these problems.

Making Choices

Every day we are exposed to the claims of advertisers: "It helps keep you drier," or "It maintains the hair's normal pH balance." We hear conflicting or confusing statements that are supposed to come from scientists. For example, some scientists have said that we will need the electricity from nuclear power plants. Other scientists have disagreed; they insist that nuclear power stations are not safe enough. Some scientists have said that putting fluorides in drinking water to reduce tooth decay is a good thing. Again, other scientists have disagreed. It is difficult for many citizens to have reasoned opinions regarding the complex, science-related issues of our times.

Nevertheless, decisions are being made which affect the use of our environment every day. If we are to make intelligent decisions, we have to know the facts on each side of the questions. If our knowledge is weak, we are at a disadvantage, and we are easy to manipulate.

Perhaps it would be pleasant to return to a less complex life style. However, we are citizens of one of the most technologically advanced countries in the world. We owe it to ourselves to become acquainted with the realities of modern life. Science is one of the most important of those realities. The first prime minister of India, Jawaharlal Nehru, said: "The future belongs to science and to those who make friends with science."

Many of the science-related issues that we face have a chemical basis. In order to understand the facts in these chemical issues, you will have to learn the basic principles of chemistry. With this knowledge you will be better able to make decisions and choices.

In the next section, we will answer two questions. What is science? Where does chemistry fit within science?

1-2 The Place of Chemistry In Science

The word science is derived from the Latin word *scientia*, which means knowledge. **Science** is a human activity which is directed toward increasing our knowledge about the composition and behaviour of matter, both living and nonliving. Matter is the material which makes up the universe. Scientific knowledge is mainly empirical knowledge. **Empirical knowledge** is knowledge gained by using the senses (Fig. 1-3), by seeing, tasting, feeling, hearing, or smelling. Do our senses provide us with an accurate picture of the real world, or does empirical knowledge create the illusion of a world that exists only in our minds? While philosophers debate this question, scientists brush it aside. They make the basic assumption that the world is real, that people are real, and that observation using our senses gives us accurate knowledge of nature.

The Types of Knowledge

Thus, scientific knowledge is gained from observation, and it is therefore empirical. Other types of knowledge are revealed, authoritative, rational, and intuitive.

Fig. 1-3 This decomposition of ammonium dichromate provides an example of empirical knowledge. We can easily *see* that a chemical reaction is occurring.

Revealed knowledge is knowledge we accept on faith. The most widely circulated source of revealed knowledge is the Bible. Millions of people accept what is written in the Bible as a matter of faith. They believe that the authors of the Bible received knowledge from God.

Authoritative knowledge is knowledge that we gain from experts. For example, when we want to learn about legal matters, we consult lawyers. When we want to install new electrical circuits in our homes, we consult electricians. Other sources of authoritative knowledge include textbooks, journals, and encyclopedias.

Rational knowledge is knowledge based on what we consider to be logical truths. For example, geometry is based on a number of axioms (also called postulates) such as the axiom of equality: "Things that are equal to the same thing are equal to each other." These axioms are not actually proven. They are accepted because they are logically acceptable—they seem obvious to everyone. Thus, geometry is largely a product of rational knowledge.

Intuitive knowledge is knowledge that people already possess without knowing where it came from. Perhaps a politician intuitively feels that he should call an election. It is not that his advisors have suggested that the time is right to call an election (authoritative knowledge). It is not that he has had a vision in which he is told to call the election (revealed knowledge). It is not that the opinion polls suggest that he is ahead of his rivals in popularity (empirical knowledge). It is not that he has analyzed the strengths and weaknesses of his party and the pros and cons of going to the voters, reaching the conclusion that he should call the election (rational knowledge). It is just that his years of serving the public have sharpened his instincts regarding the public mood. He feels that the time is right to call the election, but he cannot tell you the exact source of this feeling (intuitive knowledge).

Occasionally the different types of knowledge lead to conflicting conclusions regarding a subject or event. For example, ancient philosophers believed that it was rational to expect a large rock to fall faster than a small one. However, empirical observation showed that they fell at the same rate. Some philosophers rejected the empirical evidence. They would not accept empirical knowledge when it conflicted with rational knowledge. However, others did accept the observations. When they accepted the empirical evidence over what many felt to be rational knowledge, these people were behaving as scientists. Observation is the main activity of science, and the belief in the ability of careful observation to yield accurate information is shared by all scientists.

Science is Not...

Let us now establish what science is not. Science is not the telephone or the Dacron® shirt or the plastic heart valve. In short, science is not gadgetry. Gadgets, in many cases, have improved our lives. In most instances, these improvements have been made possible by scientific knowledge. However, gadgets do not constitute science.

Many accomplishments of science appear to be mysterious to those who are not directly involved in it. Thus, some people regard it as a sort of modern-day witchcraft. These people look at scientific advances with some fear. On the other hand, some people, noting the accomplishments of science, have unreasonably high expectations of it. They expect instant solutions for problems that scientists presently find unsolvable. Scientists can make great contributions in the fields of human welfare and knowledge, but science has not been able to solve all the problems of people. Science is neither a cure-all nor witchcraft.

Finally, science is not merely technology. Technology is directed towards the accomplishment of specific purposes. Getting a person on the moon and building a nuclear power station are examples of technology. It is true that to a large extent technology depends on scientific knowledge, and in a converse manner, technological problems often stimulate scientific research. However, science is more than just technology.

Science and Technology

Thus, there are two branches of science. First, **pure science** reveals to people the nature of the universe. It helps to expand our knowledge and our understanding. The second branch is **applied science** (also called **technology**). Applied science is the application of scientific discoveries to practical problems (Fig. 1-4). The large number of ways in which our comfort, convenience, and health have been enhanced by the use of applied science indicates the importance of this branch of science. However, we must realize that pure science is an essential basis for technology. (Is technology an essential basis for pure science?) For example, pure research revealed that the addition of sulfur to rubber improved the durability of the rubber. This information now forms the basis of the process of vulcanization. Vulcanization is part of the technology associated with the rubber industry. In this book, the word *science* will be used to mean pure science or pure research. The word *technology* will denote applied science.

Fig. 1-4 A Canadian Cancer Therapy Machine. Atomic Energy of Canada Limited (AECL) has been the pacesetter in the development of radiation equipment for cancer therapy. (Photo courtesy of Princess Margaret Hospital)

The Branches of Science

Science is divided into a number of disciplines. Among these are biology, chemistry, geology, and physics. This division is an artificial one, and the scientific disciplines are all very much alike and related. In fact, sometimes it is difficult to distinguish between physical chemistry and chemical physics, or between biochemistry and molecular biology.

However, the divisions have been made because it is really impossible for one person to be a master of all science. Thus, scientists have been forced to specialize. Many of them specialize because of necessity rather than desire.

Let us examine the place of chemistry in science. Think of a ladder (Fig. 1-5, overleaf). At the bottom of the ladder, on the first rung, is mathematics. Mathematics is not really a science since it does not depend on empirical knowledge as the other sciences do. It depends more on rational knowledge. Mathematicians have selected for study only a limited number of concepts such as number and order.

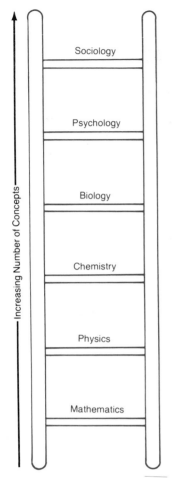

Fig. 1-5 The Science Ladder

Sociology

Psychology

Biology

Chemistry

Physics

Mathematics

Increasing Number of Concepts

Physics is placed on the rung above mathematics. Physics takes the ideas of mathematics and adds further concepts selected from the real world. Matter, energy, and electricity are some of the concepts that physics adds to those of mathematics.

By including more concepts such as the different kinds of matter and the transformation of one type of matter to another, we arrive at the next rung. Chemistry is placed on this rung. **Chemistry** is the science which deals with the composition, structure, and properties of matter and with the transformations which matter undergoes. Chemistry makes use of all the concepts of mathematics and physics. Chemistry and physics are two of the sciences which study nonliving matter. They are called physical sciences. Geology is another physical science.

Let us go up the ladder in order. If we further select the concept of living matter, we leave the physical sciences and enter the area of biology, and if we go one step further to mental behaviour, we are dealing with psychology. If we keep adding more concepts selected from the real world, we come to the social sciences, such as economics and sociology.

In the next section, we will see how scientists do their work, the rules that they follow, and some of their distinguishing characteristics.

1-3 The Methods of Scientists

In the past, writers of introductory texts have, in their desire to describe clearly the scientific method, given readers the impression that there is only one acceptable method. They have implied that all scientists use the same method. This is unfortunate because it makes science look as if it were purely mechanical. Some readers may even feel that using the scientific method is an excuse for not thinking.

The traditional form of the scientific method is first observing nature, then seeking the regularities in the obervations, formulating a **hypothesis** (a tentative explanation of the regularities), experimenting to test the hypothesis, and finally constructing a theory. This is a good method, and it may be acceptable to some scientists. However, any method which is a combination of curiosity and imagination and which uses experimentation to look for regularities in nature will be an acceptable method for scientists to use.

Scientists usually call their investigations research projects. They choose an area to study and conduct a set of experiments. An **experiment** is a planned series of observations. The use of experiments enables scientists to ask specific questions of nature rather than merely making unplanned observations and speculating as to their meaning. Some researchers might plan their projects very carefully. They might contemplate their methods, ideas, and proposed experiments for days. For these people, science is like a chess game—every move is carefully considered. Other scientists might be impatient and wish to get on with the job so that they can test out their hunches. Some aspects of their problems may make them so curious that they cannot wait to try and find some answers. Thus, the methods that scientists use really depend on their personalities.

Rules of Observation

Scientists must follow certain rules if the results of their research projects are to be acceptable to other scientists. Since observation is the very lifeblood of science, these rules apply particularly to it.

First, a scientist is expected to be **objective** in making observations. Objectivity requires an unbiased reporting of all observations. If five similar experiments give the same answer, and then a sixth gives a different answer, a scientist is not allowed to discard the different or anomalous (irregular) result. Scientists believe that nature is not capricious. That is, nature does not try to trick people by causing events to happen one way on ninety-nine occasions and another way on the hundredth occasion for no reason at all. There must be a logical explanation for an anomalous event. Time and time again scientists have found that what they thought was an anomaly was really due to a lack of knowledge. Often an anomaly will lead to a new set of observations which might well add to our understanding of nature. Consequently, since anomalous events can turn out to be disguised blessings, it is the scientist's duty to report faithfully all of the observations made (unless, of course, a mistake was made in the experiment).

A number of years ago, a chemist working for a famous company was using a gas called tetrafluoroethylene (TFE). His research project dealt with refrigeration systems. His supply of TFE was stored in a steel cylinder under pressure. One morning, he discovered that no TFE would come out of the cylinder. This surprised him, since the last time he had used the cylinder, there seemed to be plenty of TFE left. He compared the mass of the cylinder with its mass at the end of the previous usage, and established that the TFE had not leaked out. He then discovered that something rattled inside the cylinder. His curiosity led him to cut it open. Inside, he found a white, slippery solid. He experimented with the solid and found that it had interesting properties. A new product, Teflon®, was discovered because the chemist did not ignore an anomaly. He felt that there must be TFE in the steel cylinder, and he was determined to find out what had happened to it.

Second, measurements must be **reproducible**. Scientists believe that all measurements made of the same object or event under the same conditions must agree regardless of when or by whom the measurements are made. This concept of reproducibility follows from the idea that nature is not capricious. **Precision** is the term used to describe how well a group of measurements made of the same object or event under the same conditions actually do agree with one another (Fig. 1-6).

Suppose a thermometer is used to measure the temperature of some hot water. Any number of observers would agree that the temperature is between 85°C and 86°C (Fig. 1-7). However, the observers would not all likely agree on

Fig. 1-6 Precision is important. Which of these containers measures volume more precisely?

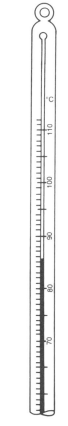

Fig. 1-7 What is the temperature reading on this thermometer?

the third digit. Some would record 85.5°C, and others would record 85.4°C or 85.6°C. In terms of the reproducibility of this measurement, the first two digits are *certain*, but the third digit is *uncertain*. Nevertheless, the third digit is useful because it tells us that the temperature is approximately halfway between 85°C and 86°C. The certain digits plus the first uncertain one are always considered to be *significant*.

Suppose the results recorded by seven people are 85.5°C, 85.7°C, 85.6°C, 85.6°C, 85.5°C, 85.4°C, and 85.6°C. The average of the results as displayed by a calculator capable of ten digits is 85.557 142 86°C. However, chemists choose to indicate only the significant digits. The average measurement is precise to three digits. It is written as 85.6°C and contains three *significant digits*. The number of significant digits written for a measurement informs us of the precision of the measurement and hence of its reproducibility. The greater the number of significant digits used for a measurement, the more precise and hence reproducible the measurement is.

Third, a scientist must make accurate observations. **Accuracy** represents the closeness of a measurement to the true value. It is important that the scientist measure what is supposed to have been measured, not something else (Fig. 1-8). If a person is trying to determine the mass of a container, it must be clean and dry. If the container holds a few drops of water, the mass of the container plus the mass of the water will be obtained, not the mass of the container alone. In addition, the balance must be in good working order, and it must be properly adjusted so that it gives a zero reading when no object is on the balance pan.

Fig. 1-8 Accuracy is important. Is the mass of this beaker being determined accurately?

Laws, Theories, and Models

Once scientists have made their observations, they seek regularities. **Laws** are statements of regularities found in observations made on a system. For example, Dalton's Law of Partial Pressures states that the total pressure exerted by several gases mixed together equals the sum of the individual pressures that each gas would exert if it were alone in the container.

Laws are a matter of convenience and are not proven beyond a shadow of a doubt. Often scientists accept a law because it is useful in anticipating or predicting what will happen if a certain experiment is performed. Occasionally a law has to be modified to explain some new observation. Scientists are not overly upset that the established law has to be modified. Over the years, they have become used to the necessity of changing or discarding scientific laws as a result of the discovery of new knowledge.

A law is a rule that nature appears to follow. A law states what happens. It does not state why it happens. Thus, scientists are not satisfied with a law alone. They would like to be able to explain why it is true. They want to know more about the underlying principles associated with the law. A **theory** is a guess at the underlying principles which can explain the group of related observations (the law).

For example, the Kinetic Molecular Theory is the modern theory which explains the behaviour of gases. This theory has, as some of its postulates (basic assumptions), the statements
a) Gases are made up of small particles called molecules.
b) These molecules are in rapid random motion.
c) They move in straight lines until their directions are changed by collisions.
d) These molecules are widely separated.

Often, we must theorize about particles that are too small or too large for us to see. A **model** is a visualization of these particles (Figs. 1-9(a) and 1-9(b)). Thus, models are useful in helping us to understand a theory. For example, the molecules described in the Kinetic Molecular Theory are much too small to be seen. As we cannot see these particles, it may be difficult to visualize them. We may resort to a model. We might visualize a closed room with a few ping-pong balls constantly moving around the room, colliding with the walls of the room and occasionally with one another in a random manner. These never-stopping ping-pong balls might constitute an acceptable model to help us understand the motion of gas molecules in a container. Of course, the model is not perfect. In reality, the ping-pong balls would fall to the floor and remain there.

Let us be clear about one thing. Theories and models, like laws, must come under constant inspection. There may be events that a certain theory cannot explain. The theory may have to be altered or discarded. Models, too, may need revision.

Moreover, models are only visualizations of the real thing. They are products of the scientists' imaginations. There may be an observation that will not fit a model or theory. We again use the word *anomaly*. The anomalous observation may contradict the accepted theory or model, but it cannot be disregarded. If the experiment was performed correctly, and if the observation

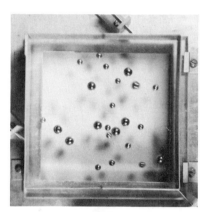

(a)

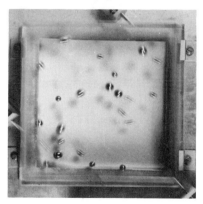

(b)

Fig. 1-9 This model is used to illustrate the movement of gas molecules. Ball bearings are kept in continuous motion by the vibrating walls of the container.
(a) This represents slower-moving molecules at a lower temperature.
(b) This represents faster-moving molecules at a higher temperature.

was made correctly, this irregular behaviour may serve as the basis for either a new theory or a modified theory. Scientists have their "pet theories," and often they argue strenuously for them; but in the final analysis, they realize that all theories must be put on display for other scientists to examine. Scientists realize that no theory or model will ever be a perfect explanation of the events it was constructed to explain.

Characteristics of Scientists

People are not born with an ability to become good scientists. Individual scientists do not differ significantly from individuals in other occupations. However, as a group, scientists do show some common characteristics.

Scientists generally have a high level of curiosity. They seem to enjoy looking for answers to unsolved problems. The Nobel Prize-winning American chemist, Linus Pauling, said: "Satisfaction of one's curiosity is one of the greatest sources of happiness in life." Scientists tend to be persistent. They are usually able to cope with the anxiety and discouragement which can result from facing unsuccessful or inconclusive experiments day after day.

Successful scientists, like successful people in other occupations, possess high standards of honesty, a desire to know the truth, open-mindedness, and focused vision. Needless to say, not all scientists will measure up to these standards; however, those who do are usually the great ones.

Fig. 1-10 Scientists can satisfy their curiosity about how the world works in many ways. This engineer works at an oil refinery in Sarnia, Ontario. (Photo courtesy of Imperial Oil Limited)

Gerhard Herzberg was born in Hamburg, Germany in 1904. He obtained his doctorate in engineering physics from Darmstadt in 1928. He continued his studies with postdoctoral years at Göttingen and Bristol.

The actions of the Nazis in the mid-thirties drove Herzberg from Germany. He went to the University of Saskatchewan. Although the university lacked research equipment and funds at that time, Herzberg had a productive stay there. He slowly obtained equipment and worked with some graduate students to produce a number of papers. He also wrote two books on molecular spectroscopy.

In 1945, Herzberg became a professor at the University of Chicago. He built up a laboratory capable of doing important experiments. However, the political atmosphere in American universities was unpleasant in 1948, and Herzberg (a Canadian citizen) accepted an invitation to set up a research laboratory in spectroscopy at the National Research Council (NRC) in Ottawa.

Herzberg was appointed director of the physics division of the NRC in 1949, and he became director of the division of pure physics when it was formed in 1955. In 1969, he became the first person to be appointed Distinguished Research Scientist with the NRC. This enabled him to continue to do research following his retirement as director that year.

Although Herzberg was trained as a physicist, much of his work has been in chemistry. His major area of research has been molecular structure. He has been called the father of atomic and molecular spectroscopy. In 1971, he was awarded the Nobel Prize in Chemistry.

Herzberg is a hard working, dedicated scientist. He has criticized some of the views presented by a Senate Special Committee on Science Policy. Herzberg believes that you cannot plan to discover something; nor can you direct or manage scientific research into undiscovered areas, because it is impossible to predict the results or consequences of the research.

Fig. 1-11 Gerhard Herzberg (1904-) (PA-128062 Public Archives Canada)

A Final Word

The value of science is real. It is a human activity which attempts to deepen our understanding and our appreciation of nature. It emphasizes honesty and clarity of thinking. It relates to the prosperity and the cultural life of a country.

The scientific method, which skeptics suggest hampers creativity, is merely a mind-freeing method. In fact, it allows the scientist to be creative. It has solved the problem of the relationship between freedom and discipline. Scientists are free to test out any hunch, knowing that the scientific method will expose any mistakes and will help to guide them on to the next step.

Now that you have finished reading this chapter, you should reread the Key Objectives to make sure that you have learned the most important points of the chapter. In addition, you should learn the meaning of each important term found in the chapter.

Key Terms

What is the meaning of each of the following terms?

science	reproducible
empirical knowledge	precision
pure science	accuracy
technology	law
chemistry	theory
hypothesis	model
experiment	objective

Questions

1. Which of the following are best considered as examples of science, and which as examples of technology? Why?
   a) The transistor has almost completely replaced the vacuum tube in its applications.
   b) It has been found that some of the so-called inert gases will react with fluorine.
   c) Fluoridation of drinking water appears to significantly decrease the incidence of tooth decay in children.
   d) Safe nuclear reactors will have to be designed to replace thermal electric generating stations due to an increasing scarcity of fossil fuels.
   e) In 1942 Enrico Fermi constructed the first atomic pile in order to prove that nuclear fission could be controlled.

2. What are two types of science? What is the purpose of each type? Give examples of each.

3. What is the most important activity of the scientist?

4. What is chemistry? How does chemistry differ from mathematics? From biology?

5. What is an anomaly? Why must an anomaly not be disregarded?

6. What is a scientific method? Are all scientists likely to use exactly the same method? Why or why not? Is there an activity that is common to all scientists?

7. Why are scientists forced to assume that nature is not capricious?

8. Which of the following statements is best considered as a law, and which as a theory?
   a) The pressure exerted by a given volume of a gas is directly proportional to its Kelvin temperature, provided the volume remains constant.
   b) Gases are made up of small particles called molecules.
   c) In all chemical reactions studied so far the total amount of matter remains constant.
   d) A solution of salt in water conducts electricity because the salt has dissociated to form mobile positive and negative particles.
   e) Carbon monoxide is poisonous because it prevents the hemoglobin in the blood from carrying oxygen to the tissues.

9. Why would you use a model when describing a scientific theory?

10. What is empirical knowledge?

11. "Even the scientific method, which skeptics suggest hampers creativity, is merely a mind-freeing method." How is the scientific method a mind-freeing method?

12. The Nobel Prize-winning chemist Linus Pauling has maintained that massive doses of Vitamin C are effective in preventing colds. Other scientists disagree with this hypothesis. What kind of experiments would you plan in order to prove or disprove Pauling's theory?

13. If technology is the application of science to industrial or commercial objectives, can there be a similar technology which applies to either art or music? Support your answer with examples.

14. List four rules that scientists must obey if their experimental results are to be acceptable to other scientists.

15. Distinguish between a law and a theory.

16. Do theories ever change? Explain your answer.

17. To what extent is it desirable, or even possible, for governments to manage or direct scientific research completely?

18. Why do you suppose that the public appears to have a more unfavourable view of chemicals and chemistry now than in the past?

19. Suggest a possible reason for which the first prime minister of India said: "The future belongs to science and to those who make friends with science."

2

Measuring and Problem Solving

Chemistry requires measurements. There can be no increase in the body of chemical knowledge unless someone carries out well-planned experiments under controlled conditions. Most of these experiments will involve careful measurement of variable quantities such as mass, volume, temperature, energy, and time. In this chapter we will see why it is important to make careful measurements. We will examine the ways in which their results are stated. Then we will examine some of the ways in which these results are manipulated in order to obtain even more information about a chemical system.

Key Objectives

When you have finished studying this chapter, you should be able to
1. express the results of a measurement in the correct SI units.
2. solve mathematical problems involving units by using the factor-label method.
3. express large and small numbers using scientific notation.
4. express the result of a measurement to the correct number of significant digits.
5. identify the significant digits in a given measurement.
6. express, rounded off to the correct number of significant digits, the results of calculations involving experimental measurements.

2-1 Communication and Science

One of the main reasons for the recent rapid growth of scientific knowledge is that scientists are now able to communicate with one another very quickly. They are able to exchange experimental observations as well as hunches and theories. Obviously, it is quite wasteful for a scientist to spend time and money trying to discover something that has already been discovered by someone else. Also, it is important for a scientist to have the latest knowledge in the field; it

may provide the key for making a great discovery. Thus, scientists are obligated to communicate their findings to other scientists. This is most often done by written descriptions which are published in scientific journals. These journals are published in countries all over the world (Fig. 2-2, overleaf). They contain descriptions of recent scientific research and are published weekly in some cases, but usually monthly. Because they are published frequently, these journals are reasonably up-to-date. Books are also used to communicate scientific information; however, scientific knowledge is growing so rapidly that books are often out-of-date by the time they are issued. Scientists often communicate their findings in lectures given at annual meetings of the various scientific societies. Occasionally special symposia are organized so that scientists investigating a certain area (e.g., cancer research) can meet and discuss their research.

Thus, because scientists communicate, scientific knowledge grows. Ideas from previous generations are used to construct modern theories. Scientists are not required to start from square one. They are able to build on what has

Fig. 2-2 Some International Chemical Journals

already been learned, and there is much to learn. This is the reason for the long period of training required by a modern scientist.

In order for scientific communication to be effective, it must have **universality**. That is, it must be interpreted the same way in Calgary as it is in Tokyo. A work of art need not have this universality. In fact, it could lose its appeal if everyone interpreted it the same way.

One of the best ways for scientists to communicate is through mathematical equations. In fact, mathematics is the language of science, and mathematics adds to the universality of science. You have probably heard of Einstein's equation, $E = mc^2$. This is understood by all scientists throughout the world to mean that energy equals mass times the square of the speed of light. It can be restated in the form of a ratio $E/m = c^2$. This means that the ratio of E to m will always be equal to the same value, c^2, regardless of the size of the quantities involved.

For these mathematical ratios to have universality, scientists must all use the same units of measurement, and they must always report those units.

If, for example, you read in a scientific report the statement, ''The experiment required ten,'' you would immediately ask, ''Ten what?'' Did the experiment require ten cents, ten minutes, or ten grams of salt? With few exceptions, all numbers are quantities of something. It is not sufficient to say only the quantity (number)—a scientist must give the quantity of *whatever* is being talked about. The ''whatever'' is called the **units** or *dimensions* of the quantity. Thus, depending on what was being measured in the reported experiment, the units of the measurement were either ''cents,'' ''minutes,'' or ''grams of salt.'' For scientific communication to be meaningful, a number must therefore always have its units written after it.

Some scientific knowledge cannot be communicated by numbers or mathematical equations, and must be communicated by means of analogies. An analogy expresses a likeness. In Chapter 1, we said that gas molecules in motion are like ping-pong balls bouncing in a room. We may say that radio waves are like water waves. Analogies are useful in science, but they do not have the universality that an equation would have. However, there are times when analogies are the only means of communicating scientific ideas.

We have seen that it is important for scientists to communicate their results to others as quickly as possible. This must be done in such a way that no other scientist can possibly misunderstand the results. This is not as easy as it might sound. In Section 2-2, we will see the standard units of measurements.

2-2 SI: The International System of Units

All measurements are made by using or making a comparison with a standard measuring device. The odometer of a car measures distances in terms of a legal standard of length. A butcher finds the mass of a steak on a scale that is set to report in terms of a standard of mass. A service station attendant dispenses gasoline with pumps that are calibrated to measure in terms of an accepted standard of volume. In the same ways, chemists use their standards when measuring length, mass, volume, and other properties of a chemical system. Until recently, many standards of measurement were in use. It was necessary for scientists to be familiar with all of them.

Scientists made many efforts to agree on a single set of standards against which all measurements would be made. In 1960 the recognized international authority on units, the General Conference of Weights and Measures, adopted the International System of Units. The abbreviation in all languages is SI (for Le Système International d'Unités). Canada has adopted this system.

Base Units

The system is constructed from seven base units. By combining various base units we obtain other units, called derived units.

The base units are the following:

Physical Quantity	Unit	Symbol
Length	metre	m
Mass	kilogram	kg
Time	second	s
Temperature	kelvin	K
Amount of substance	mole	mol
Electric current	ampere	A
Luminous intensity	candela	cd

Of these, length, mass, time, temperature, and amount of substance are the most useful to us.

The SI unit of *length* is the metre. A metre is defined as 1 650 763.73 wavelengths in vacuum of the orange-red line in the spectrum of krypton-86.

The SI unit of *mass* is the kilogram, which is defined as the mass of a cylinder of platinum-iridium alloy kept at the International Bureau of Weights and Measures in Paris.

We have defined the metre and the kilogram merely to give you an idea of the care which is taken in defining base units. The other base units are defined just as carefully.

Derived Units

Derived units have compound names. Those that have squares or cubes such as "square metre" are derived units. So are those which contain more than one unit in the name, e.g., "metre per second."

The SI unit of *area* is the square metre (m^2). The SI unit of *volume* is the cubic metre (m^3). The litre is now defined as one thousandth of a cubic metre. The use of "litre" as a unit of volume is permitted in SI.

The SI unit of *force* is the newton (N), which is defined as that force which will give a mass of one kilogram a speed of one metre per second when applied for one second. In symbols,

$$1 \text{ N} = \frac{1 \text{ kg·m/s}}{1 \text{ s}} = 1 \text{ kg·m·s}^{-2}$$

Notice that the unit of force is therefore derived from the base units of measurement. A force of about 10 N is required to lift a full one litre carton of milk.

Similarly, the SI unit for *work* and *energy* is the joule (J), which can be defined as the work done by a force of one newton when acting through a distance of one metre. In symbols,

$$1 \text{ J} = 1 \text{ N·m} = 1 \text{ N} \times 1 \text{ m} = 1 \text{ kg·m·s}^{-2} \times 1 \text{ m} = 1 \text{ kg·m}^2\text{s}^{-2},$$

and again the definition is derived from the base units. Lifting a full one litre carton of milk from the kitchen floor to the counter top takes about ten joules of energy.

The SI unit of *pressure* is the pascal (Pa). It is the force of one newton acting over an area of one square metre. In symbols,

$$1 \text{ Pa} = \frac{1 \text{ N}}{1 \text{ m}^2} = \frac{1 \text{ kg·m·s}^{-2}}{1 \text{ m}^2} = 1 \text{ kg·m}^{-1}\text{s}^{-2}.$$

Again, the definition is derived from the base units. One kilogram of sugar spread evenly over the surface of a card table exerts a pressure of about ten pascals.

The commonly used derived units are summarized in Table 2-1.

TABLE 2-1   Some Derived Units

QUANTITY	UNIT	SYMBOL	DERIVATION
Area	square metre	m^2	—
Volume	cubic metre	m^3	—
Speed	metre per second	m/s	—
Density	kilogram per cubic metre	kg/m^3	—
Force	newton	N	$kg \cdot m/s^2$
Pressure	pascal	Pa	N/m^2
Energy, Work	joule	J	$N \cdot m$
Power	watt	W	J/s

Fractions and multiples of SI units are expressed by the appropriate prefixes (Table 2-2).

TABLE 2-2   Prefixes for Fractions and Multiples of SI Units

PREFIX	SYMBOL	FACTOR	PREFIX	SYMBOL	FACTOR
exa	E	10^{18}	deci	d	10^{-1}
peta	P	10^{15}	centi	c	10^{-2}
tera	T	10^{12}	milli	m	10^{-3}
giga	G	10^9	micro	μ	10^{-6}
mega	M	10^6	nano	n	10^{-9}
kilo	k	10^3	pico	p	10^{-12}
hecto	h	10^2			
deca	da	10^1			

The prefixes in Table 2-2 tell us how many places we must move the decimal point to get the new unit. For example, moving the decimal point three places to the right (multiplying by 1000) is represented by the prefix *kilo*. Thus a *kilo*metre is a thousand metres, a *kilo*joule is a thousand joules, and a *kilo*pascal is a thousand pascals.

In Canada, certain conventions of style must be used when writing measurements in SI units. Among these are the following:

1. Digits are to be grouped in threes about the decimal point without using commas to mark off thousands, millions, etc. E.g., 1 234 567.891 23 and not 1,234,567.89123.

2. There is no period at the end of SI symbols; e.g., write "kg," not "kg.".

3. Units are not pluralized. Thus, a mass of ten kilograms is written as 10 kg, not 10 kgs.

4. Use product dots to avoid ambiguities. For example, ms could mean either "metre-second" or "millisecond." The symbol "m·s" is unambiguous: metre-second.

5. Words and symbols should not be mixed. One may write "kilograms per cubic metre" or "kg/m^3" but not "kilograms/m^3" or "kg per cubic metre," etc.

6. Symbols should be used in place of full names when units are used in conjunction with numerals. For example, write 180 cm rather than 180 centimetres.
7. Where possible, in the expression of any quantity, a prefix should be chosen so that the numeral lies between 0.1 and 1000. When similar items are compared, however, it is preferable to use the same prefix for all items.

We have just seen that a measurement consists of a number and its units. In Section 2-3, we will consider some difficulties associated with the numbers in measurements.

2-3 Exponential Numbers and Scientific Notation

Chemists frequently deal with very large and very small numbers. For example, the average mass of a single carbon atom is 0.000 000 000 000 000 000 000 019 94 g. How many carbon atoms are required to give a total mass of 12.00 g? Imagine how tedious it would be to carry out the division involved in the relation

$$x \text{ C atoms} = 12.00 \text{ g} \times \frac{1 \text{ C atom}}{0.000\ 000\ 000\ 000\ 000\ 000\ 000\ 019\ 94 \text{ g}}$$

Decimal points have a habit of slipping into the wrong places during such operations, and the answer is a large number indeed.

Exponential Notation

In order to handle both very large and very small numbers, scientists use a technique known as exponential notation. To illustrate this technique, let us consider a simple example. The number 2700 can be written as

$$2700 = 270 \times 10 = 27 \times 100 = 2.7 \times 1000 = 0.27 \times 10\ 000$$

If we recall that $100 = 10 \times 10 = 10^2$, $1000 = 10 \times 10 \times 10 = 10^3$, and $10\ 000 = 10 \times 10 \times 10 \times 10 = 10^4$, we can write

$$2700 = 270 \times 10^1 = 27 \times 10^2 = 2.7 \times 10^3 = 0.27 \times 10^4$$

Notice that each of these consists of a number (the coefficient) multiplied by ten raised to an integral power (the exponent). Each is therefore an example of exponential notation.

Scientific Notation

Any measurement which consists of a coefficient multiplied by a power of ten is said to be expressed in exponential notation. If the coefficient is 1 or a number between 1 and 10, the number is said to be expressed in *scientific notation*. In scientific notation, therefore, $2700 = 2.7 \times 10^3$. For a number greater than one, the exponent of the 10 is the same as the number of positions the decimal point must be moved *to the left* to get a coefficient between 1 and 10. E.g., 45 000 = 4.5×10^4.

Similarly, the number 0.027 can be written as

$$0.027 = \frac{27}{1000} = \frac{2.7}{100} = \frac{0.27}{10}$$

and

$$0.027 = \frac{27}{10^3} = \frac{2.7}{10^2} = \frac{0.27}{10^1}$$

$$\therefore 0.027 = 27 \times 10^{-3} = 2.7 \times 10^{-2} = 0.27 \times 10^{-1}$$

These are again examples of exponential notation. In scientific notation, we must write $0.027 = 2.7 \times 10^{-2}$. For a number less than one, the exponent of the 10 is a negative integer equal to the number of positions the decimal point must be moved *to the right* to get a coefficient between 1 and 10. For example, $0.000\,77 = 7.7 \times 10^{-4}$.

Sample Problem 2-1

Convert the following to scientific notation: **a)** 24 000; **b)** 0.000 000 61.

SOLUTION

a) The decimal point must be moved four places to the left to get a coefficient of 2.4. Therefore 24 000 = 2.4×10^4.

b) The decimal point must be moved seven places to the right to get a coefficient of 6.1. Therefore 0.000 000 61 = 6.1×10^{-7}.

Multiplying Exponential Numbers

The advantage of scientific notation is that it simplifies the manipulation of very large and very small numbers. E.g., to *multiply* exponential numbers, we multiply coefficients normally and add the exponents:

$$(3.0 \times 10^3)(2.0 \times 10^{-9}) = (3.0 \times 2.0)(10^3 \times 10^{-9}) = 6.0 \times 10^{3+(-9)}$$
$$= 6.0 \times 10^{-6}$$

Dividing Exponential Numbers

To *divide* exponential numbers, we divide the coefficients normally, then subtract the exponent of the divisor from the exponent of the dividend:

$$\frac{4.4 \times 10^6}{8.8 \times 10^{-4}} = \frac{4.4}{8.8} \times \frac{10^6}{10^{-4}} = 0.50 \times 10^{6-(-4)} = 0.50 \times 10^{10}$$

The above answer does not have a coefficient between 1 and 10. We can convert it to the standard form of scientific notation as follows:

$$0.50 \times 10^{10} = 5.0 \times 10^{10-1} = 5.0 \times 10^9$$

That is, the exponent is decreased by one for each position the decimal point of the coefficient is moved to the right (and it is increased by one for each position the decimal point of the coefficient is moved to the left) until the coefficient is a number between 1 and 10. The results of all computations in exponential notation should normally be expressed in the standard form of scientific notation.

Sample Problem 2-2

Express in scientific notation the result of the computation

$$\frac{(1.78 \times 10^{-4}) \times 2.41 \times 96.5}{0.724 \times (4.18 \times 10^{5})(1.86 \times 10^{-16})}$$

SOLUTION
Treat the coefficients and exponents in groups:

$$\frac{1.78 \times 2.41 \times 96.5}{0.724 \times 4.18 \times 1.86} \times \frac{10^{-4}}{10^{5} \times 10^{-16}} = 73.5 \times \frac{10^{-4}}{10^{-11}} = 73.5 \times 10^{7}$$

Convert to standard form: $73.5 \times 10^{7} = 7.35 \times 10^{8}$

Addition and Subtraction of Exponential Numbers

Addition and subtraction of exponential numbers is possible if the exponents are all the same. Thus

$$1 \times 10^{-3} + 2 \times 10^{-3} + 3 \times 10^{-3} = (1+2+3) \times 10^{-3} = 6 \times 10^{-3}$$

If the exponents are different, the numbers must first be converted to a form in which all exponents are the same. It is usually convenient, but not absolutely necessary, to convert all numbers so that they have the same exponent as the largest number in the group. Thus,

$$1.00 \times 10^{-3} + 2.00 \times 10^{-4} + 3.00 \times 10^{-5}$$
$$= 1.00 \times 10^{-3} + 0.200 \times 10^{-3} + 0.0300 \times 10^{-3}$$
$$= (1.00 + 0.200 + 0.0300) \times 10^{-3} = 1.23 \times 10^{-3}$$

Similarly,

$$2.0 \times 10^{10} - 6 \times 10^{9} = 2.0 \times 10^{10} - 0.6 \times 10^{10}$$
$$= (2.0 - 0.6) \times 10^{10} = 1.4 \times 10^{10}.$$

Sample Problem 2-3

What is the result of these operations?
a) $3.02 \times 10^{3} + 1.3 \times 10^{2}$
b) $5 \times 10^{-6} - 8.2 \times 10^{-5}$

SOLUTION
a) $3.02 \times 10^{3} + 1.3 \times 10^{2} = 3.02 \times 10^{3} + 0.13 \times 10^{3} = (3.02 + 0.13) \times 10^{3} = 3.15 \times 10^{3}$

b) $5 \times 10^{-6} - 8.2 \times 10^{-5} = 0.5 \times 10^{-5} - 8.2 \times 10^{-5} = (0.5 - 8.2) \times 10^{-5}$
$$= -7.7 \times 10^{-5}$$

So far, we have seen how scientists must choose the proper units for making a measurement. We have also examined some difficulties the scientist faces when dealing with very large and very small numbers. In the next section, we will see how scientists indicate the degree of confidence or certainty that is implied in their measurements.

2-4 Uncertainty and Significant Digits

When you are caught for travelling 52 km/h in a 50 km/h speed zone, you might well ask the police officer some questions. Was the speed radar recently calibrated? That is, does it actually read 50 km/h when a car is moving at that speed? You might also ask how reproducible the radar is. That is, if the officer took five different measurements of your speed, would they all be 52 km/h? Or would there be a range of values, say from 48 to 52 km/h? Should you get a ticket? That would depend on how reproducibly the radar can measure your speed, and on how close that measurement is to your actual speed.

Reading Measuring Instruments

Scientists do not deliberately make false claims about their results. However, if they do not pay attention to the degree of reliability of their measurements, they may report results to more significant figures than can be justified. A scientist must always be careful to report the reliability of all measurements. Consider, for example, the thermometer shown in Fig. 1-7. You can easily tell that the temperature is about half-way between 85°C and 86°C. If the temperature were exactly half-way between the two divisions, you would naturally record it as 85.5°. But could the temperature possibly be 85.4°C or 85.6°C? Or could it even be 85.3°C or 85.7°C? If the answer is, "Yes, the temperature might be anywhere between 85.4 and 85.6°C, but I could tell the difference if the temperature were 85.3°C or 85.7°C," then you should record the temperature as 85.5 ± 0.1°C. If you could not distinguish temperatures between 85.3°C and 85.7°C, but could distinguish temperatures outside this range, then you should record the temperature as 85.5 ± 0.2°C. The ± 0.2°C represents the experimental uncertainty in your measurement, and you have read your thermometer by estimating to tenths of the smallest division.

You should read any instrument by estimating tenths of the smallest division, even if the divisions are so close together that about the best you can do is tell that the measurement is on a division mark or between them. For example, Fig. 2-3 is a drawing of a thermometer that measures temperatures between −5°C and 365°C. Although an experienced chemist would probably estimate the temperature reading to the nearest 0.2°C or 0.3°C, most beginners would probably read the temperature as 85.5 ± 0.5°C. Such a reading would indicate that they could tell that the mercury thread was between the 85°C and 86°C divisions, but couldn't say much more about its location.

Many people would even be tempted to take the easy way out and record the temperature as either 85°C or 86°C. This would be wrong, though, because if they can tell that the mercury is between the divisions, they should indicate it when recording the measurement.

Fig. 2-3 What is the uncertainty in the temperature reading of this thermometer?

What if, for example, the mercury thread on this thermometer happens to fall exactly (as far as we can tell) on the 86°C mark? Should we record the temperature as "86°C"? The answer is, "No." On this thermometer we can distinguish readings of 85.5°C and 86.5°C. We can indeed estimate to tenths of a division. If the mercury is right on a division mark, we are estimating zero tenths. "Zero tenths" is indicated by the zero in the correct reading—86.0°C. The complete reading would be 86.0 ± 0.5°C.

Precision

An ordinary thermometer will measure temperature only to the nearest tenth of a degree. For example, we might record the temperature of an object as 85.6 ± 0.1°C. This means that the temperature is between 85.5°C and 85.7°C, but we cannot measure it any more precisely because of the limitations of our measuring instrument. If we used an electronic thermometer we might find that the temperature is 85.55 ± 0.01°C, but there is still an uncertainty (although a smaller one) in the measurement. Whatever tool we use, the result of an experimental measurement is uncertain. The precision of the measurement is indicated by the number of digits in the measurement.

Significant Digits

You must use just enough digits in a measurement to give an idea of the degree of uncertainty in your measurement. These digits are called the significant digits. The number of significant digits in a measurement is usually defined as the number of digits that are known accurately plus one that is uncertain. Thus, a measurement of 85.6°C contains three significant digits, and a measurement of 85.55°C contains four significant digits. In each of these measurements there is only one uncertain digit (the last one); the others are known accurately.

Leading zeroes are ignored when counting significant digits. For example, how many significant digits are in a measurement of 0.014 g? Since leading zeroes are ignored, there are two significant digits. You will always get the correct number if you express the measurement in scientific notation $(1.4 \times 10^{-2}$ g). The number of digits in the coefficient is the same as the number of significant digits in the measurement.

Trailing zeroes may or may not be included among significant digits. Suppose you are told, "The speed of light is 300 000 000 m/s." If this had been measured to the nearest metre per second (extremely unlikely), then all digits are significant, and the measurement contains nine significant digits. If the measurement is precise only to the nearest million metres per second (i.e., the number is between 299 000 000 and 301 000 000 m/s) then the third digit is uncertain, and there are only three significant digits. This is usually indicated either by placing a bar over the first uncertain digit ($30\bar{0}$ 000 000 m/s) or by writing the measurement in scientific notation (3.00×10^8 m/s).

Two types of numbers in science are considered to be exact and to contain an infinite number of significant digits. These are

a) Numbers obtained by counting. If there are 28 students in a classroom, there are not 27 students or 29 students or 28.32 students. There are 28.000... students (the zeroes can be extended to as many decimal places as necessary).

b) Numbers obtained by definition. In definitions such as "12 objects = 1 dozen" and "1 m = 100 cm," the numbers 12, 1, and 100 are all considered to be exact and to contain an infinite number of significant digits.

Mathematical Operations Involving Significant Digits

Measurements in chemistry are uncertain. The results of calculations involving these measurements are also uncertain. Consider a line consisting of two segments, one of length 11 ± 1 mm and one of length 17.2 ± 0.1 mm. What is the total length of the line? It is tempting to say that the length is $11 + 17.2 = 28.2$ mm. But is it, really? Both measurements are uncertain. The greatest length the line could have is $12 + 17.3 = 29.3$ mm. The shortest length it could have is $10 + 17.1 = 27.1$ mm. The actual length is somewhere between 27.1 mm and 29.3 mm. Only the first digit (2) is known for certain. The other digits are uncertain. The measurement is better expressed, then, as 28 mm. This result is quickly obtained by using the following procedure. Place a bar over the uncertain digits in each of the numbers to be added or subtracted. An uncertain digit involved in an addition or subtraction results in an answer which is also uncertain. Place bars over all uncertain digits in your answer. The answer should contain all unbarred digits plus the barred digit which is furthest to the left. E.g.,

$$1\bar{1} \quad \text{mm}$$
$$17.\bar{2} \text{ mm}$$
$$\overline{2\bar{8}.\bar{2} \text{ mm}}$$

The correct answer is 28 mm.

Sample Problem 2-4

To a beaker having a mass of 109.751 g, a student adds 10.23 g of Chemical A, 0.0639 g of Chemical B, and 19.1 g of Chemical C. What is the total mass of beaker plus chemicals?

SOLUTION

Beaker	109.75$\bar{1}$ g
Chemical A	10.2$\bar{3}$ g
Chemical B	0.063$\bar{9}$ g
Chemical C	19.$\bar{1}$ g
Total	139.$\bar{1}\bar{4}\bar{4}\bar{9}$ g

The total mass is 139.1 g.

The considerations which apply when measurements must be multiplied or divided are also straightforward. Consider the following problem. What is the area of a rectangle of sides 1.14 ± 0.01 cm and 2.3 ± 0.1 cm? The area must fall between $1.13 \times 2.2 = 2.486$ cm^2 and $1.15 \times 2.4 = 2.760$ cm^2. The answer can have only two significant digits. The rule to follow is, "When two or more measurements are multiplied or divided, the answer should contain only as many significant digits as there are in the measurement having the least number of significant digits." Thus the area obtained by multiplying 1.14 cm by 2.3 cm (2.622 cm^2) must contain only two significant digits and is written as 2.6 cm^2.

Sample Problem 2-5

What is the cross-sectional area of a piece of glass tubing with a diameter of 6.0 mm?

SOLUTION

The area is given by the formula $A = \pi r^2$. The radius is 3.0 mm (two significant digits). π is a constant with an infinite number of significant digits (3.141 592 654...). We shall use at least one more significant digit for π than is in the least accurate measurement (i.e., 3.14).

$$A = 3.14 \times (3.0 \text{ mm})^2 = 28 \text{ mm}^2$$

Rounding Off

To this point we have simply dropped all the excess uncertain digits in order to get a result with the correct number of significant digits. This process is called *truncation* (cutting off). Suppose an area of 2.622 cm^2 was truncated to 2.6 cm^2. If the area had been 2.696 cm^2, would it still have been correct to write the area as 2.6 cm^2? A more correct value would have been 2.7 cm^2, because 2.692 is closer to 2.7 than it is to 2.6. Truncation is therefore not always the correct procedure for dropping unnecessary digits. The correct procedure to use is called *rounding off*. The rules for rounding off are

a) If the first digit to be truncated is less than 5, the preceding digit stays the same. For example 2.622 becomes 2.6, because the 2 in the hundredths place is less than 5.

b) If the first digit to be truncated is greater than 5, the preceding digit is increased by one. Thus, 2.692 becomes 2.7, because 9 is greater than 5.

c) If the first digit to be truncated is 5, the preceding digit stays the same if it is even, and increases by one if it is odd. This is called rounding off to the nearest even number, and is used only when dropping a 5. Thus, to two significant figures, 2.65 is 2.6; 2.75 is 2.8; 2.85 is 2.8; 2.95 is 3.0, and so on.

It might seem strange at first glance to round off fives to the nearest even number. Think for a moment about why it is a proper procedure. Suppose you have a group of numbers, all ending in five, to be rounded off and then added together. If you round them all up, the sum will be too high. If you round them all down, the sum will be too low. It is likely that about half of the digits preceding the fives will be odd. The other half will be even. If the numbers with odd digits before the fives are rounded up, and the numbers with even digits before the fives are rounded down, any errors will cancel. The sum will be more nearly correct.

Each time a number is rounded off, a small error is introduced. Thus, if a computation is lengthy and requires the calculation of several intermediate results before a final result is obtained, rounding off after each intermediate step may introduce a significant cumulative error. It is preferable to round off only once—at the very end. The availability of inexpensive hand calculators makes it easy to do this. They will carry eight to ten digits throughout all the steps, allowing intermediate results to be stored temporarily in a memory if necessary. If, for example, we had rounded off all the masses in Sample Problem 2-4 before adding, we would have obtained

Beaker	109.8	g
Chemical A	10.2	g
Chemical B	0.1	g
Chemical C	19.1	g
Total	139.2	g

This differs from the answer earlier obtained because of the cumulative errors introduced by rounding off before adding. However, the two answers are identical within experimental uncertainty.

The process of rounding off can often be used to check a computation quickly. All that is necessary is to express each factor to only one significant figure before carrying out the calculations. An approximate answer will result. E.g., the cross-sectional area of the glass tubing of Sample Problem 2-5 is approximately given by $A = \pi r^2 \approx 3 \times (3)^2 = 27 \approx 30$ mm^2. The area is somewhere around 30 mm^2 (actually 28 mm^2). If you had obtained 2.8 mm^2 or 280 mm^2 you should have suspected a misplaced decimal point. *Always check your calculations*.

2-5 Problem Solving and the Factor-Label Method

The Problem With Problems

One of the characteristics of a good chemist is the ability to solve problems. This type of skill is useful to everyone, not just to chemists. We all have to solve problems in our daily lives. Some students give up entirely. ("I can do the chemistry, but I can't do the math.") Others adopt a trial and error approach. Yet the solving of problems in chemistry is a skill that can be developed with practice.

Consider a simple example: A newborn baby has a mass of 3640 g. Express its mass in kilograms. Student A knows that the prefix "kilo" has something to do with "a thousand" and multiplies by 1000, to get a result of 3 640 000 kg. Student B has the same knowledge, but divides by 1000, to get a mass of 3.64 kg. Student C follows a more systematic approach.

The reasoning of Student C is something like this:

1. I must convert 3640 g to kilograms. I know that there are a thousand grams in a kilogram. Since a kilogram is much bigger than a gram, I will end up with fewer kilograms than grams.
2. Therefore I will divide the number of grams by 1000.
3. Therefore 3640 g = 3.64 kg.
4. It seems reasonable that a baby should have about the same mass as three or four 1 kg bags of sugar.

Step 4 is an important step, yet it is omitted by most students to their regret. Always check the reasonableness of your answer! Student A, who presumably received a zero grade for the answer 3 640 000 kg, would have soon realized the silliness of that result after a little thought. A baby with that mass would be huge and equal in mass to about 3000 compact cars.

The Factor-Label Method

Let's try another problem. How many seconds are in two minutes? "That's easy," you say. "That's not a chemistry problem." But just *how* did you leap to the answer, "120 s," so quickly after reading the question? You probably reasoned, "There are 60 s in 1 min. Therefore, in 2 min there are 2×60 s or 120 s."

In this reasoning you used an *equality*, 60 s = 1 min. If you divide both sides of an equality by the same thing, you still have an equality. Thus, division of both sides of the equality

$$60 \text{ s} = 1 \text{ min}$$

by 1 min gives

$$\frac{60 \text{ s}}{1 \text{ min}} = \frac{1 \text{ min}}{1 \text{ min}} = 1$$

The fraction 60 s/1 min is called a *conversion factor*, and it equals 1. *All conversion factors equal 1*. The multiplication of a quantity by 1 does not change its value. That is what you did, unconsciously, when you answered the question. You multiplied 2 min by 1 in the form 60 s/1 min:

$$2 \text{ min} \times \frac{60 \text{ s}}{1 \text{ min}} = 120 \text{ s}$$

The fraction 60 s/1 min was the conversion factor for converting seconds to minutes. Note that identical units are cancelled in the same way that numbers are cancelled in algebra.

Let us return to the equality, 60 s = 1 min. If we had divided both sides by 60 s, we would have obtained

$$\frac{60 \text{ s}}{60 \text{ s}} = \frac{1 \text{ min}}{60 \text{ s}} = 1$$

Thus, 1 min/60 s is also a conversion factor. There are, then, two conversion factors—60s/1 min and 1 min/60 s. They are the same except that one is inverted compared to the other. *Any conversion factor can be inverted and it will still be a conversion factor.*

How do we use conversion factors to solve a problem? It is really quite simple. All problems ask a question whose answer will be a number *and its units*. The problems will include information which consist of numbers *and their units*. You will consider the numbers and their units separately. You will multiply the information given by conversion factors so that all units are cancelled except the one you want in your answer. You may, of course, multiply by as many conversion factors as you wish, since all conversion factors equal 1.

Here is an example. How long will it take to travel the 546 km between Toronto and Montréal at an average speed of 91 km/h? The question asked is, in effect, "How many hours?" You start by writing down the units of the answer so that you can check yourself at the end.

$$x \text{ h} = \ldots$$

Then you supply the information given.

$$x \text{ h} = 546 \text{ km} \times \ldots$$

You now want to multiply the 546 km by some conversion factor which will have the units of kilometres in the denominator (to cancel the unwanted kilometres) and hours in the numerator (to produce an answer with the required units). How about the conversion factor 91 km/1 h? That won't work because it has kilometres in the numerator. Let's try the conversion factor 1 h/91 km.

$$x \text{ h} = 546 \cancel{\text{ km}} \times \frac{1 \text{ h}}{91 \cancel{\text{ km}}} = 6.0 \text{ h}$$

We have the required cancellation and the units of the answer are in hours.

If we had used the other conversion factor we would have obtained

$$x \text{ h} = 546 \text{ km} \times \frac{91 \text{ km}}{1 \text{ h}} = 50 \ 000 \text{ km}^2/\text{h}$$

Obviously the km²/h units signal an error. Also, the 50 000 hour answer should give you second thoughts about starting on a 5.5 year trip. Always check your answers for reasonableness.

This method of solving problems by using conversion factors is usually called the "conversion factor method" or the "factor-label method," because each factor is labelled with its units.

Sample Problem 2-6

If light travels 300 000 000 m/s, how many minutes are required for light to cover the 150 000 000 km between the sun and the earth?

SOLUTION

Start with

$$x \text{ min} = 150\ 000\ 000 \text{ km} \times \ldots$$

If we are to use the conversion factor 300 000 000 m/1 s or its inverse, we must find a conversion factor relating kilometres and metres. That's easy.

$$x \text{ min} = 150\ 000\ 000 \text{ km} \times \frac{1000 \text{ m}}{1 \text{ km}} \times \ldots$$

Now convert metres to seconds.

$$x \text{ min} = 150\ 000\ 000 \text{ km} \times \frac{1000 \text{ m}}{1 \text{ km}} \times \frac{1 \text{ s}}{300\ 000\ 000 \text{ m}} \times \ldots$$

Finally, convert seconds to minutes.

$$x \text{ min} = 150\ 000\ 000 \text{ km} \times \frac{1000 \text{ m}}{1 \text{ km}} \times \frac{1 \text{ s}}{300\ 000\ 000 \text{ m}} \times \frac{1 \text{ min}}{60 \text{ s}} = 8.3 \text{ min}$$

Practice Problem 2-1

How many minutes are in three weeks? (*Answer*: 30 240 min)

The factor-label method is a versatile method of problem solving. Since it is so useful, you should make a point of remembering the steps to be followed:

1. Read the problem carefully to determine what is actually *asked for*, including units, and what is *given*, including units.
2. Write the problem as a simple equality, as we did in the example where we wrote: x h $= 546$ km $\times \ldots$
3. Decide what conversion factors are needed to make the units cancel and give the desired result. In the example, we used 1 h/91 km.
4. Do the arithmetic, and check your answer to see if it is reasonable.
5. Check to make sure that the units cancel properly.
6. Check the number of significant digits.

A Final Word

In this chapter you have learned how to express the results of a measurement correctly. You have learned how to use both the numbers and their units in arithmetic calculations. You have learned how to indicate the degree of uncertainty in your measurements and in the results obtained from them. Finally, you have learned a useful and general technique for solving mathematical problems in chemistry.

Now that you have finished reading this chapter, you should reread the Key Objectives to make sure that you have learned the most important points of the chapter. In addition, you should learn the meaning of each important term found in the chapter.

Fig. 2-4 An industrial chemist analyses samples of effluent water at the chemical plant in Redwater, Alberta. (Photo courtesy of Imperial Oil Limited)

Key Terms

What is the meaning of each of the following terms?

universality	joule
units	pascal
SI	mega-
base unit	kilo-
metre	deci-
kilogram	centi-
second	milli-
kelvin	micro-
newton	significant digit

Questions

1. The concept of universality illustrates one of the differences between science and art. What is this difference?

2. What SI units would you use to express the following measurements: the diameter of a lead pencil; the temperature in your classroom; the time required for you to say the word "cheese"; your weight; your waist measurement; the area of your classroom; the distance from the earth to the sun?

3. Complete the following table:

   a) 3.15 m   =   cm   **f)** 15.5 mg   =   g
   b) 955 g   =   kg   **g)** 1620 km   =   Mm
   c) 1630 mL =   L   **h)** 144 kg   =   mg
   d) 20.0 Mg =   mg   **i)** 0.0117 mm   =   cm
   e) 178 mm =   cm   **j)** 126 mm^3 =   cm^3

4. How many cars, each 15.0 m long, are in a freight train which requires 2.00 min to pass a station while travelling at 60.0 km/h?

5. What was the cost of gasoline for a drive from Toronto to Montréal (546 km) if the car required 15.8 L/100 km and the cost of gasoline was 36.9¢/L?

6. Express the following numbers in scientific notation:
   a) 1 003 000 000 000
   b) 0.000 000 000 399 8
   c) 58.23
   d) 0.2038
   e) 12 452

7. Convert the following numbers to decimal notation:
   a) 1.776×10^7; **b)** 2.552×10^{-9}; **c)** 1.168×10^3; **d)** 4.44×10^{-1}; **e)** 1.399×10^0.

8. Express the results of the following operations in scientific notation:
   a) $(1.39 \times 10^{-2}) + (3.11 \times 10^{-4})$ **c)** $(1.34 \times 10^{24}) - (2.22 \times 10^2)$
   b) $(1.17 \times 10^4) - (3.57 \times 10^2)$ **d)** $(2.15 \times 10^5) + (1.56 \times 10^3)$

9. Express the results of the following operations in scientific notation:
   a) $(1.81 \times 10^{-3}) \times (1.06 \times 10^{20})$ **c)** $(4.44 \times 10^{-3}) \times (2.252 \times 10^2)$
   b) $(5.77 \times 10^{-4})/(1.71 \times 10^{-11})$ **d)** $(7.99 \times 10^{-3})/(1.33 \times 10^6)$

10. How many significant digits are in the following quantities?
   a) 133.31 g; **b)** 0.02 g; **c)** 24.6 cm^3; **d)** 109.9457 mL; **e)** 29 marbles.

11. How many significant digits are there in the answers to the following problems?
    a) $24.4 + 12.692 + 14.79$ **d)** $(9.93 \times 10^{23})(6.9 \times 10^{-2})$
    b) $2.229 - 0.5710$ **e)** $73 - 36.9$
    c) 10.6×6.9

12. Identify the significant digits in each of the following:
    a) 6.29; **b)** 0.0990; **c)** 42 000 (which is 4.2×10^4);
    d) 1.81×10^{-6}; **e)** 1.772×10^{10}.

13. What is the difference between a base unit and a derived unit? Give an example of each type of unit.

14. How is information communicated among scientists?

15. Why do scientists use analogies?

16. Why is it necessary to have an international system of units?

17. Why is it necessary to define units of measurement carefully?

18. What are the SI units for the following: area, volume, force, pressure, work, and energy?

19. Make any necessary corrections to the following, using the convention of style for writing measurements with SI units:
    a) 25 gs; **b)** 10 grams/cm^3; **c)** 25,000 L; **d)** fifteen milligrams;
    e) 65 km.; **f)** 80 mg per millilitre.

20. Why is it useful to be able to express numbers in scientific notation?

21. Explain why it is important to use the correct number of significant digits in expressing a measurement.

22. Are all experimental measurements uncertain? Explain.

23. Round off each of the following numbers to two significant digits:
    a) 36.4; **b)** 729; **c)** 0.145; **d)** 8.357; **e)** 0.001 07;
    f) 6.022×10^{23}.

24. Round off each of the numbers in the preceding question to one significant digit.

25. Solve each of the following problems by using the factor-label method:
    a) What distance is covered in 4.25 h by a car travelling at 95 km/h?
    b) How much does it cost to register a car with a mass of 1800 kg if the registration fee is $2.50/100 kg?
    c) How many grams of alcohol are present in 5.00 L of blood from a person with an alcohol level of 102 mg of alcohol per 100 mL of blood?

26. The concentration of pollutants used to be expressed in "parts per million" or "ppm." The SI equivalent is "milligrams per kilogram." If one drop of a liquid pollutant has a mass of 50 mg, how many litres of water (density = 1000 kg/m^3) are required to dilute the pollutant to a concentration of 1 ppm?

3 Matter

When we look at the world around us, we see that there are always changes taking place. The eruption of volcanoes, the passing of seasons, the breaking of glass, the rusting of metals, are but a few examples of change.

We can understand these changes if we understand the nature of matter. Chemistry studies the make-up of matter; how matter is put together; its behaviour under certain conditions; and the energy involved when changes in matter occur.

In order to study chemistry, we must become acquainted with the language of chemistry. The definitions and concepts presented in this chapter serve as basic vocabulary for further study.

Key Objectives

When you have finished studying this chapter, you should be able to
1. distinguish between mass and weight; between work and energy; between kinetic and potential energy.
2. state the characteristics of solids, liquids, and gases.
3. distinguish between physical and chemical properties and identify examples of each.
4. distinguish between physical changes and chemical changes and identify examples of each.
5. distinguish between pure substances and mixtures; elements and compounds; homogeneous and heterogeneous mixtures.
6. state the main points of Dalton's atomic theory, and show how it explains the laws of chemical change.

3-1 Matter and Energy

What is the earth composed of? What makes up soil, air, water, plants, and animals? What are sound, electricity, magnetism, heat, and light? We can describe the world around us as being made of matter and energy.

Matter, Mass, and Weight

Matter is defined as anything that has mass and takes up space. Matter possesses **inertia**—the tendency for a moving body to remain in motion and

for a stationary body to remain stationary. Inertia, then, is resistance to change in state of motion. For example, if you are travelling in a car and the brakes are suddenly applied, you will tend to resist this change in state of motion by moving forward in your seat.

For the most part, matter is easily recognized: e.g., wood, bricks, and water. Some forms of matter such as air are slightly more difficult to recognize as being matter until one remembers that a hovercraft is supported by a blanket of compressed air or that the high winds of a hurricane can destroy a huge building.

Mass is a measurement of the amount of matter in an object. Since matter has inertia, mass is also defined as the quantity of inertia possessed by an object. The greater the mass of a body, the more inertia it contains. For example, a large object such as a boulder is difficult to move; however, once the boulder is moving it is difficult to stop. The boulder has a great deal of inertia (mass). The unit of mass used in chemistry is the kilogram. Since the kilogram is a relatively large unit of mass, the gram (0.001 kg) is more commonly used in practice.

Fig. 3-1 A hovercraft, supported on a cushion of compressed air, moves offshore and down the Mackenzie River in the Northwest Territories. (Photo courtesy of Imperial Oil Limited)

(b)

Fig. 3-2(a) The mass of the objects on the left pan of the balance is equal to the total mass on the right pan; the position of the pointer does not change with a change in gravitational force. The force of the earth's attraction does not influence mass.
(b) The position of the pointer on the spring scale is subject to some variation from place to place on the earth's surface due to gravitational changes. This shows how the force of the Earth's attraction influences the measurement of weight.

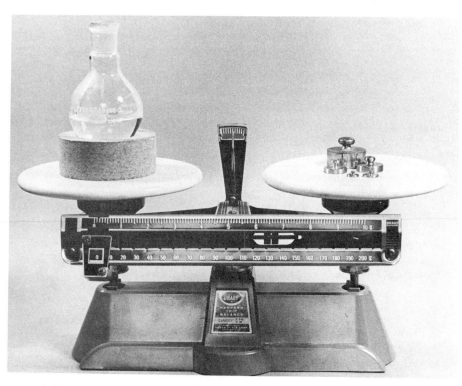

(a)

Weight is a term which is frequently confused with mass. These two terms are related, but technically they mean different things. **Weight** is a measure of the gravitational force of attraction between the earth and an object (Figs. 3-2(a) and 3-2(b)). A force is a push or a pull on an object which changes the state of rest or motion of the object. This force depends upon the mass of the object and its distance from the centre of the earth. The mass of an object is constant, but the pull of the earth's gravity is not the same everywhere on the earth's surface. Therefore, the weight of a given object does change. If that object is taken far enough from the surface of the earth, the pull of gravity becomes negligible (too small to have any effect), and the object becomes essentially weightless. However, the object still possesses the same amount of mass that it has always possessed.

Energy

A hummingbird hovers, a worm burrows through the earth, oil burns in a furnace, you turn the pages of a book—all these actions involve energy. **Energy** is the ability to do work. **Work** can be defined as the moving of matter against a force which opposes the motion. For example, when you walk up the stairs or lift a book, you are doing work. You are moving matter against a force which opposes the motion—the force of gravity. The energy required to do this work comes from the food you eat.

Energy is subdivided into two main categories: kinetic energy and potential energy. **Kinetic energy** is energy of motion. A moving object such as a stone can pass through a glass window if it has enough kinetic energy to shatter the glass. **Potential energy**, on the other hand, is the energy of position. A book held above a desk has potential energy. If the book is allowed to fall, it acquires kinetic energy. The potential energy grows smaller and the kinetic energy grows larger as the book nears the surface of the desk. When the book hits the desk, its kinetic energy is used to increase the temperature of both the book and the desk.

The potential energy of the book depends on the definition of zero potential energy. For example, we can define the potential energy of the book, when it is placed on the desk, to be zero. When the book is above the desk, its potential energy is larger than zero. As the book falls to the desk, its potential energy decreases to zero. However, if the book were to fall past the desk to the floor, its potential energy would become less than zero. Thus the potential energy can have values greater than zero, equal to zero, or less than zero. The actual value depends on where we have defined the zero level of potential energy to be. In this example negative values of potential energy can be eliminated simply by defining floor level rather than desk level as zero potential energy.

There are many forms of potential energy. The energy stored in a tightly wound spring, for example, is a form of *mechanical energy* which is able to drive the hands of a clock. When energy from the sun reaches the earth, a portion of it is absorbed by green plants and converted by photosynthesis into *chemical energy* (another form of potential energy). The chemical energy stored in plants is useful because it can be converted into heat energy or, by use of thermal generating stations, into *electrical energy* (Fig. 3-3).

The transformation of energy from one form to another is the basis for change in the material world (Fig. 3-4). When the radiant energy of the sun

Fig. 3-3 This oil-fired thermal generating station located at Dartmouth, Nova Scotia produces 350 MW of power.

Fig. 3-4 Energy Transformations

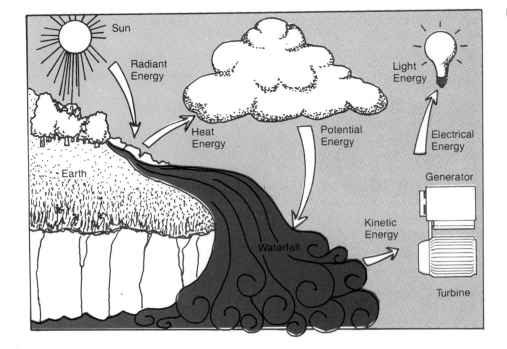

reaches the earth, some of it is converted to heat energy. This heat causes water to evaporate and rise to form clouds. When the water falls to earth again and flows in waterfalls such as the one at Churchill Falls, Labrador, the potential energy of the water is converted to kinetic energy. This can be used to drive the blades of a turbine and produce the mechanical energy necessary to operate a generator. The generator converts part of it to electrical energy, which may in turn be used to toast bread (heat energy) and to light a room (light energy).

Law of Conservation of Mass and Energy

What is the relationship between matter and energy? At one time it was believed that there was a constant quantity of matter (i.e., mass) in the universe. It was also believed that there was a constant quantity of energy in the universe. These generalizations were known as the Laws of Conservation of Mass and Conservation of Energy respectively. The study of nuclear reactions has led to the discovery that in some cases mass can be converted into energy, and vice versa. This knowledge gave rise to the **Law of Conservation of Mass and Energy**. This law states that the total quantity of matter and energy in the universe is constant. An increase in the amount of matter must be balanced by an equivalent decrease in the amount of energy, and vice versa. In chemical processes, any change of mass into energy is too small to be detected. However, in nuclear processes, the change in the quantity of matter is large enough to be measured.

3-2 The Three States of Matter

Solid

The three states of matter are the solid, liquid, and gaseous states. Matter in the **solid** state has a definite shape and volume (Fig. 3-5). A solid object will have a

Fig. 3-5 Solids, Liquids, and Gases
(a) Bulk properties
(b) Explanation of those properties

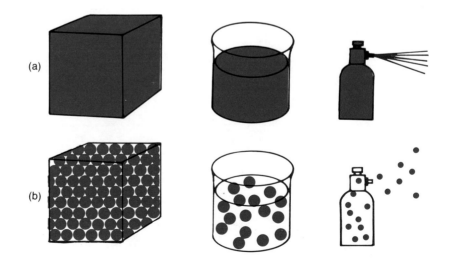

(a)

(b)

constant size and shape regardless of the container in which it is placed. Factors such as temperature and pressure have little effect on solids. That is, solids do not expand or contract very much when they are heated or cooled, and they are not easily compressed. These and many other properties of solids can be explained. We assume that the particles which make up the solid are held closely together in fixed positions by strong attractive forces.

Liquid

Matter in the **liquid** state has a definite volume, but it does not have a definite shape. A liquid takes the shape of the container into which it is poured (Fig. 3-5). Liquids may be compressed slightly, but for most purposes, it is safe to assume that they do have a constant volume. This incompressibility of liquids means that a pressure exerted on a liquid will be transmitted equally in all directions. Use is made of this property in the automotive hydraulic brake system. When the brakes are applied, the pressure is transmitted from the master-cylinder by the brake fluid to the slave-cylinders connected to the brake shoes. The brake shoes press against the revolving brake drums to slow or stop the car. It is easy to explain these properties by assuming that the particles of a liquid are held together by attractive forces which are not quite as strong as those in solids. The particles are not as close to each other as they are in solids, and are able to slide, glide, and slip over one another with relative ease.

Gas

Matter in the gaseous state has neither definite volume nor a definite shape (Fig. 3-5). A **gas** takes both the shape and the volume of the container in which it is placed. Factors such as temperature and pressure have such a large effect on a gas that it is pointless to consider a given volume of gas unless both its temperature and pressure are known. The tank on a scuba diver's back would contain enough air to supply his lungs for only a very short time if it were at normal atmospheric pressure. By forcing more air into the tank at pressures of one thousand to two thousand times that of the atmosphere, the supply of air can be enormously increased with no change in the size of the container. This principle is also used by firefighters, mine rescue personnel, and others who require a self-contained supply of air for work in the presence of toxic gases. These properties are understandable if we assume that the particles of a gas are extremely small and far apart from each other, so that their volume is negligible in comparison with the volume of the container. Furthermore, the attractive forces between the particles are also negligible.

According to modern theories, these gas particles are so small that in a room at normal temperature only about 0.05% of the volume of the room is occupied by the particles. The rest is empty space. This means that the total volume of all the air particles in a room (4 m long, 3 m wide, and 2.5 m high) is less than the volume of a standard basketball.

3-3 Changes in States of Matter

As you know, one substance, water, can exist in three different states. In the form of ice, it exists in the solid state; as water, it is in the liquid state; and when it evaporates or boils away into the atmosphere as water vapour, it is in the gaseous state. Many other substances exhibit similar properties.

How can we explain what is happening when a solid changes to a liquid or a liquid changes to the gaseous state, or vice versa? Suppose, for example, we remove an ice cube from the freezer and measure its temperature—assume it is −20°C. Now we gradually add heat energy to the cube, and notice that its temperature rises smoothly until it reaches 0°C. At this point the temperature stops rising, even though heat energy is still being added to the ice cube, and we notice that the solid ice is being converted to liquid water. We have reached the melting point of the ice. When all the ice has melted the water warms up until the liquid reaches a temperature of 100°C. The temperature of the water again remains constant as heat is added, but again we notice something happening— bubbles of a gas are forming within the body of the liquid. They rise to the surface and break. The liquid is being converted into a gas, and we have reached the boiling point of the liquid. If the container is closed, the temperature of the gas will again start to rise after the last drop of water has been converted to a gas. These changes are indicated schematically in Fig. 3-6.

Fig. 3-6 Warming Curve for a Pure Substance (Water)

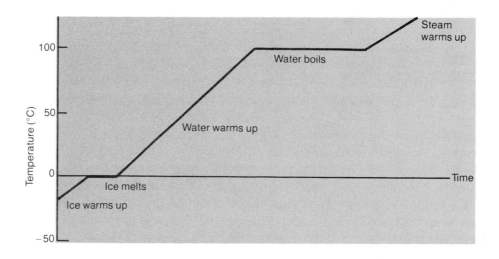

What is happening within the water sample in each of these states as the various changes take place? We have already noted that the particles of a solid are held closely together in a fixed position by strong attractive forces (Fig. 3-5). The various parts of these particles can vibrate back and forth, much as you might rhythmically move your arms in and out from your sides. The particles have vibrational energy (Fig. 3-7). The particles are held so rigidly in position in the ice crystal, however, that they can move only minute distances from their original positions. They do not have much sideways motion or translational energy (Latin *trans*, across + *latus*, carried) in any direction. The situation is analogous to a dance floor in which the couples are crowded together near the band. They can move arms and legs, and perhaps change distances between partners, but the couples do not move far from their starting positions on the dance floor.

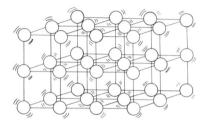

Fig. 3-7 Vibration of Particles in a Simple Solid Crystal

As heat energy is added the translational energy of the water particles increases, and they begin to move greater distances from their original positions. Eventually some of them are able to overcome the attractive forces of their neighbours. In addition to their increased translational motions, the particles rotate more freely. They have increased translational and rotational energies. There is so much movement that the crystal starts to fall apart. The ice starts to melt. At this point the addition of more heat does not cause the temperature to rise. It is simply used to overcome the attractive forces. That is, it raises the potential energy of the particles. Fig. 3-8 represents translational, vibrational, and rotational motions of a dumbbell-shaped particle. Similarly, an increase in tempo and loudness of music will cause couples on the dance floor to move ever more vigorously. The couples will move further apart until eventually some of them will be able to move back and forth through the sea of bodies surrounding them.

Water particles are able to slide past each other, but the attractive forces still hold the particles relatively closely together. As heat energy is added to a liquid, the particles gain ever more translational and rotational energies until eventually many of them are able to overcome the restraining attractive forces between particles and escape into the gaseous state. At this point the temperature will remain constant, because the heat energy is being used to move the particles away from each other in opposition to the attractive forces, thus increasing their potential energy.

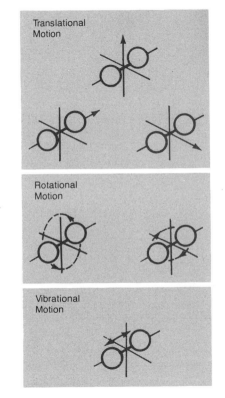

Translational Motion

Rotational Motion

Vibrational Motion

Fig. 3-8 Motions of a Dumbbell-Shaped Particle

Finally, when the last bit of water has boiled away, the temperature of the gas will again begin to rise, because the heat energy is used to increase the total kinetic energy of the particles.

In summary, then, the addition of energy to a substance such as ice will bring about changes by causing the particles to move further apart. The internal energy, that is, the total energy contained in a sample of matter is increased, largely because the translational kinetic energy of the particles is increased. This increase in internal energy results in either a rise in the temperature or a change in the state (melting or boiling) of the system.

3-4 Physical and Chemical Properties

Different kinds of matter are recognized by their properties. A **property** is a quality or characteristic. For example, diamonds are hard; copper wire is a good conductor of electricity; oxygen gas is colourless; and iron rusts. The properties of matter can be divided into two classes: physical and chemical properties.

Physical Properties

The **physical properties** of a substance are those properties which can be determined without changing its composition or make-up. Mercury, for example, is an odourless liquid with a characteristic silvery luster. It does not dissolve in water. It is an excellent conductor of electricity. It freezes at $-39°C$ and boils at $357°C$. Properties such as colour, odour, hardness, melting point, boiling point, electrical conductivity, and many others are examples of physical properties. They do not involve changing the composition of the mercury to that of some other substance. Thus, the density of mercury is also one of its physical properties. **Density** is defined as the mass of an object per unit volume of the object. One cubic centimetre of mercury has a mass of 13.6 g. Hence the density of mercury is 1.36×10^4 kg/m^3. Since density can be measured using only devices for determining mass and volume, and without changing the mercury into some other substance, it is a physical property.

Chemical Properties

The **chemical properties** of a substance are those properties which can be observed only when the substance undergoes a change in composition. It is difficult to distinguish pyrite (fool's gold) from gold because they are physically so much alike. Yet it is quite easy to distinguish them chemically. Concentrated nitric acid has no effect on gold, but it reacts with pyrite to give a soluble product, iron(III) nitrate, and a residue of insoluble sulfur. Charcoal (carbon) burns in air to give a mixture of two gases, carbon monoxide and carbon dioxide. An iron nail immersed in water gradually becomes coated with a layer of rust. These properties are all chemical properties because they involve changing various kinds of matter into other substances with different compositions, different structures, and different properties. Such changes or transformations are called **chemical reactions**. The formation of iron(III) nitrate and sulfur by the action of nitric acid on pyrite is an example of a chemical reaction. Burning charcoal involves a reaction between carbon and oxygen; the rusting of iron involves a chemical reaction between iron and oxygen.

A substance can often be identified by observing its chemical and physical properties. Silver and platinum are both beautiful silvery white metals used extensively in jewelry. Silver melts at $961°C$, boils at $2212°C$, and has a density of 1.05×10^4 kg/m^3. Platinum melts at $1769°C$, boils at $3827°C$, and has a density of 2.14×10^4 kg/m^3. They can be distinguished and identified by these differences in their physical properties. For a chemist, perhaps the easiest way to distinguish them would be to test a small amount of each metal with nitric acid. Silver dissolves readily in nitric acid with a vigorous chemical reaction, whereas platinum is completely unaffected by the acid.

Quantitative and Qualitative Properties

Both physical and chemical properties can be further subdivided into two categories, quantitative and qualitative properties. A **quantitative property** is one that can be measured. Numbers will be used in expressing a quantitative property. Thus, to say that aluminum has a melting point of 660°C, a boiling point of 2467°C, and a density of 2.7×10^3 kg/m^3, is really to give a list of some quantitative physical properties of aluminum. On the other hand, statements to the effect that 1 g of aluminum will react with dilute hydrochloric acid to produce 112 mg of hydrogen gas, or that the burning of 32.1 g of sulfur to form sulfur dioxide releases 297 kJ of heat energy, are examples of quantitative chemical properties of those elements.

Qualitative properties, on the other hand, are those which cannot be expressed numerically, such as appearance and odour. To say that carbon monoxide is a colourless, odourless gas is to state two of its qualitative physical properties. If we state that it is poisonous and burns with a pale blue flame we are mentioning some of its qualitative chemical properties.

3-5 Physical and Chemical Changes in Matter

Now we shall consider the two types of change that substances undergo: physical and chemical change.

Physical Change

A **physical change** is a change which alters one or more of the properties of the substance with no change in its composition or identity. When liquid water freezes to ice, one of its properties changes: it no longer pours—but it is still water. When water boils and is converted into water vapour, another property changes: it no longer has a definite volume—but again it is still water. Water retains the same chemical composition whether it is in the form of a solid, a liquid, or a gas. Changes of state, such as melting, freezing, or boiling are physical changes because they do not change the composition or chemical identity of the substance. The tungsten filament in a light bulb becomes white hot when electricity is passed through it, but it is still tungsten. This is again a physical change because the tungsten filament is not converted to any other substance during the passage of the electric current.

Chemical Change

A **chemical change** is a change in a substance which converts it into a different kind (or different kinds) of matter each with a different composition and new properties. When paper burns, it is converted mainly into two gases, carbon dioxide and water vapour, both of which differ in composition and properties from the original paper. The rusting of iron gives a product, rust, which is different in composition and properties from the original iron. At least one new substance, different in composition and properties from the original sub- stances, must be produced whenever a chemical change occurs. The burning of gasoline in an automobile engine and the preparation of caramel by heating sugar are other examples of chemical changes.

3-6 Classification of Matter

Pure Substances

A **pure substance** is a homogeneous (uniform) material. It consists of only one particular kind of matter and has the same properties throughout. It always has the same composition. Diamond is a pure substance. It consists only of carbon. Pure substances are classified into two categories: elements and compounds.

Elements are pure substances that cannot be broken down into simpler substances by ordinary chemical methods. Carbon, oxygen, and iron are examples of elements.

Compounds are pure substances, consisting of two or more elements in combination. Compounds may be decomposed into two or more simpler substances by ordinary chemical methods. Pure water is a *pure substance* by virtue of the fact that it is homogeneous and consists of only one kind of matter. It is a *compound* by virtue of the fact that it can be broken down into hydrogen and oxygen.

When a compound is prepared, the original components lose their identities, and they can then be separated only by chemical means. When compounds are prepared, evidence of chemical reaction (e.g., heat or light) can usually be observed.

Mixtures

A **mixture** is a combination of two or more pure substances each of which retains its own physical and chemical properties. Many mixtures are heterogeneous (nonuniform). A **heterogeneous mixture** consists of more than one phase. The word **phase** is used to mean any region with a uniform set of properties. For example, a mixture of sand and water is composed of two phases. One phase is the solid sand. The second phase is the liquid water. A heterogeneous mixture is easily identified because the borderline or interface between the different phases is easily seen. A salami, mushroom, and cheese pizza is a heterogeneous mixture with several identifiable components. If you look carefully, you will see that even the salami itself is a heterogeneous mixture. If you had the time and patience you could manually separate the pizza into its components.

Milk is actually a heterogeneous mixture. If you examine it closely with a microscope, you will see that it consists of small fat droplets suspended in a water layer. The fat droplets are less dense than water and eventually rise to the top as cream. This process can be speeded up by spinning the milk in a separator.

The important point to note is that heterogeneous mixtures are not uniform throughout. Different portions have different properties (salami is different from mushroom). Furthermore, heterogeneous mixtures can be of variable composition—you can always ask for more salami and less mushroom. A mixture of oil and vinegar can contain any proportion of oil and

Fig. 3-9 Examples of Heterogenous Mixtures
(a) A two-phase system consisting of a solid and a liquid
(b) A four-phase system consisting of four different liquids
(c) A three-phase system consisting of solid ice, liquid water, and water vapour in air

(a)   **(b)**   **(c)**

vinegar. This variability of composition is a feature that distinguishes mixtures from pure substances. Figure 3-9 illustrates a number of heterogeneous mixtures consisting of different numbers of phases.

A **homogeneous** or one-phase mixture is called a **solution**. A homogeneous mixture is uniform throughout. A solution of sugar dissolved in water is an example of a homogeneous mixture. What has been said about heterogeneous mixtures can also be said about homogeneous mixtures or solutions but with one caution. A homogeneous mixture of sugar and water cannot be prepared using *any* quantity of sugar and *any* quantity of water. One cannot dissolve one kilogram of sugar in a drop of water.

Except for certain solutions (e.g., ethyl alcohol and water) the solubility of one substance in another is limited (or has a maximum value). A solution of one metal (or several) in another is called an **alloy**. Mixtures do have variable composition, but usually the composition of a solution can vary only within certain limits. The various ways in which matter can be classified are summarized in Fig. 3-10.

It is fairly easy in principle to tell whether a homogeneous sample of matter is a pure substance or a mixture. If it is a solid we can determine its

Fig. 3-10 Classification of Matter

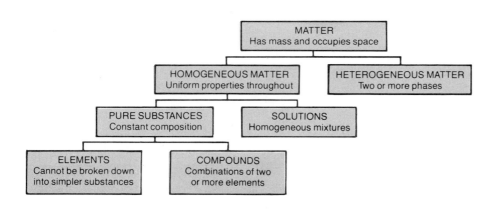

melting point. We have already seen that if a pure solid substance is heated slowly it melts at a characteristic temperature (the melting point of ice is 0°C). As long as any solid remains the temperature will stay constant (Fig. 3-6). The temperature rises only when the sample is completely melted. Thus, a pure substance has a sharp, characteristic melting point.

An impure solid, on the other hand, does not have a sharp melting point. It melts over a range of temperatures. The solid begins to melt at a temperature lower than that of the pure substance, and the temperature rises steadily as more of the solid continues to melt (Fig. 3-11). Thus a mixture usually has a melting point which is lower and covers a wider range of temperatures than a pure substance does. This is a familiar phenomenon to residents of Canada's Atlantic coast. When the temperature is cold enough, both fresh water and salt water will freeze. When the weather warms up, however, the impure salt-water ice begins to melt at a much lower temperature than does the ice on fresh-water streams and ponds.

Fig. 3-11 Warming Curve for an Impure Substance (Salt Solution)

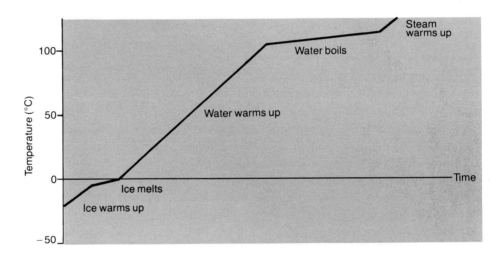

In a similar manner it is possible to test for the purity of a liquid. In this case we will look for a constant temperature as the liquid boils. A pure liquid has a characteristic boiling point. For example, at sea level water boils at 100°C. This temperature remains constant as long as any liquid is present. (It is only after the water has completely boiled away that the bottom of a kettle can get hot enough to melt.) If the liquid is impure the temperature usually rises steadily as the liquid boils (Fig. 3-11). On this fact is based the secret of making successful fudge—water is boiled away from the mixture of sugar and other ingredients until the temperature has risen to an appropriate level.

3-7 Discovery of the Elements

The earliest source of chemical energy was fire. Long before members of the human race had learned to start a fire—thought to be about two million years ago—they had learned how to keep it going. Once they had managed this, they were able to practise chemistry.

Using fire, these people found about eight thousand years ago that shiny materials sometimes melted out of heated rocks. Thus they discovered soft metals such as copper, silver, and gold. These substances were easily hammered into various shapes and could be used to make pieces of jewelry, tools, or weapons. Lead, tin, iron, mercury, carbon, and sulfur had also been discovered by this time. Then, about five thousand years ago, it was found that a little tin added to melted copper changed its properties. The new substance (bronze) was much tougher and made superior tools and weapons. Thus began the Bronze Age. Whole empires were built around this technological breakthrough. There was a thriving tin trade between Phoenicia and the tin mines in Cornwall, England at least as long ago as 1000 B.C., and a prehistoric mine near Salzburg, Germany, is believed to have produced 20 kt (kilotonnes) of copper during this period.

Elements have also been responsible for the fall of empires. The Romans used lead goblets and lead water pipes. Small amounts of lead dissolved in the wine, fruit juices, and water are believed to have caused a form of chronic lead poisoning which weakened the population and led to its eventual overthrow by the barbarians.

The art of working with metals had interesting effects for chemistry. When the Greek philosophers saw ordinary minerals going into the foundries at Alexandria, Egypt, and large amounts of gold and silver coming out, they naturally assumed that the craftsmen were changing base substances into gold and silver. The craftsmen did not give out their trade secrets. Thus the search for the elusive ''philosopher's stone,'' a magical substance which could change base substances into gold and silver, began.

The alchemists (Arabic *al*, the + Greek *chymeia*, pouring, as of molten metal) continued the search for centuries without success. In the process, however, they made many important discoveries. By the middle of the 18th century they had isolated phosphorus, zinc, arsenic, antimony, and bismuth.

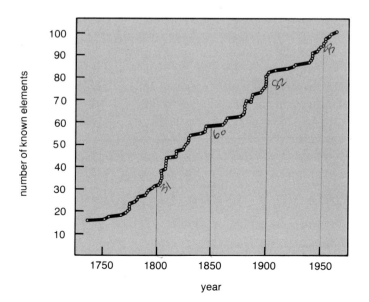

Fig. 3-12 Chronology of the Discovery of the Elements

Fig. 3-13 Humphrey Davy (1778-1829) (Photo courtesy of The Bettman Archive, Inc.)

Humphrey Davy was born in Cornwall, England, the eldest of eight children. He did badly at school, mainly because of his love of sport. At age 16 he started assisting a local physician with the preparation of remedies, but his taste for startling experiments and explosions quickly got him fired.

At 19, he began his study of chemistry, using materials and apparatus at hand. He made such progress that he was placed in charge of patients at the Pneumatic Institution, which had been established to study the medical effects of the gases discovered in the previous twenty years. He inhaled many gases such as N_2O, CH_4, CO_2, N_2, H_2, and NO. Somehow, he managed to survive.

He prepared N_2O in large quantities by heating NH_4NO_3. Sniffing N_2O became a fad, and Davy's resulting popularity led to his appointment at the age of 22 as an assistant lecturer at the Royal Philosophical Institution of London. Here he prepared a treatise on agricultural science which was the authority for the next 50 years.

He began studies on electrolysis, and quickly isolated for the first time the elements K, Na, Ba, Sr, Ca, and Mg. He discovered H_2Te and PH_3, and proved that Cl_2 and I_2 were elements. He invented the safety lamp for miners. He also discovered that he could protect the copper sheathing of naval vessels from corrosion by attaching to it a more reactive metal. At the age of 34 he was knighted and six years later he was made a baronet. At age 42 he became President of the Royal Society.

His health began to decline in 1826, and in 1829 at the age of 51 he died, one of the most remarkable men of his time.

The crudeness of their experimental techniques, however, still limited them to discovering only the easily obtainable elements.

The number of known elements increased from 21 to about 50 between 1775 and 1830. During these years new techniques were devised and new theories were proposed. The theories led to predictions about the existence of new elements, and the search for new elements was based on principles rather than chance. Advances in experimental technique were usually responsible for rapid increases in the number of known elements (Fig. 3-12 , previous page).

An example of the importance of new experimental technique is shown in the work of Sir Humphrey Davy (Fig. 3-13). At that time the scientific world was interested in the study of ''voltaic'' electricity. Davy, with a well-equipped laboratory at the Royal Philosophical Institution at his disposal, enthusiastically joined in these studies. He succeeded in constructing cells (batteries) which were more efficient than previous ones. By 1807 he had succeeded in producing sodium and potassium by passing an electric current through certain of their compounds. The following year in quick succession he isolated boron, magnesium, calcium, strontium, and barium. In less than two years one person had added seven elements to the list, all as the result of an improved experimental technique. Other sharp rises in the curve in Fig. 3-12 are due to similar advances in experimental technique.

Few new elements were discovered in the first half of this century, and by about 1940 all the 90 naturally-occurring elements had been discovered. Since

4-3 The Nuclear Atom

It had finally been shown that the atom was not a solid, indestructible particle. By the late 1800s, the atom was known to be made up of at least two kinds of particles—electrons and protons.

Thomson's Model of the Atom

In 1898, J.J. Thomson proposed a model to explain the arrangement of protons and electrons in the atom. Thomson considered the atom to be a sphere of positive electricity in which negative electrons were embedded like raisins in a plum pudding (Fig. 4-7). It had been shown that protons had more mass than electrons, and therefore most of the atom's mass was thought to be associated with the positive charge.

Meanwhile, the discovery of radioactivity was made by the French physicist Henri Becquerel in 1896. While studying metals that fluoresce (give off light), he found accidentally that a covered photographic plate became fogged when it was placed near a uranium ore. He wrapped photographic plates in thin sheets of aluminum and copper and placed them near the uranium ore. Again the photographic plates were blackened when they were developed. Becquerel decided that the uranium salts emit invisible rays which, unlike light, are able to pass through black paper and thin sheets of metal. A substance that gives off these invisible rays is said to be *radioactive*.

The New Zealand-born British physicist Lord Rutherford (Fig. 4-8) discovered that the invisible rays from radium were actually composed of three different rays. Some were positively charged, some were negatively charged, and others were uncharged. He named these alpha, beta, and gamma rays, respectively. The experiment which led Rutherford to these conclusions is described in Section 19-3. It is worth noting that Rutherford performed this important experiment while he was head of the physics department at McGill University in Montréal. Later, Rutherford conclusively proved that alpha particles were positive helium ions—helium atoms which had each lost both their electrons. These experiments with radioactivity set the stage for an experiment by Lord Rutherford which shed considerable light on the structure of the atom.

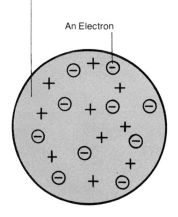

Fig. 4-7 J.J. Thomson's Plum Pudding Model of the Atom

The Gold Foil Experiment

In 1911, Lord Rutherford investigated the scattering of alpha particles by thin sheets of gold metal (Fig. 4-9). Alpha particles from a radioactive source passed through a hole in a lead plate and were allowed to strike a sheet of gold foil. The movable zinc sulfide detector gave off a flash of light whenever it was struck by an alpha particle.

Fig. 4-8 Ernest Rutherford (1871 – 1937) (C-18230 Public Archives Canada)

Ernest Rutherford was born in New Zealand, the fourth in a family of twelve children.

After graduating in mathematics and physics from the University of New Zealand, Rutherford was the first research student to join J.J. Thomson at Cambridge University. One of his research projects at Cambridge involved ingenious methods for measuring the velocities of ions. Rutherford once said: "Ions are jolly little beggars, you can almost see them!"

From 1898 to 1907 Rutherford was professor of physics at McGill University in Montréal, where he worked on radioactivity. In 1903, he published important results on the nature and properties of alpha particles which led him to believe that they are helium ions.

Rutherford became a professor of physics at the University of Manchester in 1907. It was there that he proved that alpha particles are helium ions. However, Rutherford's greatest contribution to atomic theory came in 1911, when he proposed the nuclear model for the atom.

Rutherford spent the years from 1919 until he died in 1937 at Cambridge University. In 1919, he became the first person to change one element into another, when he bombarded nitrogen with alpha particles to produce oxygen atoms. Changing elements into other elements was the crowning achievement of his life's work and held for Rutherford a deep fascination.

Rutherford was awarded the Nobel Prize in Chemistry in 1908, and he was knighted in 1914. In 1931, he was made Baron Rutherford of Nelson and took his seat in the House of Lords. Sir James Jeans said, "Rutherford was ever the happy warrior—happy in his work, happy in its outcome, and happy in its human contacts." Rutherford had great energy, intense enthusiasm, and an immense capacity for work.

A writer once said to him, "You are a lucky man, Rutherford, always on the crest of the wave." Rutherford laughingly replied, "Well! I made the wave, didn't I?"

Fig. 4-9 Rutherford's Gold Foil Experiment

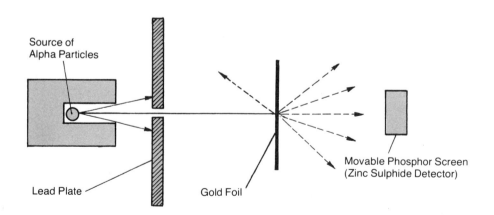

Source of Alpha Particles

Lead Plate

Gold Foil

Movable Phosphor Screen (Zinc Sulphide Detector)

According to the Thomson model of 1898, atoms are essentially a sphere of uniform positive charge in which the negative particles are embedded. Since alpha particles have high speed, they should penetrate the foil. If the positive charge of an atom is uniformly distributed, an alpha particle would have little reason to swerve from its original path. It should pass through the foil without being deflected (Fig. 4-10).

Rutherford found that most of the alpha particles did pass through the gold undeflected, but some were deflected quite a lot. In fact, some were reflected back towards the lead plate. Rutherford was astonished. He said "it was almost as incredible as if you fired a 15-inch shell at a piece of tissue paper and it came back and hit you."

The Thomson model could not explain this result. According to that model, an alpha particle would never encounter a large enough obstacle to force it to be reflected. Rutherford proposed his own model to account for his experiment. He suggested that the mass and the positive charge in the gold atoms must be concentrated in very small regions. Most of the alpha particles could pass through; however, occasionally one came close to a high concentration of positive charge and mass. The large amount of mass made the positive charge immovable. As the positive alpha particles came near these positive particles in the atom, the repulsion of like charges caused the alpha particles to swerve (Fig. 4-11).

Rutherford suggested that an atom had a **nucleus** or center in which the positive charge and most of the mass were located. This nucleus occupied only a tiny portion of the volume of the entire atom. If a large football stadium were to represent the volume of the entire atom, a housefly in the center of the stadium could represent the size of the nucleus. In the nuclear atom, the electrons occupy the volume of the atom which surrounds the nucleus.

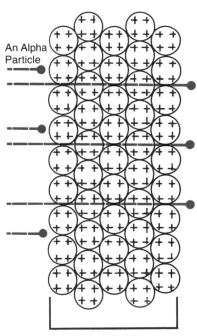

Fig. 4-10 **Predicted Passage of Alpha Particles Through a Thomson Model of the Atom. (The electrons have been omitted to simplify the diagram.)**

Neutrons

The third fundamental particle of the atom was not discovered until 1932, when the British physicist James Chadwick bombarded atoms of beryllium with high-speed particles. He found that a beam of rays was emitted from the beryllium during the bombardment. Since these rays travelled at only about one-tenth the speed of light, they could not be true radiation. Also, since the rays were unaffected by a magnet, they could not be charged. Chadwick was able to show that they were actually a stream of uncharged particles. These particles were called **neutrons**. The atomic mass of a neutron was found to be 1.0087 u. In the nuclear atom, the neutrons occupy the nucleus along with the protons.

Rutherford's gold foil experiment has improved our view of the atom. We believe that the atom has a dense, tiny centre or nucleus. The protons and neutrons are located in this nucleus, and are the major contributors to the mass of the atom. The protons contribute the positive charge of the atom. The electrons surround the nucleus, and occupy most of the volume of the atom. They do not contribute very much to the mass of the atom, but they do contribute its negative charge.

In the next section we will find out why atoms of the same element are able to have different masses.

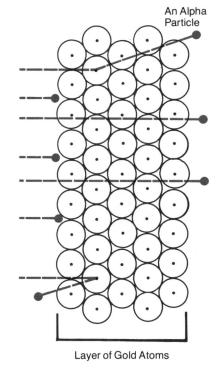

Fig. 4-11 **Passage of Alpha Particles Through a Nuclear Atom**

4-4 The Structure of the Atom

The nuclear atom is the basis of our present theory of atomic structure. The protons and neutrons are called **nucleons**. Together they reside in the nucleus, which is a minute but very dense part of the atom. The positive charge of the protons in the nucleus is balanced by the negative charge of the electrons around the nucleus in a neutral atom. The neutrons have no charge. The extranuclear (outside the nucleus) region, which makes up virtually all of the volume of the atom, contains only the electrons. The radii of atoms are around 10^{-10} m, but nuclei have radii in the range of 10^{-15} to 10^{-14} m. The nucleus contributes almost no volume to the atom, but it contains essentially the entire mass of the atom.

Atomic Number

The number of protons in the nucleus is called the **atomic number** (Z). Every atom of each element has a particular number of protons. That is, all oxygen atoms have 8 protons. If an atom has a number of protons other than 8, it is not an oxygen atom. In a neutral atom, Z is also the number of electrons. Oxygen is element number 8, and a neutral oxygen atom has 8 protons and 8 electrons.

Mass Number

The atomic mass of the proton is 1.0073 u. The atomic mass of the neutron is 1.0087 u. Thus, the approximate masses of the proton and of the neutron are 1 u. The mass of the electron is 0.000 55 u or approximately 0 u compared to the mass of the nucleons. The total number of protons and neutrons in an atom is called the **mass number**, A, and it is approximately equal to the mass of the whole atom. A specific atom may be referred to by using a symbol with both the atomic number and the mass number. For example, the symbol $^{12}_{6}C$ indicates a carbon atom that has $Z = 6$ and $A = 12$. The atom has 6 protons and a total mass of 12 u. The atom contains a total of 12 protons and neutrons, but it contains 6 protons. Therefore, it must also contain 6 neutrons. This atom is the carbon-12 mentioned in Chapter 3.

Sample Problem 4-1

How many electrons, protons, and neutrons are in an atom for which the atomic number is 92 and the mass number is 235?

SOLUTION

The atomic number is the number of protons in the atom.

$\therefore$ There are 92 protons.

The number of electrons must equal the number of protons.

$\therefore$ There are 92 electrons.

The mass number is the sum of the number of protons and the number of neutrons.

$\therefore$ The number of neutrons is $235 - 92 = 143$.

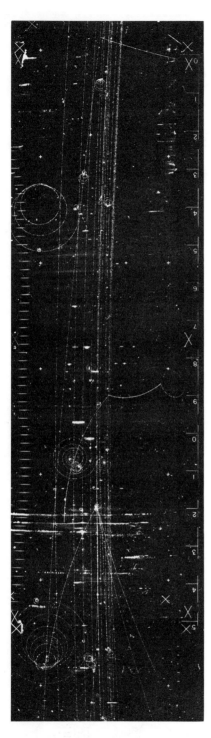

Fig. 4-12 A beam of high energy particles enters a hydrogen bubble chamber at the top of the photograph. Electrons knocked out of the hydrogen atoms produce tightly curled tracks, while protons and other particles result in tracks at an angle to the beam.

Practice Problem 4-1

How many electrons, protons, and neutrons are in an atom for which the atomic number is 103 and the mass number is 257?

Isotopes

All atoms of the same element must have the same number of protons, but they need not all have the same number of neutrons. Atoms which have the same number of protons but different numbers of neutrons are called **isotopes**. Isotopes are atoms that have the same atomic number but different mass numbers. For example, two isotopes of lithium are ^6_3Li and ^7_3Li. The first isotope has three neutrons, and the second one has four neutrons. These isotopes have the same chemical properties, but they have slightly different physical properties.

The atomic mass for lithium found in the table of atomic masses is calculated from the masses of the two isotopes: ^6_3Li makes up 7.4% of all lithium atoms, and ^7_3Li makes up the other 92.6%. Of 1000 lithium atoms, 74 have a mass number of 6 (actual mass 6.015 u) and 926 have a mass number of 7 (actual mass 7.016 u). The average mass is

$$(74 \times 6.015 \text{ u} + 926 \times 7.016 \text{ u}) \div 1000 = 6.94 \text{ u}.$$

The existence of isotopes explains why some elements have average atomic masses that are not close to whole numbers. For example, the atomic mass for chlorine is calculated from the masses of two isotopes: $^{35}_{17}Cl$ makes up 75.5% of all naturally occurring chlorine atoms, and $^{37}_{17}Cl$ makes up the other 24.5%. The average atomic mass of chlorine is 35.5 u. The compositions of the isotopes of a number of elements are given in Table 4-1.

Sample Problem 4-2

Natural carbon consists of 98.89% carbon-12 and 1.11% carbon-13 (actual mass 13.0033 u). What is the average atomic mass of natural carbon?

SOLUTION
Assume you have 10 000 atoms of carbon. Then there will be 9889 atoms of $^{12}_6C$ and 111 atoms of $^{13}_6C$.

$$\text{Total atomic mass} = 9889 \times 12.000 + 111 \times 13.0033$$
$$= 120\ 111 \text{ u}$$
$$\text{Average atomic mass} = 120\ 111 \text{ u}/10\ 000 = 12.0111 \text{ u}$$

Practice Problem 4-2

Natural neon contains 90.92% $^{20}_{10}Ne$ (mass 20.0 u), 0.26% $^{21}_{10}Ne$ (mass 21.0 u) and 8.82% $^{22}_{10}Ne$ (mass 22.0 u). Show that this gives an average atomic mass for neon of 20.2 u.

TABLE 4-1 Table of Isotopes

ATOMIC NUMBER	ELEMENT	SYMBOL OF ISOTOPE	ABUNDANCE IN NATURE (%)	ATOMIC MASS
1	Hydrogen	^1_1H	99.985	1.007 825
		^2_1H	0.015	2.014 0
2	Helium	^3_2He	0.000 13	3.016 03
		^4_2He	100	4.002 60
3	Lithium	^6_3Li	7.42	6.015 12
		^7_3Li	92.58	7.016 00
4	Beryllium	^9_4Be	100	9.012 18
5	Boron	$^{10}_5B$	19.78	10.012 9
		$^{11}_5B$	80.22	11.009 31
6	Carbon	$^{12}_6C$	98.89	12.000 0
		$^{13}_6C$	1.11	13.003 3
7	Nitrogen	$^{14}_7N$	99.63	14.003 07
		$^{15}_7N$	0.37	15.000 11
8	Oxygen	$^{16}_8O$	99.759	15.994 91
		$^{17}_8O$	0.037	16.999 14
		$^{18}_8O$	0.204	17.999 16
9	Fluorine	$^{19}_9F$	100	18.998 40
10	Neon	$^{20}_{10}Ne$	90.92	19.992 44
		$^{21}_{10}Ne$	0.257	20.993 95
		$^{22}_{10}Ne$	8.82	21.991 38
11	Sodium	$^{23}_{11}Na$	100	22.989 8
12	Magnesium	$^{24}_{12}Mg$	78.70	23.985 04
		$^{25}_{12}Mg$	10.13	24.985 84
		$^{26}_{12}Mg$	11.17	25.982 59
13	Aluminum	$^{27}_{13}Al$	100	26.981 53
14	Silicon	$^{28}_{14}Si$	92.21	27.976 93
		$^{29}_{14}Si$	4.70	28.976 49
		$^{30}_{14}Si$	3.09	29.973 76
15	Phosphorus	$^{31}_{15}P$	100	30.973 76
16	Sulfur	$^{32}_{16}S$	95.0	31.972 07
		$^{33}_{16}S$	0.76	32.971 46
		$^{34}_{16}S$	4.22	33.967 86
		$^{36}_{16}S$	0.014	35.967 09
17	Chlorine	$^{35}_{17}Cl$	75.53	34.968 85
		$^{37}_{17}Cl$	24.47	36.965 90
18	Argon	$^{36}_{18}Ar$	0.337	35.967 55
		$^{38}_{18}Ar$	0.063	37.962 72
		$^{40}_{18}Ar$	99.60	39.962 38

4-5 The Bohr Model of the Hydrogen Atom

The nuclear model of the atom raised some interesting questions. Why are the negative electrons not pulled into the positive nucleus because of the attraction of unlike charges? The electrons must be in some type of motion which prevents them from falling into the nucleus. Rutherford and his colleagues suggested that the electrons move around the nucleus in orbits, much as the planets orbit the sun.

This planetary model of the atom did not solve the problem completely. Physicists had observed that a moving electric charge which changes its direction in space will give off radiant energy. Thus, an electron moving around a nucleus in an orbit would be expected to lose energy. Do electrons lose energy? If so, the loss of energy would cause electrons to slow down and to be more strongly attracted to the nucleus, and they would gradually spiral into the nucleus. The result would be the collapse of the atom. However, atoms do not collapse. Therefore, there must be a flaw in the argument.

A clue to the problem is obtained from a study of the light given off from high energy substances. If a tungsten wire is in a high energy state due to the heating effect caused by an electric current, it releases the extra energy in the form of white light. White light is composed of all colours or frequencies of light. Each frequency has a characteristic energy.

The relationship between energy and frequency was shown by the German physicist, Max Planck. He assumed that light is made up of discrete (separate) little packages of energy. Each package is called a **quantum** (plural *quanta*) or a photon. The relationship between energy and frequency is $E = h\nu$, where E is the amount of energy possessed by a quantum, h is Planck's constant, and ν is the frequency of the quantum. According to this theory, red light consists of a stream of quanta, each of which is a certain amount of energy and has a characteristic frequency. Violet light also consists of a stream of quanta. However, quanta of violet light have more energy and a higher frequency than do quanta of red light.

White light is composed of all frequencies and all energies of visible light. White light can be broken down into its component colours by a prism or a diffraction grating. A spectrum of colours is obtained. It is called a **continuous spectrum** because it consists of all the colours or frequencies of visible light. In order of increasing frequencies (and increasing energies) the colours are red, orange, yellow, green, blue, indigo, and violet.

When hydrogen gas is excited (forced into a higher energy state) by an electric current passing through it, it will emit energy in the form of visible light. However, the visible light is violet, not white. This violet light can be passed through a prism to show its component colours or frequencies. The visible spectrum of hydrogen atoms consists of four prominent coloured lines (red, bluish-green, indigo, and violet), each of which corresponds to a characteristic energy. This is called a line spectrum because it is made up of only certain frequencies (coloured lines) of visible light. When different elements are excited (as hydrogen is excited) by the passing of an electric current through gaseous samples of the elements, it is found that each element has a characteristic line spectrum.

Fig. 4-13 Niels Bohr (1885–1962) (Photo courtesy of The Bettman Archive Inc.)

Niels Bohr was born in Copenhagen, Denmark in 1885, the son of a university professor. He was the second of three children in a wealthy family. He was given much encouragement at home and grew up in a social and intellectual environment. Bohr showed his skill as an investigator while a student at the University of Copenhagen, where he won a gold medal from the Academy of Sciences for his precise measurement of the surface tension of water. He received his doctorate in 1911 for his electron theory of metals.

For a time he worked with Rutherford at Manchester. As a result of this contact with Rutherford, Bohr laid the foundations for the quantum theory of the atom in 1913 and 1914. His work on the structure of the atom won him the Nobel Prize in Physics in 1922.

Bohr visited the United States in 1939 and brought with him the news that Hahn and Strassman in Germany had been able to split the uranium atom. This prompted the Americans to increase their own research efforts in the same direction. Bohr returned to Denmark in 1940. Three years later, he was forced to leave Denmark in order to escape Nazi occupation. He fled to Sweden, then to England, and finally went to the United States. There he acted as an adviser to the physicists working on the development of the atomic bomb. However, he did not work directly on the bomb, and he was opposed to its use. After the war, he returned to Denmark. In 1950, he wrote an open letter making a plea for world peace to the United Nations. He spent most of the rest of his life working as a director of the Institute for Theoretical Physics in Denmark. He died in Copenhagen in 1962 at the age of 77.

Niels Bohr (Fig. 4-13), a Danish physicist working with Rutherford, proposed a model for the hydrogen atom in 1913. The Bohr model explained why the hydrogen atom does not collapse. It also successfully explained the line spectrum of hydrogen. Although it was used by chemists for only about 13 years, several of the postulates of the Bohr model are still considered valid. In the following paragraphs some of Bohr's postulates will be listed and discussed.

Postulates of the Bohr Theory

First, in every hydrogen atom, there are only certain states in which an electron is allowed to move. Each of these states has a definite, fixed energy. These states are called **energy levels** (Fig. 4-14). Bohr suggested that the energy of an electron in a hydrogen atom is **quantized**, which means that the energy is limited to a number of definite quantities that can be calculated by use of the equation

$$E_n = -\frac{R}{n^2}$$

where n is the number of the energy level and R is called the Rydberg constant.

The equation means that the energy of an electron in the first energy level equals $-R/1$. The energy of an electron in the second energy level equals $-R/4$. In the third energy level, the energy of an electron equals $-R/9$, and so on. From these energies it can be seen that the larger the value of n, the more energy (less negative value) an electron possesses.

You may be wondering why the energy of an electron in a hydrogen atom is negative. The answer lies in the way scientists have defined the point of zero energy. For example, if you hold a book over a table, the book has potential energy. You could define the table as being the point of zero energy. If you drop the book to the table, the book loses energy and has zero potential energy on the table. However, if the book were to fall from the table to the floor, it would lose more energy. Thus, the book would have a negative potential energy if it were resting on the floor.

Let us return to the case of an electron in a hydrogen atom. The electron in a hydrogen atom has a negative energy because scientists have decided to define zero energy as the point at which the electron is separated from the hydrogen nucleus by an infinite distance. As a negative electron approaches a positive nucleus, it feels an increasing force of attraction and gives off energy. Since the electron starts at zero energy outside the energy levels of a hydrogen atom and loses energy as it enters these energy levels, the energy of an electron in a hydrogen atom is negative.

Second, each of these energy levels corresponds to an **orbit**, a circular path in which the electron can move around the nucleus. Thus, Bohr retained the notion of orbits, which was part of the planetary model. (This is the only postulate of the Bohr model listed here which is now considered to be incorrect.) The first orbit has the smallest radius, the second orbit has a larger radius, and so on (Fig. 4-15, overleaf). In the first orbit, the energy of an electron equals $-R/1$. In the second, third, and n^{th} orbits, the energy of an electron equals $-R/4$, $-R/9$, and $-R/n^2$, respectively. For these orbits, only certain radii and energies are possible.

If the motion of an electron in an orbit is not limited to a single plane, the three-dimensional path traced by an electron will describe a spherical shell. As with orbits, the shell closest to the nucleus corresponds to the first energy level. It is called the K shell. Shells farther from the nucleus correspond to higher energy levels: the L shell corresponds to the second energy level, the M shell to the third energy level, the N shell to the fourth energy level, and so on. Thus, an electron in the first energy level is said to be in the first orbit or the K shell. For our purposes, the terms energy level, orbit, and shell are essentially interchangeable.

Third, Bohr assumed that an electron could travel in one of the allowed orbits (energy levels) without a loss of energy.

Fourth, the only way an electron can change its energy value is to "jump" from one allowed energy level (orbit) to another. The jump cannot be gradual—it must occur all at once. To illustrate this point, imagine a person climbing or descending a flight of stairs: the steps can be taken one, two, or even three at a time, but the person can never land between the steps.

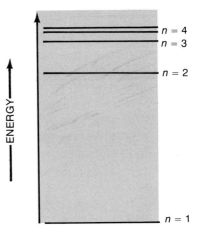

Fig. 4-14 Allowed Energy Levels for a Hydrogen Atom

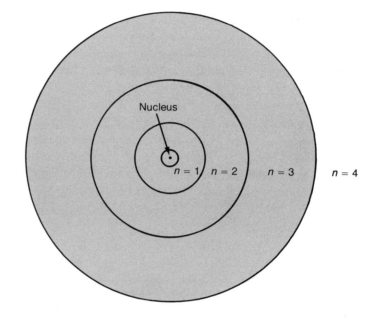

Fig. 4-15 The First Four Bohr Orbits for the Hydrogen Atom

When a hydrogen atom is excited, the electron gains an exact quantity of energy and jumps instantly from a lower allowed energy level to a higher allowed energy level. We say that the electron is promoted from one energy level to another. The quantity of energy required for this promotion equals the difference in energy between the two energy levels. When the electron drops back to a lower energy level, some or all of the previously gained energy is given off in the form of radiation of a definite frequency (Fig. 4-16). The

Fig. 4-16 Allowed Transitions Between Energy Levels. (Upward arrows indicate transitions that require energy, and downward arrows indicate transitions which give off energy.)

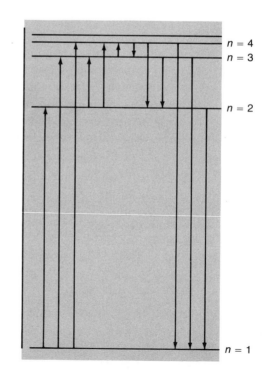

frequency of the radiation depends on the amount of energy emitted and can be calculated using the equation $E = h\nu$.

If the electron is already at the lowest energy level, no more energy can be emitted, and thus the atom does not collapse. This is similar to being at the bottom of the flight of stairs. One can descend no further.

In summary, if an electron is promoted from an orbit with a smaller radius (lower energy level) to an orbit with a larger radius (higher energy level), energy is absorbed by the atom. When an electron goes from an orbit with a larger radius to an orbit with a smaller radius, energy is emitted by the atom (Fig. 4-17).

Since there are only certain allowed orbits or energy levels in the atom, only certain energies can be absorbed or emitted as the electron changes orbits. In addition, since energy is related to frequency, only certain frequencies of radiation can be absorbed or emitted during these changes.

The frequencies of the coloured lines in the visible spectrum of hydrogen agree with the predicted frequencies calculated using the Bohr model of the hydrogen atom. In a hydrogen discharge tube having enormous numbers of hydrogen atoms, all possible jumps from one orbit to another occur simultaneously. That is why we see four coloured lines in the hydrogen spectrum simultaneously.

The frequency of the red line agrees with the calculated frequency due to a jump from the 3rd to the 2nd orbit. Also, the frequencies of the bluish-green line, the indigo line, and the violet line agree with the calculated frequencies due to jumps from the 4th to the 2nd orbit, the 5th to the 2nd orbit, and the 6th to the 2nd orbit, respectively.

In addition, Bohr was able to predict an undiscovered set of lines corresponding to jumps from the 6th, 5th, 4th, 3rd, and 2nd orbits to the 1st orbit. He said that these lines would occur in the ultraviolet region of the hydrogen spectrum. These lines were discovered, and their observed frequencies did agree with the predicted frequencies using the Bohr model of the hydrogen atom.

The Bohr model explained why the hydrogen atom did not collapse, and it explained the line spectrum of hydrogen. Also, Bohr was correct in arguing that Newton's laws of motion (classical mechanics), which describe the motion of objects of large mass, do not describe adequately the motion of particles of very small mass. Empirical evidence suggests that these small particles obey a new set of laws of motion. **Quantum mechanics** is the study of the laws of motion which describe the motion of particles of very small mass.

The basic principle of quantum mechanics is that electrons are allowed to have only certain energy values when they are in atoms. No electrons can have energy values that lie between these allowed energy values. When an electron shifts from one allowed energy value (or energy level) to another allowed energy level, the shift must be instantaneous.

However, Bohr was incorrect on a number of points. He wrongly supposed that the electron is a particle whose position and motion can be specified exactly at a given time. He was also wrong in thinking that the electron moves in an orbit at a fixed radius which changes only when the electron "jumps" to another orbit having a different fixed radius. Another difficulty of the Bohr model is that it agrees well with experimental evidence only in the case of a

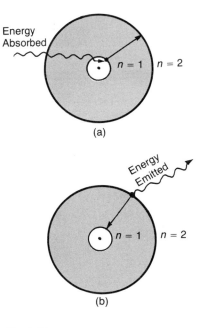

Fig. 4-17
(a) Energy is absorbed, causing the electron to move from the first to the second orbit.
(b) When the electron moves from the second to the first orbit, energy is emitted.

one-electron atom. Thus, the Bohr model had to be replaced; however, many of its key postulates were retained.

4-6 Energy Levels and Many-Electron Atoms

We will not use the Bohr model to describe many-electron atoms. However, we will use two principles of quantum mechanics and some of Bohr's terminology to develop a straightforward view of the first twenty elements. The first principle is that electrons exist in energy levels in atoms. Electrons in atoms can have only energies that are calculated by the equation $E_n = -R/n^2$. The number of the energy level, n, is called the principal quantum number. The second principle is that each energy level can hold up to $2n^2$ electrons. Thus the 1st energy level can hold $2(1)^2 = 2$ electrons, the 2nd energy level can hold $2(2)^2 = 8$ electrons, the 3rd energy level can hold 18 electrons, and so on.

The energy level populations for the first twenty elements are given in Table 4-2. Normally, as we go from one element to the next, the additional electron goes into the lowest unfilled energy level. In the cases of potassium

TABLE 4-2 Energy Level Populations for the first Twenty Elements

ELEMENT	SYMBOL	NUMBER OF PROTONS IN THE NUCLEUS	1st Level (max. = 2)	2nd Level (max. = 8)	3rd Level (max. = 18)	4th Level (max. = 32)
Hydrogen	H	1	1			
Helium	He	2	2			
Lithium	Li	3	2	1		
Beryllium	Be	4	2	2		
Boron	B	5	2	3		
Carbon	C	6	2	4		
Nitrogen	N	7	2	5		
Oxygen	O	8	2	6		
Fluorine	F	9	2	7		
Neon	Ne	10	2	8		
Sodium	Na	11	2	8	1	
Magnesium	Mg	12	2	8	2	
Aluminum	Al	13	2	8	3	
Silicon	Si	14	2	8	4	
Phosphorus	P	15	2	8	5	
Sulfur	S	16	2	8	6	
Chlorine	Cl	17	2	8	7	
Argon	Ar	18	2	8	8	
Potassium	K	19	2	8	8	1
Calcium	Ca	20	2	8	8	2

and calcium, the last electron(s) go(es) into the 4th energy level even though the 3rd energy level (maximum population = 18) is not filled. We will discuss this again in Chapter 5; however, we can say that the third energy level does have eighteen electrons in all elements with thirty or more electrons.

The energy level population of an atom can be written in a short form. For example, the energy level population of element number 11, sodium, can be written 2,8,1. This indicates that two of the sodium electrons occupy the 1st energy level; eight occupy the 2nd energy level; and the last sodium electron occupies the 3rd energy level. Using Table 4-2, you should be able to verify that the energy level population of phosphorus is 2,8,5. We are going to make use of the simple, but valuable, concept of energy level populations in Chapters 5 and 6.

4-7 Wave Mechanics—The Present Model

One of the problems that led to the discarding of the Bohr model was that in some experiments electrons behaved as particles while in other experiments electrons behaved as waves. That is, they could be reflected and diffracted just as light waves can be. Bohr, on the other hand, supposed that the electron is a particle whose position and motion in an orbit can be specified exactly at any given time. In order to describe the motion of electrons in atoms, taking into account both their wave nature and their particle nature, the German mathematician Erwin Schrödinger in 1924 devised a type of mathematics called **wave mechanics**.

The basic idea of wave mechanics is that we cannot measure both the position and velocity of a body as small as an electron at the same time. The best we can do is to calculate the probability of an electron being in a certain place at a certain time. This may seem rather vague, but much can be learned about an atom by studying electron position probabilities. Many problems of atomic and molecular structure can be solved by use of wave mechanics.

A **wave equation** is a mathematical expression describing the energy and motion of an electron around a nucleus. Such a wave equation exists for the hydrogen atom. It is possible to solve this wave equation and obtain a three-dimensional **wave function**. This wave function is linked to the probability of finding an electron in a certain volume of space around the nucleus. Just as -2 and $+3$ are both solutions for the equation $x^2 - x - 6 = 0$, there are a number of wave functions which are all solutions to the wave equation for the hydrogen atom. They describe regions in space where the electron is most likely to be found. These regions are called **orbitals**. This word was coined to resemble the term *orbit* used in the Bohr model.

The Orbitals

The **principal quantum number** (n) identifies the energy possessed by an electron in any orbital under study. It is the same as the n used in the equation $E_n = -R/n^2$. Also, as in the Bohr model, n goes from 1 to infinity by units: $n = 1, 2, 3, \ldots \infty$.

For every value of n, there are n types of orbitals and n^2 actual orbitals. Thus, the first energy level (n = 1) has one type of orbital and one (1^2) orbital. This orbital is called the 1s orbital. It is spherically shaped. If an electron is in this orbital, it is possible to calculate its energy, but it is not possible to calculate its position or motion. The electron is moving so fast that it seems to occupy all the space in a sphere around the nucleus. It is possible to say only that an electron in the 1s orbital of a hydrogen atom spends 95 percent of its time somewhere in a sphere with a radius of about 1×10^{-10} m around the nucleus, and that it is most likely to be at a distance of 5×10^{-11} m from the nucleus.

The second energy level (n = 2) has two types of orbitals and four (2^2) orbitals. The first orbital in this level is called the 2s orbital. This orbital is much like the 1s orbital except that it is larger. In addition, there are three 2p orbitals in the second energy level. They all have the same shape, size, and energy, but they point in different directions and are called p_x, p_y, and p_z orbitals (Fig. 4-18).

Fig. 4-18 Shapes of s and p Orbitals. It is impossible to draw a picture of an orbital since theoretically it extends through all space. However, 95 percent of the time the electron can be found in some small region near the nucleus. The shapes drawn here represent contour boundaries within which the electron can be found 95 percent of the time.

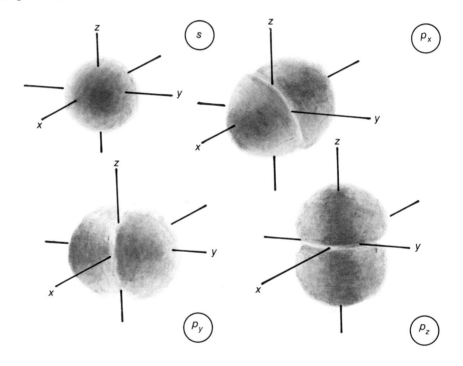

The third energy level (n = 3) has three types of orbitals and nine (3^2) orbitals. The first orbital is called the 3s orbital. Like all s orbitals, the 3s orbital is spherical; however, it is larger than either the 1s or the 2s orbital. An electron in the 3s orbital has more energy than it would have if it were in the 1s or 2s orbital, and it can move further from the nucleus more often. Next there are three 3p orbitals. The 3p orbitals are like the 2p orbitals except that an electron in a 3p orbital is more likely to be further from the nucleus than an electron in a 2p orbital. Also it would have more energy than an electron in a 2p orbital. Finally there are five 3d orbitals. In the third energy level, there are s, p, and d type orbitals, for a total of 9 orbitals (1 s-type + 3 p-type + 5 d-type).

The Hydrogen Energy Level Diagram

The energy level diagram of the orbitals derived for the hydrogen atom is shown in Fig. 4-19. Notice that orbitals having the same principal quantum number have the same energy. Orbitals that are at the same level of energy are said to be *degenerate*. For example, the 3s, the three 3p, and the five 3d orbitals are degenerate in a hydrogen atom.

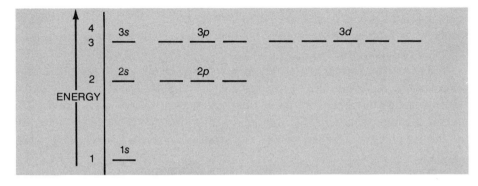

Fig. 4-19 The Energy Level Diagram for a Hydrogen Atom

There are higher energy levels containing more orbitals; however, the trend seems to be clear. A large number of orbitals can be derived mathematically for the hydrogen atom. This may seem to be a waste of time inasmuch as there is only one electron in the hydrogen atom. This electron can occupy only one orbital at a time. The other orbitals are empty. It must be remembered that in a large sample of hydrogen atoms most of the atoms would have their one electron in the lowest energy orbital, the 1s. However, some atoms could be in an excited state, and they would have electrons in the orbitals of the second, third, fourth, or higher energy levels.

Summary

The Bohr model supposed that an electron is a particle whose position and motion can be specified exactly; however, the present wave mechanical model allows us to calculate only the probability of finding an electron in a certain place at a certain time. The mathematical equation which is used in wave mechanics can be solved; the solutions are called wave functions. These wave functions are mathematical descriptions of regions surrounding the nucleus where a hydrogen electron is most likely to be found. These regions are called orbitals.

For every energy level, there are n types of orbitals and n^2 actual orbitals, where n is the number of the energy level. The first energy level consists of one orbital called the 1s. The second energy level consists of two types of orbitals totaling four orbitals, one 2s and three 2p orbitals. The third energy level consists of three types of orbitals totaling nine orbitals, one 3s, three 3p, and five 3d orbitals.

The wave mechanical energy level diagram for the hydrogen atom is shown in Fig. 4-19. A sample of hydrogen gas consists of many hydrogen atoms. Each hydrogen atom has one electron. The electrons of most of these hydrogen atoms occupy 1s orbitals. However, the electrons of some of them do occupy orbitals of the second, third, or higher energy levels.

4-8 Wave Mechanics and Many-Electron Atoms

The Bohr model was dropped because it was useful only for a one-electron system. Is this theory of orbitals useful for a many-electron system? The theory is useful as long as we are willing to learn some new rules and to modify the energy level diagram slightly.

The **Aufbau principle** states that in going from a hydrogen atom to a larger atom, you add protons to the nucleus and electrons to orbitals having the same shape as those derived for the hydrogen atom. You start at the orbitals having the lowest energy and fill them, in order of increasing energy, until you run out of electrons. Stated briefly, electrons go into the lowest energy level available.

The modified energy level diagram is shown in Fig. 4-20. This diagram shows that the second level is divided into two sublevels. That is, the 2s orbital is no longer degenerate with the three 2p orbitals. The first sublevel consists of the 2s orbital, and the second sublevel consists of the three 2p orbitals. In the same way, the third, fourth, and fifth energy levels are divided into sublevels of different energies. Also, the energy levels begin to overlap. For example, the fourth energy level begins before the third level is completed (i.e., the 4s sublevel is of lower energy than the 3d sublevel). The reasons for having to modify the original energy level diagram, when describing a many-electron system, have been discussed by chemists; however, they are beyond the scope of an introductory course.

Fig. 4-20 The Energy Level Diagram for a Many-Electron Atom

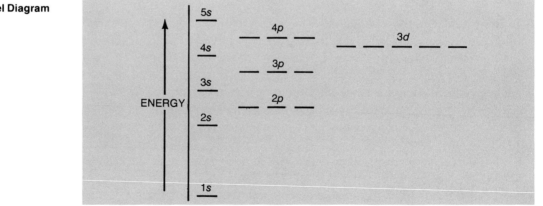

Two rules that must be used in connection with the Aufbau principle are the Pauli exclusion principle and Hund's rule. The **Pauli exclusion principle** states that an orbital can be empty, have one electron, or at most have two electrons. **Hund's rule** states that electrons in the same sublevel will not pair up until all the orbitals of the sublevel are at least half-filled (Fig. 4-21).

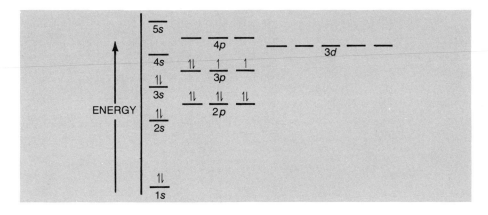

Number of Electrons in the 2p Sublevel	Distribution		
	$2p_x$	$2p_y$	$2p_z$
1	↿	__	__
2	↿	↿	__
3	↿	↿	↿
4	↿⇂	↿	↿
5	↿⇂	↿⇂	↿
6	↿⇂	↿⇂	↿⇂

Fig. 4-21 Distribution of Electrons in the 2p Sublevel. (An arrow represents an electron in an orbital. A pair of arrows indicates that an electron pair occupies the orbital.)

An example will show how these rules can be used to describe many-electron atoms. Consider the element sulfur. Sulfur has 16 protons and 16 electrons. It also has 16 neutrons, but the number of neutrons is of no concern to us at this point. Sixteen electrons can be placed into the energy level diagram as shown in Fig. 4-22. Each arrow in the diagram represents one electron.

Fig. 4-22 The Energy Level Diagram for a Sulfur Atom

Practice Problem 4-3

Draw an energy level diagram for element 7, nitrogen, and for element 14, silicon. The energy levels for these elements may be checked by consulting Fig. 4-24.

Practice Problem 4-4

Draw an energy level diagram for element 10, neon, and for element 20, calcium. The answers are given in Fig. 4-24.

The distribution of electrons among the various orbitals of an atom is called its **electronic configuration**. In this text, the ground state electronic configurations are given. This means that each electron in an atom is in the lowest possible orbital available to it. The electronic configuration of sulfur is written as

$$_{16}S \ 1s^2 \ 2s^2 \ 2p^6 \ 3s^2 \ 3p^4$$

The superscripts indicate the number of electrons occupying each sublevel. Thus, the first and second energy levels are completely filled. However, the third energy level is only partly filled. The $3s$ and one of the $3p$ orbitals are filled. The other two $3p$ orbitals are half-filled. The $3d$ and all orbitals of the fourth, fifth, and higher levels are empty. The electronic configurations of the first 20 elements are given in Table 4-3.

TABLE **4-3 Electronic Configurations of the First Twenty Elements**

ELEMENT	ELECTRONIC CONFIGURATION
H	$1s^1$
He	$1s^2$
Li	$1s^2\,2s^1$
Be	$1s^2\,2s^2$
B	$1s^2\,2s^2\,2p^1$
C	$1s^2\,2s^2\,2p^2$
N	$1s^2\,2s^2\,2p^3$
O	$1s^2\,2s^2\,2p^4$
F	$1s^2\,2s^2\,2p^5$
Ne	$1s^2\,2s^2\,2p^6$
Na	$1s^2\,2s^2\,2p^6\,3s^1$
Mg	$1s^2\,2s^2\,2p^6\,3s^2$
Al	$1s^2\,2s^2\,2p^6\,3s^2\,3p^1$
Si	$1s^2\,2s^2\,2p^6\,3s^2\,3p^2$
P	$1s^2\,2s^2\,2p^6\,3s^2\,3p^3$
S	$1s^2\,2s^2\,2p^6\,3s^2\,3p^4$
Cl	$1s^2\,2s^2\,2p^6\,3s^2\,3p^5$
Ar	$1s^2\,2s^2\,2p^6\,3s^2\,3p^6$
K	$1s^2\,2s^2\,2p^6\,3s^2\,3p^6\,4s^1$
Ca	$1s^2\,2s^2\,2p^6\,3s^2\,3p^6\,4s^2$

Some people use a shortened form of the electronic configuration. The shortened form of the electronic configuration of sulfur is $_{16}$S [Ne] $3s^2\,3p^4$. The electronic configuration of neon is $_{10}$Ne $1s^2\,2s^2\,2p^6$, and the [Ne] replaces the $1s^2\,2s^2\,2p^6$ in the electronic configuration of sulfur. When we write the shortened electronic configuration of an element, we always start with the symbol of the nearest noble gas that has fewer electrons than the element. The shortened form of the electronic configuration of calcium can be written $_{20}$Ca [Ar] $4s^2$. This indicates that calcium has all of the electrons that argon has plus two electrons in the $4s$ orbital.

Summary

In this section, we learned that the wave mechanical model of the atom can be adapted to include many-electron atoms. We learned a number of rules:
1. In going from a hydrogen atom to a larger atom, we add protons to the nucleus and electrons to orbitals that resemble the orbitals derived for the hydrogen atom.

2. The energy level diagram must be modified; the modified version is shown in Fig. 4-20.
3. We fill the orbitals having the lowest energy first.
4. We must place no more than two electrons in an orbital.
5. We cannot place two electrons in any one orbital of a sublevel until all the orbitals of that sublevel are at least half-filled.

Finally, we learned how to draw energy level diagrams and how to write electronic configurations for elements. The electronic configuration tells us the number of electrons that occupy each sublevel in an atom.

4-9 The Quantum Numbers

Each of the orbitals can be identified by its quantum numbers: n, ℓ, and m. The quantum numbers are a necessary part of the solution of the wave equation of an atom. We cannot solve the wave equation because it is beyond the scope of an introduction to chemistry. However, we can use the quantum numbers that come from the solution of the wave equation to help us figure out the various orbitals that are allowed for each energy level.

The first quantum number is the principal quantum number, n. We discussed it in Sections 4-5 to 4-7. The principal quantum number identifies the energy of an electron in an orbital. Also, n goes from 1 to infinity by units:

$$n = 1, 2, 3 \ldots \infty$$

The second quantum number, ℓ, is the **secondary** or **azimuthal quantum number**. It identifies the shape of the orbital. For any given value of n, ℓ can start at 0 and go to the number which is one unit smaller than n:

$$\ell = 0, 1, 2, \ldots, n - 1$$

If $\ell = 0$, the orbital is called an *s* orbital and has a spherical shape. If $\ell = 1$, the orbital is called a *p* orbital. If $\ell = 2$, the orbital is a *d* orbital, and it has a more complicated shape. If $\ell = 3, 4, 5, \ldots$, the orbitals are called *f, g, h, . . .* orbitals, and they have even more complicated shapes.

The third quantum number, m, is the **magnetic quantum number**. It identifies the direction of orientation (pointing) of the orbital with respect to an external magnetic field. For a given value of ℓ, m takes every integral value starting at $-\ell$, and going to $+\ell$. For example, if $\ell = 0$, then m = 0; if $\ell = 1$, then m = -1 or 0 or 1; if $\ell = 2$, then m = -2 or -1 or 0 or 1 or 2.

We can use the quantum numbers to work out the orbitals for any value of the principal quantum number. As examples, we can consider the orbitals which have n equal to 1, 2, and 3. If n = 1, then ℓ must equal 0 and m must also equal 0. The values of n and ℓ indicate that this is the 1*s* orbital. The symbol used is nℓ, where the numerical value of n is used, but the numerical value of ℓ is not used. Instead, letters are used to replace the numerical value of ℓ. That is, if $\ell = 0, 1, 2, 3, 4, 5, \ldots$, the orbitals are called *s, p, d, f, g, h, . . .* orbitals respectively.

If n = 2, ℓ can equal both 0 and 1. If ℓ = 0, m must equal 0, and the orbital is the 2s orbital. However, if ℓ = 1, then there are three acceptable values of m (−1, 0, 1), and hence there are three 2p orbitals.

If n = 3, ℓ can equal 0, 1, and 2. If ℓ = 0, m must equal 0, and the orbital is the 3s orbital. If ℓ = 1, there are three values of m (−1, 0, 1), and hence there are three 3p orbitals. If ℓ = 2, the orbitals are d type, and because m can have five values (−2, −1, 0, 1, 2), there are five 3d orbitals. Table 4-4 summarizes the use of quantum numbers.

TABLE 4-4 Orbital Names for Different Sets of Quantum Numbers

n	ℓ	m	NAME OF ORBITAL
1	0	0	1s
2	0	0	2s
2	1	−1	2p
2	1	0	2p
2	1	1	2p
3	0	0	3s
3	1	−1	3p
3	1	0	3p
3	1	1	3p
3	2	−2	3d
3	2	−1	3d
3	2	0	3d
3	2	1	3d
3	2	2	3d
4	0	0	4s
4	1	−1	4p
4	1	0	4p
4	1	1	4p
4	2	−2	4d
4	2	−1	4d
4	2	0	4d
4	2	1	4d
4	2	2	4d
4	3	−3	4f
4	3	−2	4f
4	3	−1	4f
4	3	0	4f
4	3	1	4f
4	3	2	4f
4	3	3	4f

Sample Problem 4-3

What orbital has quantum numbers n = 3, ℓ = 2, m = 1?

SOLUTION
If ℓ = 2, the orbital is d type. Since n = 3, it must be a 3d orbital. We could use the value of m to tell us which one of the five 3d orbitals is being described. However, it is sufficient for us to say merely that the orbital in question is a 3d orbital.

Practice Problem 4-5

What orbital has quantum numbers **a)** $n = 5$, $\ell = 3$, $m = -3$?
b) $n = 4$, $\ell = 1$, $m = -1$? **c)** $n = 7$, $\ell = 4$, $m = 0$?

(*Answers*: a) 5*f*, b) 4*p*, c) 7*g*)

According to the Pauli exclusion principle an orbital can contain as many as two electrons. If two electrons are in the same orbital, they must have opposite spins. This introduces the final quantum number, s. The **spin quantum number**, s, can have only two values, $+\frac{1}{2}$ and $-\frac{1}{2}$. That is, an electron behaves as if it were a charged particle that can spin clockwise or counterclockwise. The Pauli exclusion principle means that no two electrons in the same atom can have four identical values for the four quantum numbers.

In the caption for Fig. 4-21, it was stated that an arrow represents an electron in an orbital, and a pair of arrows represents an electron pair. We can now add to this by stating that the spin direction of an electron is indicated by the direction of the arrow. Two paired electrons in an orbital are indicated by two arrows, one pointing up and one pointing down—meaning that they have opposite spins.

If we know the possible values for the quantum numbers, we can figure out the orbitals for each value of the principal quantum number. If we also know the order in which the orbitals fill with electrons, along with Hund's rule and the Pauli exclusion principle, we can construct energy level diagrams for large atoms. We can also write electronic configurations for these atoms.

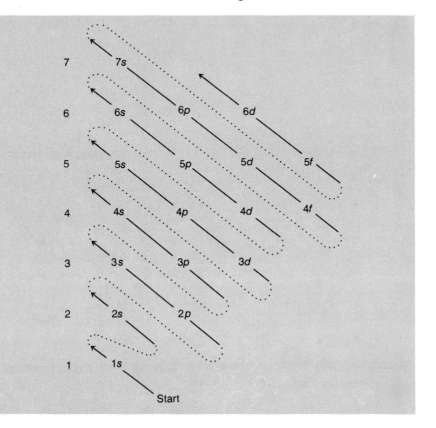

Fig. 4-23 Mnemonic for Filling Orbitals

The energies of the orbitals are approximately in the order $1s < 2s < 2p < 3s < 3p < 4s \lesssim 3d < 4p < 5s \lesssim 4d < 5p < 6s \simeq 4f \simeq 5d < 6p$. They fill with electrons in this order. It is possible to remember the order of filling by studying Fig. 4-23 (on previous page).

Practice Problem 4-6

Draw an energy level diagram for element 28, nickel. The answer is shown in Fig. 4-24.

Fig. 4-24 Solutions for Practice Problems 4-3, 4-4, and 4-6

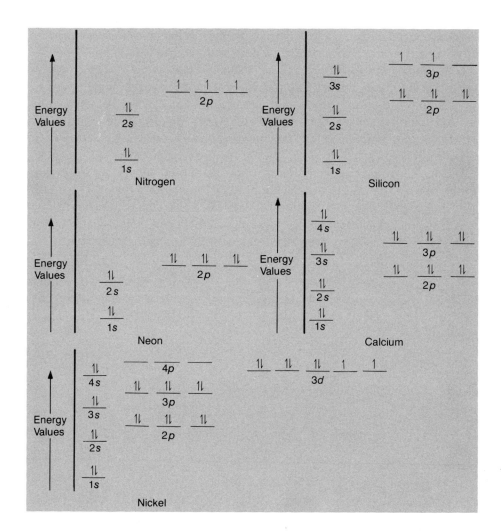

Sample Problem 4-4

Predict the electronic configuration of element number 24, chromium.

SOLUTION
When electrons are added according to the order given in Fig. 4-23 the predicted electronic configuration becomes

$$Cr\ 1s^2\ 2s^2\ 2p^6\ 3s^2\ 3p^6\ 4s^2\ 3d^4$$

The actual electronic configuration of chromium deviates slightly from that predicted. It is found that chromium actually has the configuration

$$\text{Cr } 1s^2\, 2s^2\, 2p^6\, 3s^2\, 3p^6\, 4s^1\, 3d^5$$

This deviation from the predicted behavior usually occurs in those elements which are close to filling or half-filling a sublevel. Hund's rule implies that half-filled sublevels would be relatively stable. Full sublevels, whether they are s, p, or d, also confer a measure of stability on an atom. When $3d$ sublevels are involved, with energies near those of the $4s$ sublevel, the stability effect is large enough to allow promotion of a $4s$ electron in chromium to the $3d$ sublevel. This gives a chromium atom a half-filled $3d$ sublevel containing five electrons.

Practice Problem 4-7

Predict the electronic configuration of element number 35, bromine. *(Answer:*

$$1s^2\, 2s^2\, 2p^6\, 3s^2\, 3p^6\, 4s^2\, 3d^{10}\, 4p^5$$

or

$$1s^2\, 2s^2\, 2p^6\, 3s^2\, 3p^6\, 3d^{10}\, 4s^2\, 4p^5)$$

Practice Problem 4-8

Predict the electronic configuration of element number 60, neodymium. *(Answer*: $1s^2\, 2s^2\, 2p^6\, 3s^2\, 3p^6\, 4s^2\, 3d^{10}\, 4p^6\, 5s^2\, 4d^{10}\, 5p^6\, 6s^2\, 4f^4$ or $[\text{Xe}]\, 6s^2\, 4f^4)$

Summary

The quantum numbers are
a) Principal quantum number, n, energy of an electron in an orbital:

$$n = 1, 2, 3, \ldots, \infty$$

b) Azimuthal quantum number, ℓ, shape of an orbital:

$$\ell = 0, 1, 2, \ldots, n-1$$

c) Magnetic quantum number, m, direction of pointing of an orbital:

$$m = -\ell, \ldots, -1, 0, 1, \ldots, +\ell$$

d) Spin quantum number, s, spin of an electron:

$$s = +\tfrac{1}{2} \text{ and } -\tfrac{1}{2}$$

Numerical values of the first three quantum numbers (n, ℓ, m) specify orbitals. Numerical values of all four quantum numbers specify electrons in orbitals. The order of filling of the orbitals is $1s$, $2s$, $2p$, $3s$, $3p$, $4s$, $3d$, $4p$, $5s$.

A Final Word

In this chapter, we traced the development of atomic theory from Dalton's theory, through Thomson's model, the nuclear model, and Bohr's model, to the present wave mechanical model of the atom. We described the three most important particles in the atom—electrons, protons, and neutrons. Most importantly, we laid the foundation for our descriptions of the chemical properties of elements and the chemical combinations of elements to form compounds.

Now that you have finished reading this chapter, you should reread the Key Objectives to make sure that you have learned the most important points of the chapter. In addition, you should learn the meaning of each important term found in the chapter.

Key Terms

What is the meaning of each of the following terms?

cathode rays	quantum mechanics
electron	wave mechanics
proton	wave equation
neutron	wave function
nucleon	orbital
atomic number	principal quantum number
mass number	Aufbau principle
isotope	Pauli exclusion principle
quantum	Hund's rule
continuous spectrum	electronic configuration
line spectrum	secondary or azimuthal quantum
energy level	number
quantized	magnetic quantum number
orbit	spin quantum number

Questions

1. Where do the rays in a gas discharge tube orginate? How do we know?
2. Contrast the Thomson model with the nuclear model of the atom.
3. Describe the experiment which caused the Thomson model to be replaced by the nuclear model of the atom.
4. What particles are found in the nucleus of the atom? Describe these particles. Describe the third particle found in an atom.
5. How many neutrons are found in one atom of $^{60}_{27}$Co? $^{90}_{38}$Sr? $^{108}_{47}$Ag? $^{207}_{82}$Pb? $^{210}_{85}$At? $^{238}_{92}$U?
6. How many electrons, protons, and neutrons are in an atom for which the atomic numer is 38 and the mass number is 90? For which the atomic number is 82 and the mass number is 207?
7. Natural boron consists of 19.8% $^{10}_{5}$B (mass 10.0 u) and 80.2% $^{11}_{5}$B (mass 11.0 u). What is the average atomic mass of natural boron?
8. Natural potassium consists of 93.1% $^{39}_{19}$K (mass 39.0 u) and 6.9% $^{41}_{19}$K (mass 41.0 u). What is the average atomic mass of natural potassium?

9. Natural thallium consists of 29.50% $^{203}_{81}$Tl (mass 203.0 u) and, 70.50% $^{205}_{81}$Tl (mass 205.0 u). What is the average atomic mass of natural thallium?

10. Natural erbium consists of 33.41% $^{166}_{68}$Er (mass 165.9 u), 22.94% $^{167}_{68}$Er (mass 166.9 u), 27.07% $^{168}_{68}$Er (mass 167.9 u), and 14.88% $^{170}_{68}$Er (mass 169.9 u). What is the average atomic mass of natural erbium?

11. What experimental evidence did Bohr have to support his belief that the energy of the electrons in a hydrogen atom is quantized?

12. When a hydrogen atom is excited, what happens to the electron in the atom?

13. Give two reasons why the Bohr model was eventually discarded.

14. What is one difference between the idea of a Bohr orbit and the idea of an orbital?

15. Account for the bluish-green line in a hydrogen spectrum in terms of the Bohr model.

16. Write the energy level population of element number 13; of element number 17.

17. How many types of orbitals are there for n = 4? How many orbitals are there for n = 4?

18. Use Hund's rule to place seven electrons in the orbitals of the 3d sublevel. Use Hund's rule to place two electrons in the orbitals of the 4p sublevel.

19. Draw the energy level diagram for element number 5 (boron), number 9 (fluorine), number 12 (magnesium), and number 17 (chlorine).

20. Write the electronic configurations for $_6$C, $_{10}$Ne, $_{15}$P, $_{19}$K.

21. What are the quantum numbers n, ℓ, and m for each of the orbitals of the 5p sublevel? Of the 6d sublevel?

22. What orbital (1s, 2s, 2p, etc.) has quantum numbers **a)** n = 2, ℓ = 1, m = 0? **b)** n = 4, ℓ = 2, m = $-$2? **c)** n = 6, ℓ = 3, m = 1?

23. Draw the energy level diagram for element number 22 (titanium), number 25 (manganese), number 32 (germanium), number 46 (palladium), and number 55 (cesium).

24. Write the electronic configurations for $_{23}$V, $_{34}$Se, $_{40}$Zr, $_{50}$Sn, $_{56}$Ba.

25. Why can there be no d orbitals in the second (n = 2) energy level?

26. Suppose the spin quantum number had the values 0, $+\frac{1}{2}$, $-\frac{1}{2}$. How many electrons could one orbital hold? Why?

27. If the magnetic quantum number, m, took every integral value starting at 0 and going to $+\ell$, how many orbitals would have n = 5?

28. Suggest an atom (other than chromium), with atomic number smaller than 38, which might be expected to deviate from the predicted electronic configuration.

29. How do the 2s and 3s orbitals differ? How are they similar?

30. Which of the following are designations for orbitals which are not possible in wave mechanics? 1d, 4f, 2s, 1p, 6d, 2f.

31. Which of the following are sets of quantum numbers for orbitals which are possible in wave mechanics?
    a) n = 1, ℓ = 1, m = 1
    b) n = 2, ℓ = 1, m = 2
    c) n = 2, ℓ = 0, m = 0
    d) n = 3, ℓ = 3, m = 1
    e) n = 3, ℓ = 2, m = $-$2
    f) n = 4, ℓ = 3, m = 2

5 Periodic Law

Dalton's atomic theory was such an effective stimulus in the search for elements that by the 1860s more than 60 elements were known. However, there was a problem. It was not possible to predict what elements were still undiscovered or to foretell their properties. In this chapter we shall see how, as time went on, various regularities were recognized in the properties of elements; how this led to the discovery of the periodic law and the development of the modern periodic table; and how the relationship between the properties of elements and their atomic structures finally became clear.

Key Objectives

When you have finished reading this chapter you should be able to
1. state the Periodic Law.
2. locate, in a modern periodic table, the representative elements, the transition metals, the lanthanides, and the actinides.
3. locate, in a modern periodic table, the noble gases, the alkali metals, and the halogens.
4. locate, in a modern periodic table, the metals, nonmetals, and metalloids.
5. using energy level populations for the first twenty elements, identify pairs of elements which should have similar chemical properties.
6. write electron dot symbols for the first 20 elements.
7. predict trends in atomic size, ionization potential, and electron affinity as one goes across a period or down a family in the periodic table.

5-1 Periodic Law

Döbereiner's Triads

Within twenty-five years after Dalton had proposed his atomic theory, enough elements had been discovered for some patterns of relationship to appear. In 1829, the German chemist Johann Döbereiner noticed similarities among certain elements. Similar elements seemed to appear in groups of three: sulfur, selenium, and tellurium; chlorine, bromine, and iodine; lithium, sodium, and potassium. He called them "triads."

Dmitri Mendeleev was the fourteenth and youngest child of a Siberian teacher. He studied at a teacher's training college in St. Petersburg and at the University of St. Petersburg. After he obtained his doctorate in chemistry, he became Professor of General Chemistry in the University of St. Petersburg in 1866.

Mendeleev is best known for his work on the periodic law. He treated the periodic law not only as a system for classifying the elements according to their properties, but as a "law of nature" which could be used to predict new facts. He presented his periodic law in 1869, and two years later gaps in his tables led him to predict the existence of three new elements. He called them eka-boron, eka-aluminum, and eka-silicon, and he predicted their properties. Within 15 years he was proven correct by the discovery of gallium in 1871, scandium in 1879, and germanium in 1886.

Mendeleev was one of the greatest teachers of his day. His lecture room was always crowded with students. His students thought of him as a comrade, and on more than one occasion he supported students in their disputes with the university administration.

Mendeleev had strong views about the Russian education system. He believed that education should not be based on a study of the classics. He wrote, "We could live at the present day without a Plato, but a double number of Newtons is required to discover the secrets of nature, and to bring life into harmony with the laws of nature."

In 1890, because of a dispute with the university administration, Mendeleev resigned his professorship at St. Petersburg. A probable cause of this resignation was his outspoken criticism of the classical system of education which irritated officials in the Ministry of Education. However, in 1893 he was appointed Director of the Bureau of Weights and Measures, and he retained this position until his death in 1907.

Fig. 5-1 Dmitri Mendeleev (1834-1907) (Photo courtesy of The Bettman Archive, Inc.)

Newlands' Law of Octaves

In 1864 the English chemist John A. R. Newlands arranged the known elements in order of increasing atomic mass. He noticed that similar chemical and physical properties occurred after every eight elements. For example, atoms 2, 9, and 16 in his list (lithium, sodium, and potassium) resembled each other chemically. He was ridiculed for this suggestion. One prominent contemporary even asked if he had ever examined the elements according to the order of their initial letters. Nevertheless, it was Newlands who pointed out more clearly than anyone else had done previously the existence of the periodic recurrence of properties among the elements. But there was one flaw in his scheme. His proposed table had no gaps and therefore left no room for new elements.

Mendeleev's Periodic Table

This flaw was corrected by two chemists working independently. The Russian chemist Dmitri Mendeleev (Fig. 5-1) and his German counterpart Lothar

Meyer both discovered the periodic law in 1869. Mendeleev, however, is usually given priority because he published his ideas first.

In 1869 Mendeleev presented his periodic law. It stated that when elements are arranged in order of increasing atomic mass, elements with similar properties recur at regular intervals. Mendeleev prepared a periodic table to illustrate his arguments, and made predictions based on it. A version of his table is given in Table 5-1. Mendeleev's table had several gaps. He predicted that new elements would be found to fill these gaps. The discoveries of scandium and gallium filled two of the gaps in the table. These discoveries created interest in Mendeleev's theory, since he had predicted with remarkable accuracy the properties of these elements before they were discovered. The table made it possible to predict their properties.

TABLE 5-1 Mendeleev's Periodic Table

Row	Group I	Group II	Group III	Group IV	Group V	Group VI	Group VII	Group VIII
1	H = 1							
2	Li = 7	Be = 9	B = 11	C = 12	N = 14	O = 16	F = 19	
3	Na = 23	Mg = 24	Al = 27	Si = 28	P = 31	S = 32	Cl = 35.5	
4	K = 39	Ca = 40	Sc = 44	Ti = 48	V = 51	Cr = 52	Mn = 55	Fe = 56 Co = 58.5 Ni = 59
5	Cu = 63	Zn = 65	Ga = 70	Ge = 72	As = 75	Se = 79	Br = 80	
6	Rb = 85	Sr = 87	Y = 89	Zr = 90	Nb = 94	Mo = 96		Ru = 103 Rh = 104 Pd = 106
7	Ag = 108	Cd = 112	In = 113	Sn = 118	Sb = 120	Te = 125	I = 127	
8	Cs = 133	Ba = 137	La = 138	Ce = 140				
9								
10			Yb = 173		Ta = 182	W = 184		Os = 191 Ir = 193 Pt = 196
11	Au = 198	Hg = 200	Tl = 204	Pb = 206	Bi = 208			
12				Th = 232		U = 240		

In Mendeleev's table the elements were placed in horizontal rows or **periods**. Elements with similar properties were arranged in vertical groupings called **families**. The periodic occurrence of properties noticed by Newlands is reflected in the table. Chlorine, bromine, and iodine are all found in Group VII. The reactive metals lithium, sodium, and potassium are found in Group I; so are the coinage metals copper, silver, and gold.

Mendeleev's table has stood the test of time with few alterations. The only major modification was required by the discovery of the first noble gas (argon) by Lord Rayleigh and Sir William Ramsay in 1894.

5-2 The Modern Periodic Table

The discovery of the noble gases meant that a new family had to be added to Mendeleev's table. After the discovery of electrons and protons and the development of the nuclear model of the atom, the Dutch physicist A. van den Broek suggested in 1911 that several minor inconsistencies would be removed if the table were arranged according to atomic number instead of atomic mass.

In 1913 the English physicist Henry Mosely studied the wavelengths of X-rays produced by every element that he could possibly use in his apparatus. He discovered the relationship between the atomic number of an element and the wavelength of the X-rays produced. His work confirmed conclusively that the properties of elements depended on atomic number rather than atomic mass.

The result of the new arrangement is the modern periodic table which is shown at the back of the book. The revision required a change in the periodic law to its modern form. The modern **periodic law** states that when the elements are arranged in order of increasing atomic number, elements with similar properties occur at regular intervals. Another way of stating the periodic law is that the physical and chemical properties of the elements are a periodic function of the atomic numbers.

Features of the Modern Periodic Table

The modern periodic table differs slightly from the arrangements used by Mendeleev and Meyer. In 1920 the Danish physicist Niels Bohr devised a long-form version of the periodic table, with the elements arranged in order of increasing atomic number instead of increasing atomic mass. There are still horizontal rows or periods, but these periods have different lengths. The first period is short, consisting of only two elements. Periods 2 and 3 contain eight elements each. Periods 4 and 5 are long periods, each containing 18 elements. Period 6 is the longest, with 32 elements, and Period 7 is incomplete. Elements 57 through 70 and 89 through 102 are put into separate groupings below the main table to maintain compactness. Elements having similar properties still appear in vertical columns called groups or families. As new elements were discovered, all of the gaps of Mendeleev's time have become filled. A simplified version of the modern periodic table, based on Bohr's design, is shown in Fig. 5-2 (overleaf).

Groups I and II, on the left-hand side of the periodic table, and Groups III to VII, on the right-hand side, together constitute what are called the **represent-**

GROUP →

	I	II											III	IV	V	VI	VII	0
1	1																	2
2	3	4											5	6	7	8	9	10
3	11	12	← Transition Metals →										13	14	15	16	17	18
4	19	20	21	22	23	24	25	26	27	28	29	30	31	32	33	34	35	36
5	37	38	39	40	41	42	43	44	45	46	47	48	49	50	51	52	53	54
6	55	56	71	72	73	74	75	76	77	78	79	80	81	82	83	84	85	86
7	87	88	103	104	105	106												

6	57	58	59	60	61	62	63	64	65	66	67	68	69	70
7	89	90	91	92	93	94	95	96	97	98	99	100	101	102

Fig. 5-2 Arrangement of Elements in the Periodic Table According to Increasing Atomic Number

ative elements. The middle elements in the periodic table, between Groups II and III, are responsible for the extra length of the long periods and are called the **transition metals**. The very long periods, 6 and 7, are compressed in the table by removing 14 of their members and representing them separately below. These elements are called the **lanthanides** (rare-earth elements) and **actinides**, respectively.

The periodic table is useful for organizing chemical knowledge. The elements on the left of the zigzag line in the table are metals. Those on the right side are nonmetals. The most metallic elements are located in the lower left corner of the periodic table. The most nonmetallic (least metallic) elements are located in the upper right corner. There is a gradual transition from metallic to nonmetallic properties as one goes from left to right within a period. Since there is no sharp dividing line between metals and nonmetals, those elements near the zigzag line will exhibit properties of both metals and nonmetals. These elements are called metalloids (Section 3-9). Boron, aluminum, silicon, germanium, and arsenic fall into this category.

The Noble Gases

When the elements are arranged according to this scheme, elements with atomic numbers 2, 10, 18, 36, 54, and 86 are found in Group 0. These six elements—helium, neon, argon, krypton, xenon, and radon—are the least reactive of all the elements known. Since they are all gases at room temperature and pressure they are known as the **noble gas** family.

The Alkali Metals

The elements with atomic numbers one greater than the noble gases—3, 11, 19, 37, 55, and 87—are lithium, sodium, potassium, rubidium, cesium, and francium. They all exhibit metallic properties and are highly reactive. For example, they all react vigorously with water to liberate hydrogen, and they all react with chlorine to form colourless compounds which crystallize in cubic shapes and have simiar formulas—$LiCl$, $NaCl$, KCl, $RbCl$, $CsCl$, $FrCl$. These chemically similar elements are called the **alkali metals** and are found in Group I of the periodic table. The word alkali comes from an Arabic term: the ashes of saltwort. Saltwort was a general term referring to any one of a number of plants from whose ashes the carbonates of sodium and potassium were obtained.

The Halogens

The elements with atomic numbers 9, 17, 35, 53, and 85 are found in Group VII. They are fluorine, chlorine, bromine, iodine, and astatine. These elements all exhibit nonmetallic properties. They react with hydrogen to form compounds which dissolve in water to form acidic solutions. They react with the alkali metals to form compounds with similar formulas and crystal shapes. These chemically similar elements are called the **halogen** family. The word halogen comes from a Greek term: salt-former. The halogens combine readily with metals to form compounds called salts. A salt is a type of compound resulting from the union of a metallic element with a nonmetallic element.

Hydrogen

Hydrogen, with atomic number 1, is unique. It is usually included in Group I even though its chemical properties do not resemble those of the alkali metals. The fact is that hydrogen does not really fit anywhere in the table. There is no other element with properties like those of hydrogen.

Why do the periods contain different numbers of elements, such as 2, 8, 18, or 32 elements? The answer must lie in the way the atoms are constructed from their neutrons, protons, and electrons. Some arrangements must be preferred over others. In Section 5-3, we shall see that certain energy level populations are the preferred ones, and periods are completed as these energy level populations are achieved.

5-3 The Periodic Law and Energy Levels

In Chapter 4, the energy level populations were given for the first 20 elements. Three of those elements (helium, neon, and argon) belong to the noble gas family. They are all inert when one attempts to react them with almost any compound or element. Element 2, helium, has a filled outer energy level (1st level). Element 10, neon, has a filled outer energy level (2nd level). Element 18, argon, has only eight electrons in its outer energy level (3rd level). Since the 3rd energy level can hold 18 electrons, argon might not be expected to be inert. Nevertheless, argon is as chemically inert as helium and neon. Apparently, eight electrons in the 3rd level of argon behave like a filled outer level.

Three of the first 20 elements belong to the family of alkali metals. They have similar chemical properties, and each of them has one electron in its outer energy level. They are lithium, sodium, and potassium.

Two more of the first 20 elements which have similar properties are fluorine and chlorine. They are strongly nonmetallic, and they belong to the halogen family. Each of them has seven electrons in its outer level.

Apparently, the existence of families of chemically related elements in the periodic table can be explained by assuming that the properties of atoms depend significantly on the number of electrons present in the outer energy level. Atoms which have the same number of electrons in their outer energy levels are usually members of the same family.

Why do the last electron of potassium and the last two electrons of calcium go into the 4th energy level even though the 3rd energy level is not filled? Why does argon, and each succeeding noble gas, exhibit the same chemical properties as neon, even though each one has only eight electrons in an outer energy level that is capable of holding many more electrons? In this section, we will attempt to give an answer to these questions.

Studies of the spectra of different elements indicate that each shell or energy level actually consists of one or more energy sublevels grouped closely together. The number of energy sublevels equals the numerical value of the

Fig. 5-3 Energy Levels of a Hydrogen Atom Compared with the Energy Sublevels of a Many-Electron Atom

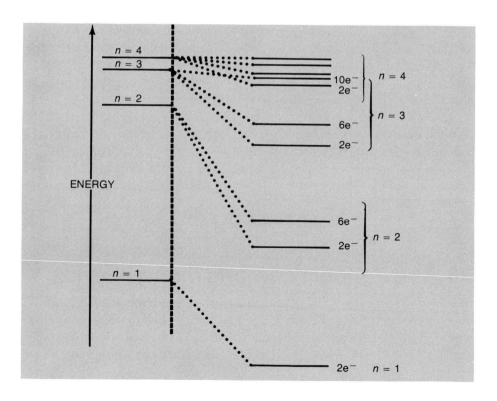

principal quantum number, n. The two electrons of the 1st energy level have only one possible energy value. However, the eight electrons of the 2nd energy level can have two possible energy values. That is, the 2nd energy level consists of two energy sublevels. Two electrons can occupy the first sublevel, and the other six electrons occupy the second sublevel. The 3rd energy level consists of three energy sublevels, the 4th energy level consists of four energy sublevels, and so on.

An energy level diagram is shown in Fig. 5-3. To the left of the dashed line are the first four energy levels of a hydrogen atom. To the right of the dashed line are the corresponding energy sublevels of a many-electron atom. For any energy level, the first sublevel can hold up to two electrons. For the 2nd and all subsequent energy levels, the second sublevel can hold up to six electrons. For the 3rd and all subsequent energy levels, the third sublevel can hold up to ten electrons. For the 4th and all subsequent energy levels, the fourth sublevel can hold up to 14 electrons.

Another feature shown in Fig. 5-3 is the overlapping of the 3rd and 4th energy levels. That is, the first sublevel of the 4th energy level is below the third sublevel of the 3rd energy level *in terms of energy*. This overlapping would be even more complicated if the sublevels of the 5th and 6th energy levels were added to Fig. 5-3. The overlapping of the 3rd and 4th energy levels

TABLE 5-2 Energy Sublevel Populations for the First Twenty Elements

ELEMENT	SYMBOL	NUMBER OF PROTONS IN NUCLEUS	1ST LEVEL	ENERGY SUBLEVEL POPULATIONS								
				2ND LEVEL		3RD LEVEL			4TH LEVEL			
				FIRST SUB-LEVEL	SECOND SUB-LEVEL	FIRST SUB-LEVEL	SECOND SUB-LEVEL	THIRD SUB-LEVEL	FIRST SUB-LEVEL	SECOND SUB-LEVEL	THIRD SUB-LEVEL	FOURTH SUB-LEVEL
Hydrogen	H	1	1									
Helium	He	2	2									
Lithium	Li	3	2	1								
Beryllium	Be	4	2	2								
Boron	B	5	2	2	1							
Carbon	C	6	2	2	2							
Nitrogen	N	7	2	2	3							
Oxygen	O	8	2	2	4							
Fluorine	F	9	2	2	5							
Neon	Ne	10	2	2	6							
Sodium	Na	11	2	2	6	1						
Magnesium	Mg	12	2	2	6	2						
Aluminum	Al	13	2	2	6	2	1					
Silicon	Si	14	2	2	6	2	2					
Phosphorus	P	15	2	2	6	2	3					
Sulfur	S	16	2	2	6	2	4					
Chlorine	Cl	17	2	2	6	2	5					
Argon	Ar	18	2	2	6	2	6					
Potassium	K	19	2	2	6	2	6		1			
Calcium	Ca	20	2	2	6	2	6		2			

provides an answer for the first of the two questions posed in this section. The last electron of potassium and the last two electrons of calcium go into the 4th energy level before the 3rd energy level is filled, because the lowest (first) sublevel of the 4th energy level is below the highest (third) sublevel of the 3rd energy level.

The existence of sublevels also explains why argon behaves as an unreactive gas with only eight (instead of 18) electrons in its outer energy level. Argon has completely filled 1st and 2nd energy levels. The first two sublevels of its 3rd energy level are also filled (Table 5-2, on previous page). Because the next available sublevel is so much higher in energy than the second sublevel of the 3rd energy level, argon behaves as an inert element just as if it had a filled outer energy level. There seems to be a special stability associated with having eight electrons in an outer energy level. Every atom that has eight electrons in its outer energy level is chemically stable and is a member of the noble gas family.

Sample Problem 5-1

Which one of the first 20 elements should have similar chemical properties to, and be a member of, the same family as phosphorus? Why?

SOLUTION
Phosphorus has five electrons in its outer energy level. The only other element of the first 20 elements to have five electrons in its outer energy level is nitrogen. Thus, nitrogen and phosphorus should be members of a chemically related family.

Practice Problem 5-1

Which one of the first 20 elements should have similar chemical properties to, and be a member of, the same family as oxygen? Why? (*Answer*: sulfur)

5-4 Electron Dot Symbols

In Section 5-3 we discussed how electrons are found in various energy levels. The electrons in the outer energy levels are the ones which usually participate in chemical reactions. The inner electrons are not usually involved. These outer electrons allow us to explain the combining powers of atoms. They are called **valence electrons**. In the case of chlorine, the 1st and 2nd energy levels contain ten electrons, and those electrons are considered to be inner electrons. The seven electrons in the 3rd energy level are the valence electrons. In the case of potassium, the 1st, 2nd, and 3rd energy levels contain 18 inner electrons. The one electron in the 4th energy level is the valence electron. These two examples illustrate the point that the *valence electrons of an atom* are those in the energy levels with the *highest principal quantum number*.

Since the valence electrons of an atom are so important in determining its chemical properties, chemists have developed a special symbol, the **electron** dot symbol, to represent an atom and its valence electrons. In an ordinary chemical symbol such as N, Al, or Cl, the letters in the symbol represent the whole atom: nucleus, inner electrons, and valence electrons. In an electron dot symbol, however, the letters represent only the **kernel** of the atom, that is, the *nucleus* and the *inner electrons*. The *outer* or *valence electrons* are written as dots surrounding the kernel. Thus, the electron dot symbol for chlorine is ·C̈l̤:. The Cl represents the nucleus and the ten inner electrons in the first two energy levels. The seven dots represent the seven valence electrons in the 3rd energy level. The positions of the dots have no relationship to the actual positions of the electrons. The main function of the dots is to remind us of the number of valence electrons belonging to the atom. The electron dot symbols of some representative elements are shown in Table 5-3. You will notice that the number of electron dots is the same as the number of the group to which the element belongs. The atoms of Group 0, however, have eight electron dots (helium, of course, has only two). This grouping of eight electrons is called an **octet**. The term octet draws attention to the special stability associated with having eight electrons in an outer energy level.

TABLE 5-3 Electron Dot Symbols of Some Elements

I	II	III	IV	V	VI	VII	0
H·							He:
Li·	Be:	Ḃ:	·Ċ:	·N̈:	:Ö:	·F̈:	:N̈e:
Na·	Mg:	A̤l:	·Si̤:	·P̤:	:S̤:	·C̈l:	:Ä̤r:
K·	Ca:					·B̈r:	:K̈r:

Sample Problem 5-2

Write the electron dot symbols for rubidium and strontium.

SOLUTION
Rubidium, in Group I, has one valence electron. Its electron dot symbol is therefore Rb·.
Strontium, in Group II, has two valence electrons. Its electron dot symbol is therefore Sr:.

Practice Problem 5-2

Write the electron dot symbols for indium and tin.

5-5 The Periodic Table and Electronic Configurations

The number of electrons in the outer energy level of an atom of an element depends on the position of that element in the periodic table. Consider, for example, element number 38, strontium.

Fig. 5-4 Order of Filling Energy
Sublevels

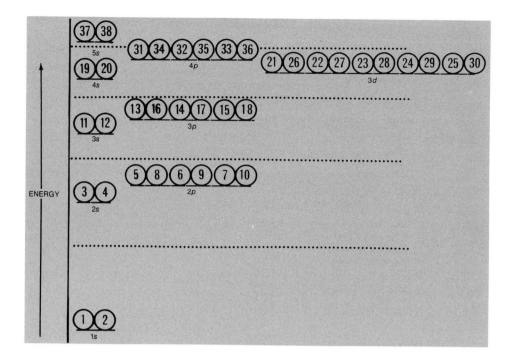

The energy level diagram for strontium is shown in Fig. 5-4. Each of the 38 electrons of strontium is represented by a numbered circle. The diagram shows the order in which the 38 electrons are placed in the 19 orbitals of lowest energy. You can use this diagram to give the electronic configuration of any element below number 38. For example, the energy level diagram for element 16, sulfur, would contain only the first 16 electrons. You would make a mental note to omit electrons 17 to 38 from the diagram. Thus, the electronic configuration of sulfur is $_{16}$S $1s^2\,2s^2\,2p^6\,3s^2\,3p^4$. The energy level diagram for element 28, nickel, would contain only the first 28 electrons. You would make a mental note to omit electrons 29 to 38 from the diagram. The electronic configuration of nickel is $_{28}$Ni $1s^2\,2s^2\,2p^6\,3s^2\,3p^6\,4s^2\,3d^8$.

In Fig. 5-4, the energy sublevels are grouped into clusters of roughly similar energy by horizontal dotted lines. The $1s$ sublevel stands alone. The $2s$ and $2p$ sublevels are grouped together, as are the $3s$ and $3p$ sublevels. The next grouping, however, consists of $4s$, $3d$, and $4p$ sublevels, and they are filled in the relative order s, then d, then p. Although it is not shown in Fig. 5-4, the energy sublevels in the next cluster are also filled in the order s, then d, then p.

You can also obtain a table similar to the periodic table by listing the elements in a pattern according to the way their electrons fill up the energy level diagram. Place two columns for the atoms with electronic configurations ending in s^1 and s^2 at the left side of a piece of paper. Place six columns for the atoms with electronic configurations ending in p^1 to p^6 at the right side of the paper. In the middle, place ten columns for the atoms with electronic configurations ending in d^1 to d^{10}. These d columns are placed in the middle because the orbitals of the fourth grouping are filled in the order s, then d, then p. The elements are now listed in such a way that every atom with an electronic configuration ending in s^1 will appear in the first column. Every atom with an electronic configuration ending in s^2 will appear in the second column and so on:

s^1	s^2	d^1	d^2	d^3	d^4	d^5	d^6	d^7	d^8	d^9	d^{10}	p^1	p^2	p^3	p^4	p^5	p^6
1	2																
3	4											5	6	7	8	9	10
11	12											13	14	15	16	17	18
19	20	21	22	23	24	25	26	27	28	29	30	31	32	33	34	35	36
37	38																

The similarity of this table to the periodic table is not accidental. The periodic table was originally constructed to group elements according to their chemical properties. However, we have seen that it can also be constructed using energy level diagrams. Thus, chemical properties are apparently related to the electronic configurations of elements.

Consider elements 10, 18, and 36. Their electronic configurations are

$$_{10}\text{Ne} \quad 1s^2 \, 2s^2 \, 2p^6$$
$$_{18}\text{Ar} \quad 1s^2 \, 2s^2 \, 2p^6 \, 3s^2 \, 3p^6$$
$$_{36}\text{Kr} \quad 1s^2 \, 2s^2 \, 2p^6 \, 3s^2 \, 3p^6 \, 3d^{10} \, 4s^2 \, 4p^6*$$

All of these elements are noble gases. They all have filled outer s and p orbitals. It appears that whenever the outer s and p orbitals are filled with a total of *eight* electrons, the atom is chemically unreactive. Helium is also chemically unreactive because two electrons are sufficient to fill the first energy level. Thus, it is included in the noble gas family, not in the second column (Group II).

Consider elements 3, 11, 19, and 37:

$$_{3}\text{Li} \quad 1s^2 \, 2s^1$$
$$_{11}\text{Na} \quad 1s^2 \, 2s^2 \, 2p^6 \, 3s^1$$
$$_{19}\text{K} \quad 1s^2 \, 2s^2 \, 2p^6 \, 3s^2 \, 3p^6 \, 4s^1$$
$$_{37}\text{Rb} \quad 1s^2 \, 2s^2 \, 2p^6 \, 3s^2 \, 3p^6 \, 3d^{10} \, 4s^2 \, 4p^6 \, 5s^1$$

These elements all have electronic configurations ending in s^1. That is, their outer (or highest energy) orbitals are half-filled s orbitals. These elements all have similar properties.

Finally, consider elements 9, 17, and 35:

$$_{9}\text{F} \quad 1s^2 \, 2s^2 \, 2p^5$$
$$_{17}\text{Cl} \quad 1s^2 \, 2s^2 \, 2p^6 \, 3s^2 \, 3p^5$$
$$_{35}\text{Br} \quad 1s^2 \, 2s^2 \, 2p^6 \, 3s^2 \, 3p^6 \, 3d^{10} \, 4s^2 \, 4p^5$$

---

*If the d sublevel is incomplete (as in nickel), it is written at the end of the electronic configuration to show that the d sublevel is still being filled. If the d sublevel is complete (as in krypton), we write the $4s$-$4p$ unit at the end of the electronic configuration so that the actual number of valence electrons is more obvious.

These elements are the halogens, and experiments have shown that they all have similar chemical properties. Their electronic configurations all end in $s^2 p^5$. That is, they have a total of *seven* electrons in their outer s and p orbitals.

Sample Problem 5-3

Consider elements 4, 12, 20, and 38. Show why they should all belong in the same family.

SOLUTION
Their electronic configurations are

$$
\begin{array}{ll}
\text{Be} & 1s^2\, 2s^2 \\
\text{Mg} & 1s^2\, 2s^2\, 2p^6\, 3s^2 \\
\text{Ca} & 1s^2\, 2s^2\, 2p^6\, 3s^2\, 3p^6\, 4s^2 \\
\text{Sr} & 1s^2\, 2s^2\, 2p^6\, 3s^2\, 3p^6\, 3d^{10}\, 4s^2\, 4p^2\, 5s^2
\end{array}
$$

The electronic configurations of these atoms all end in s^2, that is, these atoms all have two electrons in their outermost shells.

Practice Problem 5-3

Consider elements 5, 13, and 31. Show why they should belong in the same family.

In fact, the electronic configuration of any element in Group I ends in s^1; for any element in Group II it ends in s^2; for any element in Group III it ends in $s^2 p^1$; and so on. It appears that the important chemical properties of any element depend on the number of electrons in its outermost s and p orbitals.

The series of elements in which the d orbitals are being filled (elements 21 to 30) are all metals and have similar properties. Apparently, partially filled d orbitals do not contribute as much to the chemical properties of an element as partially filled s and p orbitals.

The outer s and p orbitals are called the **valence orbitals**, and they contain the valence electrons. However, partially filled d orbitals are not valence orbitals. For example, an iron atom has an electronic configuration:

$$_{26}\text{Fe}\ 1s^2\, 2s^2\, 2p^6\, 3s^2\, 3p^6\, 4s^2\, 3d^6$$

The valence electrons of iron are the two electrons in the $4s$ orbital. The six $3d$ electrons are considered *not* as valence electrons but as *inner electrons* even though the $3d$ orbitals fill *after* the $4s$ orbital fills. The electron dot symbol for iron is Fe: . (On some occasions, one of the $3d$ electrons of iron is promoted to a vacant $4p$ orbital, and this electron *does* take part in chemical reactions. It is considered to be a third valence electron, and the electron dot symbol for iron would then be Fė: . Iron, therefore, has either two or three valence electrons, depending on the reaction taking place.)

Germanium has the electronic configuration

$$_{32}Ge \ 1s^2 \ 2s^2 \ 2p^6 \ 3s^2 \ 3p^6 \ 3d^{10} \ 4s^2 \ 4p^2$$

Germanium has four valence electrons, those in the $4s$ and $4p$ orbitals. The electrons in the $3d$ sublevel are included among the inner electrons. The electron dot symbol for germanium would be $\cdot\dot{Ge}\colon$. The valence electrons of an atom are in those orbitals with the highest principal quantum number.

5-6 Trends in the Periodic Table—Atomic Size

You might expect that atoms would become larger as you move from the left to the right of a period. However, this does not happen. If we think of an atom as being a sphere, the size of the atom depends on its radius. The radii of atoms decrease as one moves from the left hand side of a period to the right hand side. This is due to the fact that as one goes from the left of a period to the right, electrons are all being placed in sublevels of the same energy level. Electrons in sublevels of the same energy level would be predicted to be approximately the same distance from the nucleus. However, as one passes from the left to the right side of the period, protons are being added to the nucleus, increasing the nuclear charge. As the nuclear charge increases, all the electrons are being pulled closer to the nucleus, and the size of the atom decreases.

Sample Problem 5-4

Of Si, Mg, and S, which element has the largest atomic radius? Why?

SOLUTION
The atomic radius decreases as one moves from left to right in the periodic table since, as the nuclear charge increases, all the electrons are being pulled closer to the nucleus, and the size of the atom decreases. Thus, the atom with the largest atomic radius should be the farthest left in the periodic table. In this case the element is Mg.

Practice Problem 5-4

Of the elements Al, Na, and Cl, which one has the largest atomic radius? Why?

The atomic radii increase when one goes from the top of a group of the periodic table to the bottom of the same group. This happens because, as one moves from the top of a group to the bottom, the extra electrons are going into energy levels that place the electrons farther from the nucleus. Even though the nuclear charge increases from the top to the bottom of a group, it is less effective at attracting electrons which are much farther away from the nucleus.

5-7 Trends in the Periodic Table— Ionization Potential

When a marble is aimed at a group of marbles inside a circle, the skillful player is able to cause one or more marbles to be knocked outside the circle. In the same way, an electron can be knocked out of an atom by being hit with a high-speed electron aimed at it from outside:

$$\text{Li·} \xrightarrow[\substack{\text{bombard with a high-} \\ \text{speed electron}}]{} \text{Li}^+ + e^-$$

The remaining positive particle is a lithium ion, and the process (changing an atom into an ion) is called **ionization**. The symbol e^- represents a free electron.

The bombarding electron acquires its energy when it passes between two plates to which a voltage (or potential) is applied. The electron is attracted toward the positive plate at a speed which is proportional to the applied voltage, just as in a cathode ray tube. If the voltage is too low, the bombarding electron will not have enough energy to knock an electron out of the target atom. As the voltage is increased, however, a point will be reached at which ionization just begins. The minimum voltage which is just sufficient to remove one electron from an isolated atom of a gaseous sample of the element is called the **ionization potential** of that element. The ionization potential of lithium is 5.4 V (volts). This means that if a bombarding electron is subjected to a potential of 5.4 V, it will have just enough energy to remove one electron from a lithium atom.

Fig. 5-5 Ionization Potential as a Function of Atomic Number

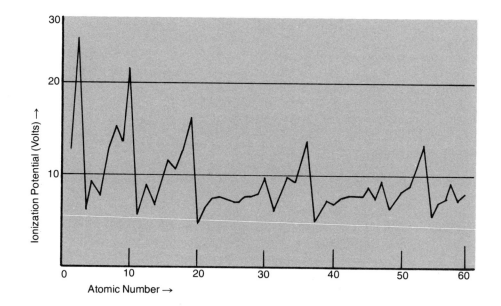

The most easily removed electron will be the one in the highest energy level. Since energy levels depend on the electron populations which are summarized in the periodic table, we should expect to find that ionization potentials would vary in a periodic manner. This variation is quite apparent in Fig. 5-5. The exceptional stability of the noble gases is readily apparent. These gases have filled outer *s* and *p* orbitals, that is, they have achieved a completed octet of electrons. An atom with a completed octet is in a relatively stable state, and it is quite difficult to remove an electron from such an octet. Thus, the noble gases have very high ionization potentials.

The alkali metals all have very low ionization potentials. They all readily lose their single valence electron in order to form a stable positive ion with a completed electron octet exposed.

The ionization potentials of the first 54 elements are arranged in the form of a periodic table in Fig. 5-6. The ionization potential increases as one goes from the left side to the right side of a period. This occurs because there are more protons in the atoms of the right side of a period than there are in the atoms of the left side of the same period. That is, the positive nuclear charge increases as one moves from the left to the right of a period. This increased positive nuclear charge makes it more difficult to pull electrons from atoms on the right side of the periodic table. As a general rule, the atoms have a large ionization potential if they are on the right-hand side of the periodic table. They have a small ionization potential if they are on the left side of the periodic table.

Variations of the ionization potentials of the atoms in a group are predictable. The ionization potential decreases as one goes from the top of a group to the bottom, because the outermost electrons of the small atoms of a group are closer to the nucleus and are more tightly held than the outer electrons of a larger atom in the group.

Fig. 5-6 Ionization Potentials (Volts) of the First 54 Elements

I	II											III	IV	V	VI	VII	0
13.6																	24.6
5.4	9.3											8.3	11.3	14.5	13.6	17.4	21.6
5.1	7.6	←				Transition Metals					→	6.0	8.1	11.0	10.4	13.0	15.8
4.3	6.1	6.6	6.8	6.7	6.8	7.4	7.9	7.9	7.6	7.7	9.4	6.0	8.1	10.0	9.8	11.8	14.0
4.2	5.7	6.6	7.0	6.8	7.2	—	7.5	7.7	8.3	7.6	9.0	5.8	7.3	8.6	9.0	10.4	12.1

Sample Problem 5-5

Of the elements Ca, Be, and Mg, which has the highest ionization potential? Why?

SOLUTION

Since the outermost electrons of the small atoms of a group are closer to the nucleus and are more tightly held than the outer electrons of larger atoms in the group, the ionization potential decreases as one goes from the top to the bottom of a group. The atom with the highest ionization potential should be at the top of the group. In this case that element is Be.

Practice Problem 5-5

Of the elements B, Al, and Ga, which has the highest ionization potential? Why?

5-8 Trends in the Periodic Table—Electron Affinity

In Section 5-7 we saw that some atoms have a tendency to lose electrons easily. Now we shall see that some atoms have a tendency to pick up additional electrons. They do so because this results in a lowering of energy of the system, i.e., the achievement of a more stable state for the added electrons. Energy will be given off since an added electron is moved into the positive field of the nucleus. **Electron affinity** is a measure of the energy given off when an electron is added to a neutral atom:

$$:\ddot{\text{X}}\cdot + 1\,e^- \rightarrow :\ddot{\text{X}}:^-$$

We can view the process of addition of an electron to a neutral atom to form a *negative ion* as the reverse of the removal of an electron from a negative ion to form a neutral atom. Since it is more difficult to remove an electron from a smaller ion (more energy is required because the electrons are closer to the nucleus), the electron affinity increases as the size of the atom decreases. That is, more energy is given off as a smaller atom accepts an additional electron to become an ion.

Because the size of atoms decreases from left to right across a period from Groups I to VII, the Group VII elements would be expected to have the highest electron affinities. Within a group it appears that the elements at the top generally have a higher electron affinity than do the elements at the bottom. This is also to be expected since the smaller atoms are at the top of a group. The halogens all react to form the halide ions F^-, Cl^-, Br^-, and I^-. The smallest halogen, fluorine, is the most reactive element known.

A Final Word

In this chapter we have seen that there are regular and periodic variations in the properties of elements. Eventually, regularities led to the discovery of the periodic law and the development of the modern periodic table. The periodic table arranges the elements so that the ones with similar chemical properties are grouped together in columns. We also learned that the electronic configuration of an element is related to its position in the periodic table. Thus, the periodic table is a powerful aid for memory and for making predictions about the properties of elements.

   Now that you have finished reading this chapter, you should reread the Key Objectives to make sure that you have learned the most important points of the chapter. In addition, you should learn the meaning of each important term found in the chapter.

Key Terms

What is the meaning of each of the following terms?

period	valence electron
family	electron dot symbol
periodic law	kernel
noble gas	octet
alkali metal	valence orbital
halogen	ionization
representative element	ionization potential
transition metal	electron affinity

Questions

1. For each of the following triads, compare the average of the atomic masses of the first and third elements with the atomic mass of the second element: sulfur, selenium, and tellurium; chlorine, bromine, and iodine; lithium, sodium, and potassium. What regularity do you notice?
2. What would you predict for the atomic mass of the missing element in Group VII, Row 6, of Mendeleev's periodic table?
3. Find two adjacent elements in the modern periodic table which would appear in a different order when arranged in order of increasing atomic mass.
4. Write the electronic configurations for phosphorus and arsenic. Show why they belong to the same family.
5. Consider elements 8, 16, and 34. Show why they should belong in the same family.

6. Which element of the first 20 elements should belong to the same family of chemically related elements as silicon? Why?

7. Write the electron dot symbols for gallium; germanium; arsenic; selenium.

8. How many valence electrons do nitrogen, phosphorus, and arsenic have?

9. The elements whose electronic configurations end in $s^2 p^2$ belong to which group in the periodic table?

10. What are elements that have some metallic and some nonmetallic properties called?

11. Which family of the periodic table contains the most metallic element? The most nonmetallic element?

12. Which group contains the elements which are hardest to ionize?

13. Which element should have the largest atomic radius and why? **a)** B, Li, or F; **b)** K, Li, or Na.

14. Which element loses an electron most readily and why? **a)** B, Li, or F; **b)** K, Li, or Na.

15. Which element has the largest electron affinity and why? **a)** B, Li, or F; **b)** Br, Cl, or I.

16. How many electrons would the following elements tend to gain or lose: Mg, Cl, N, Al, S, Ar? State whether the element gains or loses electrons.

17. In which energy level are the valence electrons of the following elements found: iodine, calcium, gallium, fluorine, francium?

18. State the periodic law. What is meant by periodicity of properties?

19. **a)** Draw a blank outline of the periodic table as in Fig. 5-2. Indicate the position of the representative elements, the transition metals, the lanthanides, and the actinides.

   b) On a similar blank outline indicate the positions of the noble gases, the alkali metals, and the halogens.

20. Using the energy level populations given in Table 5-2, indicate which elements should have similar chemical properties to **a)** carbon, **b)** neon, and **c)** sulfur.

21. Explain why sodium forms only ions with a +1 charge, and calcium forms only ions with a +2 charge.

22. Without looking at the periodic table, indicate the groups in which elements having the following atomic numbers will be found: **a)** 4, **b)** 7, **c)** 9, **d)** 13, **e)** 16, **f)** 18.

23. Using the periodic table, identify each of the following:

   a) an element which has seven electrons in each atom;

   b) an element with seven electrons in its outer energy level;

   c) an element for which the second energy level is half-filled;

   d) a representative element which forms ions by losing only s electrons.

24. You have landed on a strange planet and have been taken prisoner. You are told that your life will be spared if you are able to construct a periodic table for the natives. Their atomic theory is the same as ours except that their spin quantum numbers are $+\frac{1}{2}$, 0, and $-\frac{1}{2}$ and their magnetic quantum numbers take the values 0, 1, 2, ... ℓ.

   a) Construct an energy level diagram for the natives. This will differ from ours only because of the changes in the spin quantum numbers and the magnetic quantum numbers. Everything else, including the ordering of the orbitals and the naming of the orbitals, will be the same.

b) Construct a periodic table. Use atomic numbers instead of symbols and go as far as element number 35.

c) What are the atomic numbers of their first three noble gases?

d) What is the electronic configuration of their element number 24?

e) Which of the following elements should have similar chemical properties: 4, 7, 15, 16, 20, 27, 34, 35?

f) Which of the following elements should have the highest electron affinity: 13, 11, 27, 12?

25. The energy required to remove a second electron from magnesium (second ionization potential) is only about twice as great as the energy required to remove the first electron (first ionization potential). However, the energy required to remove the third electron from magnesium (third ionization potential) is about ten times as great as the first ionization potential. Why does it take so much more energy to remove the third electron?

26. The first ionization potential of boron is slightly less than the first ionization potential of beryllium. Use electronic configurations of these two elements to provide an explanation for this fact.

27. The electronic configurations for six neutral atoms are

A) $1s^2 2s^2 2p^6 3s^1$ **D)** $1s^2 2s^2 2p^6$

B) $1s^2$ **E)** $1s^2 2s^1$

C) $1s^2 2s^2 2p^6 3s^2$ **F)** $1s^2 2s^2 2p^3$

a) Which of these would have the highest first ionization potential?

b) Which of these would have the lowest first ionization potential?

c) Which of these would have the lowest second ionization potential?

d) Which of these would likely have the lowest third ionization potential?

6 Chemical Bonding

Individual atoms possess the ability to unite with one another. Thus, compounds are formed by the union of atoms of elements. A **molecule** is any electrically neutral group of atoms that is held together tightly enough to be considered a single particle. Atoms are therefore the smallest particles of an element, and molecules are the smallest particles of a compound. **Chemical bonds** are the attractions between the atoms within a molecule.

Some compounds are familiar to almost everyone. For example, water vapour consists of molecules, each containing two hydrogen atoms and one oxygen atom (H_2O). Carbon dioxide gas is found in soda water and in fire extinguishers, is used by plants in photosynthesis, and is a product of food burned in our bodies. It consists of molecules, each containing one carbon atom and two oxygen atoms (CO_2). Methane molecules are the most abundant molecules in natural gas. Methane is also found in coal mines and in bogs and marshes. Each methane molecule consists of one carbon atom and four hydrogen atoms (CH_4). Figure 6-1 shows models of water and methane.

Why do atoms bond together? Is there more than one type of chemical bond? Why is there a specific number of each type of atom in a molecule? For example, why does a methane molecule have four hydrogen atoms but only one carbon atom? These questions and others are answered in this chapter.

Key Objectives

By the time you have finished reading this chapter, you should be able to
1. explain the role of electrons in bonding.
2. predict whether a given bond will be ionic or covalent.
3. write equations, using electron dot symbols, for the formation of ionic compounds.
4. predict the formulas of ionic compounds.
5. write Lewis structures to represent the formation of covalent bonds in simple molecules.
6. use VSEPR Theory to predict the shapes of simple molecules.
7. draw orbital diagrams for simple covalent molecules.

Fig. 6-1 Models of Water (H$_2$O) and Methane (CH$_4$)

6-1 The Role of Electrons in Bonding

Before the types of chemical bonds are described and examples are given, one important question should be asked. Why do atoms bond together? The formation of a chemical bond indicates that a molecule is more stable, that is, it has less energy than the isolated atoms from which it is formed. This answer leads to another question: Why is a molecule more stable than the isolated atoms from which it is formed?

In a single atom, the electrons come under the influence of only one nucleus. The atom has a certain amount of potential energy associated with the distribution of its electrons in the energy levels. The atom is most stable when its electrons are in the lowest possible energy levels. When the electrons of an atom are in the lowest possible energy levels, the atom is said to be in the *ground state*. The ground state energy level populations for the first 20 elements are given in Table 6-1 (overleaf). For example, the sodium atom is most stable when two of its electrons are in the first energy level, eight more electrons are in the second energy level, and its eleventh electron is in the third energy level. Its ground state energy level population is 2, 8, 1.

When any two atoms come close together, the electrons of each atom come under the influence of the nucleus and the electrons of the other atom. We can consider two distant hydrogen atoms (Fig. 6-2 (a)), and two hydrogen atoms which are near to one another (Fig. 6-2 (b)). In the distant hydrogen atoms, the only force is the attraction of the electron of each atom to the proton of the same atom. In the near hydrogen atoms, there are both attractive and repulsive forces. First, there are the same proton-electron attractions. In addition, there is an electron-electron repulsion; there is a proton-proton repulsion; and the electron of each atom is attracted to the proton of the other atom (two new attractions).

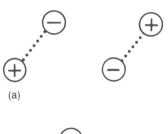

(a)

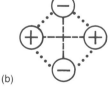

(b)

Fig. 6-2 (a) Two Distant Hydrogen Atoms
(b) Two Near Hydrogen Atoms
(The dotted lines represent attractions, and the dashed lines represent repulsions.)

TABLE 6-1 Energy Level Populations for the First Twenty Elements

ELEMENT	SYMBOL	ATOMIC NUMBER	ENERGY LEVEL POPULATIONS				ENERGY LEVEL POPULATION ABBREVIATIONS
			1st Level	2nd Level	3rd Level	4th Level	
Hydrogen	H	1	1				1
Helium	He	2	2				2
Lithium	Li	3	2	1			2,1
Beryllium	Be	4	2	2			2,2
Boron	B	5	2	3			2,3
Carbon	C	6	2	4			2,4
Nitrogen	N	7	2	5			2,5
Oxygen	O	8	2	6			2,6
Fluorine	F	9	2	7			2,7
Neon	Ne	10	2	8			2,8
Sodium	Na	11	2	8	1		2,8,1
Magnesium	Mg	12	2	8	2		2,8,2
Aluminum	Al	13	2	8	3		2,8,3
Silicon	Si	14	2	8	4		2,8,4
Phosphorus	P	15	2	8	5		2,8,5
Sulfur	S	16	2	8	6		2,8,6
Chlorine	Cl	17	2	8	7		2,8,7
Argon	Ar	18	2	8	8		2,8,8
Potassium	K	19	2	8	8	1	2,8,8,1
Calcium	Ca	20	2	8	8	2	2,8,8,2

The fact that two hydrogen atoms *do* bond together to form a molecule indicates that the hydrogen molecule is more stable (of lower energy) than the distant hydrogen atoms. The *original* proton-electron attractions do not contribute to this *new* increase in stability. Furthermore, the electron-electron repulsion and the proton-proton repulsion act against the increase in stability which results in bond formation. The two hydrogen atoms bond together because the electron of each atom is attracted to the proton of the other atom. These attractive forces are greater than the repulsive forces between electrons and those between protons. The electrons are simultaneously attracted to two nuclei and this causes a more stable (lower energy) state. A chemical bond can form between two atoms when electrons are simultaneously attracted to the two nuclei.

It is important to know that a molecule is more stable than the isolated atoms from which it is formed, and that the increased stability is caused by electrons being simultaneously attracted to two nuclei. However, it is not easy to calculate all of the attractions and repulsions in molecules formed by larger atoms. Less complicated theories of bonding are therefore necessary for a discussion of the formation of compounds. The basis of the present theories of chemical bonding was presented in 1916 by W. Kossel (a German physicist) and G. N. Lewis (Fig. 6-3) in separately published papers.

The electrons in the outer (highest) energy level of an atom are the ones which usually participate in chemical bonding. These electrons are called

Gilbert Lewis was born in West Newton, Massachusetts, in 1875, the son of a lawyer. He received his early education at home from his parents. He was able to read at the age of three and attended university preparatory school in Nebraska in 1889. He later went to the University of Nebraska and after two years transferred to Harvard University. In 1899, he obtained his doctorate, doing research into electrochemistry. After studying in Germany, he returned to teach at Harvard and then at the Massachusetts Institute of Technology. His early research was in the area of thermodynamics.

In 1912, Lewis became dean and chairman of the College of Chemistry at the University of California at Berkeley. There he recruited many people who would later make great contributions to chemistry and to chemical education. Lewis' work in chemical education set the standard for other chemists to follow and is one of his greatest achievements.

In 1916, he proposed a theory of chemical bonding in which electron pairs were shared between atoms. An octet of valence electrons resulted in stability for an atom.

In 1918, Lewis became a major in the Chemical Warfare Service in France. He was later decorated for his war efforts. Lewis went on to work in the areas of acid-base theory, heavy water, and photochemistry. He died in 1946 in Berkeley, California.

Fig. 6-3 Gilbert Newton Lewis (1875–1946) (Photo courtesy of The Bettman Archive, Inc.)

valence electrons. The number of valence electrons possessed by an atom determines the number of other atoms with which that atom can combine.

Except for helium, the noble gases each have eight valence electrons. Helium has only two valence electrons. However, since its outer level (the first energy level) is capable of holding only two electrons, helium also behaves like a noble gas. The noble gases are stable and virtually inert. There appears to be a special stability associated with an atom's having eight valence electrons. The term **stable octet** draws attention to this special stability.

Kossel believed that some atoms could acquire a stable octet by the loss or gain of electrons. Lewis suggested that other atoms might achieve a stable octet and at the same time be held together by sharing electrons between them, that is, by chemically bonding to one another. In the following sections, the ideas of Kossel and Lewis will be described in some detail. We will see that atoms can acquire a stable octet and an energy level population similar to that of the noble gases. This stability is obtained by losing, gaining, or sharing valence electrons.

6-2 Ionic Bonding

The most chemically reactive metals are found in Groups I, II, and to a lesser extent III of the periodic table. These metals have low ionization potentials. That is, a relatively small amount of energy is required to cause them to lose electrons. The most active nonmetals are found in Groups VI and VII. These nonmetals have relatively large electron affinities. That is, they tend to gain electrons readily. When an active metal reacts with an active nonmetal, electron(s) are transferred from the metal to the nonmetal. The atoms of the nonmetal, having gained electrons, become negatively charged ions. The atoms of the metal, having lost electrons, become positively charged ions. These oppositely charged ions attract each other. **Ionic bonding** is the type of chemical bonding resulting from the attraction between oppositely charged ions formed when metallic atoms transfer electrons to nonmetallic atoms.

The sodium atom has an energy level population of 2,8,1 and could become **isoelectronic** with (i.e., have the same energy level population as) neon (2,8) by losing its valence electron. The chlorine atom has an energy level population of 2,8,7 and could become isoelectronic with argon (2,8,8) by gaining one electron from the sodium atom. The equations for these processes are

$$Na\cdot + Energy \rightarrow Na^+ + 1e^-$$

$$:\overset{\cdot\cdot}{\underset{\cdot\cdot}{Cl}}\cdot + 1e^- \rightarrow :\overset{\cdot\cdot}{\underset{\cdot\cdot}{Cl}}:^- + Energy$$

Both the sodium ion (Na^+) and the chloride ion (Cl^-) are isoelectronic with stable, noble gases.

A positive and a negative ion are produced when the sodium atom collides with the chlorine atom. These ions attract one another because they have opposite charges. An ionic bond is formed and more energy is released once again:

$$Na^+ + Cl^- \rightarrow NaCl + Energy$$

The ionic compound formed is sodium chloride, also known as table salt.

Sample Problem 6-1

Why does each lithium ion require one fluoride ion in the compound, lithium fluoride? Large crystals of lithium fluoride are used in certain optical instruments.

SOLUTION

The energy level populations are Li (2,1) and F (2,7). Each lithium atom tends to lose its valence electron to form a lithium ion which is isoelectronic with the noble gas, helium (2). Each fluorine atom tends to gain one electron from the lithium atom to form a fluoride ion which is isoelectronic with the noble gas, neon (2,8). The lithium ion attracts the fluoride ion because they have opposite charges:

$$Li\cdot + Energy \rightarrow Li^+ + 1e^-$$

$$:\overset{\cdot\cdot}{\underset{\cdot\cdot}{F}}\cdot + 1e^- \rightarrow :\overset{\cdot\cdot}{\underset{\cdot\cdot}{F}}:^- + Energy$$

$$Li^+ + F^- \rightarrow LiF + Energy$$

Practice Problem 6-1

Why does each rubidium ion require one bromide ion in the compound, rubidium bromide?

When an ionic bond is formed by electron transfer between a metal and a nonmetal, there must be a balance of electrons gained and lost. After reaction the sodium ion and the chloride ion are each left with a filled outer energy level. When ionic bonds are formed, enough electrons are transferred so that each ion produced has a filled outer energy level.

A Group II metal (such as calcium) has two valence electrons located in its highest energy level. Calcium (2,8,8,2) can become isoelectronic with the noble gas argon (2,8,8) if it loses two valence electrons. Therefore, calcium atoms lose their two valence electrons:

$$Ca\!:\, + \text{ Energy} \rightarrow Ca^{2+} + 2e^-$$

If calcium is reacting with chlorine (2,8,7), two chlorine atoms will be required to accept the two electrons from each calcium atom and two chloride ions will be formed:

$$2:\ddot{\underset{..}{C}}l\cdot\, + 2e^- \rightarrow 2:\ddot{\underset{..}{C}}l:^- + \text{ Energy}$$

The two chloride ions will be attracted to the calcium ion:

$$Ca^{2+} + 2Cl^- \rightarrow CaCl_2 + \text{ Energy}$$

The subscript 2 indicates that there are two chloride ions ionically bonded to a calcium ion. Calcium chloride is used as a drying agent and is spread on roads to melt ice and snow.

Calcium could react with an element from Group VI. Oxygen (2,6) is such an element. Oxygen atoms have six valence electrons. Oxygen atoms would have to gain two electrons to become isoelectronic with the noble gas, neon (2,8):

$$:\ddot{O}\cdot\, + 2e^- \rightarrow :\ddot{\underset{..}{O}}:^{2-}$$

Thus one calcium atom could transfer two electrons to one oxygen atom and the ionic compound calcium oxide would be formed:

$$Ca^{2+} + O^{2-} \rightarrow CaO$$

Calcium oxide is also known as lime or quicklime. It is a white solid used as a component of cement and fertilizers.

Sample Problem 6-2

Predict the formula of the ionic compound, beryllium oxide, which is found in emeralds.

SOLUTION
The energy level populations are Be (2,2) and O (2,6). Each beryllium atom can give up its two valence electrons to form a beryllium ion which is isoelectronic with the noble gas, helium (2). Each oxygen atom gains two electrons from the beryllium atom to form an oxide ion which is isoelectronic with the noble gas, neon (2,8).

$$Be\!:\, \rightarrow Be^{2+} + 2e^-$$
$$:\ddot{O}\cdot\, + 2e^- \rightarrow :\ddot{\underset{..}{O}}:^{2-}$$

Therefore one beryllium ion requires one oxide ion:

$$Be^{2+} + O^{2-} \rightarrow BeO$$

The formula is BeO.

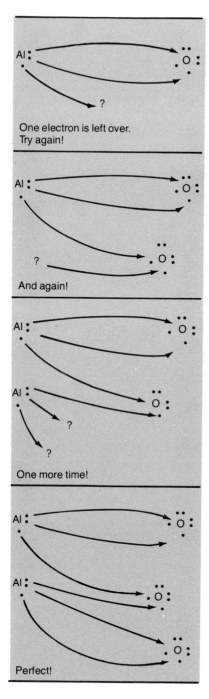

One electron is left over.
Try again!

And again!

One more time!

Perfect!

Fig. 6-4 Establishing the 2:3 Ratio of Ions in Al_2O_3

Practice Problem 6-2

Predict the formula of magnesium sulfide.

Let us consider the example of the Group III metal aluminum (2,8,3) reacting with oxygen (2,6):

$$Al: \rightarrow Al^{3+} + 3e^- \text{ and } :\ddot{O}\cdot + 2e^- \rightarrow :\ddot{O}:^{2-}$$

$$\therefore 2\ Al: \rightarrow 2\ Al^{3+} + 6e^- \text{ and } 3\ :\ddot{O}\cdot + 6e^- \rightarrow 3\ :\ddot{O}:^{2-}$$

$$2\ Al^{3+} + 3\ O^{2-} \rightarrow Al_2O_3$$

Two aluminum atoms have lost 6 electrons and three oxygen atoms have received the 6 electrons. The formula Al_2O_3 indicates that there are three oxide ions for every two aluminum ions in aluminum oxide. Fig. 6-4 shows schematically how the two to three ratio of aluminum ions to oxide ions can be obtained for aluminum oxide.

Sample Problem 6-3

When magnesium burns in air it reacts not only with oxygen to form magnesium oxide, but also with nitrogen to form magnesium nitride. What is a reasonable formula for magnesium nitride?

SOLUTION

The energy level populations are Mg (2,8,2) and N (2,5). Each magnesium atom can give up its two valence electrons to form a magnesium ion which is isoelectronic with the noble gas, neon (2,8). However, each nitrogen atom must gain three electrons to form a nitride ion which is also isoelectronic with the noble gas, neon (2,8).

$$Mg: \rightarrow \quad Mg^{2+} + 2e^-$$

$$:\dot{\ddot{N}}\cdot + 3e^- \rightarrow \quad :\ddot{\ddot{N}}:^{3-}$$

Three magnesium atoms will lose six electrons. These electrons can be accepted by two nitrogen atoms:

$$3\ Mg^{2+} + 2\ N^{3-} \rightarrow Mg_3N_2$$

The formula is Mg_3N_2.

Practice Problem 6-3

What is a reasonable formula for lithium nitride? For gallium sulfide? (*Answers:* Li_3N; Ga_2S_3)

The atoms and the ions of an element have different chemical properties. Sodium is a soft, silvery-white metal and chlorine is a poisonous, greenish-yellow gas. However, sodium chloride (sodium ions and chloride ions) is white, solid, table salt and it is not poisonous except in large quantities.

In general, the ionic compounds which are formed when the elements of Groups I, II, or III react with the elements of Groups VI or VII resemble sodium chloride. They are usually white, brittle solids which melt at high temperatures. Their molten form or water solutions contain mobile positive and negative ions which conduct electricity.

	GROUP I METALS	GROUP II METALS	GROUP III METALS
GROUP VII NONMETALS	MX (1)	MX_2 (2)	MX_3 (3)
GROUP VI NONMETALS	M_2X (2)	MX (2)	M_2X_3 (6)

Fig. 6-5 Formulas of Ionic Compounds. Each rectangle contains the formula of the compound that results when the metal (M) from the indicated group combines with the nonmetal (X) from the indicated group to form an ionic compound. The number in parentheses indicates the total number of electrons transferred.

Fig. 6-5 can be used to obtain the formulas of many ionic compounds. Suppose we wish to know the formula of aluminum selenide. Aluminum is a Group III metal and selenium is a Group VI nonmetal. The formula must have the form M_2X_3. The formula is Al_2Se_3. Six electrons have been transferred from the two aluminum atoms to the three selenium atoms.

One point should be made regarding the naming of the ionic compounds which we have considered. The name of the metallic ion is the same as the name of the metallic atom. Hence, during the formation of an ionic compound, a sodium atom becomes a sodium ion. However, the name of the nonmetallic ion differs from the name of the nonmetallic atom. The ending of the name of the nonmetallic atom is dropped and replaced with the suffix -ide. During the formation of an ionic compound, a chlorine atom becomes a chloride ion, an oxygen atom becomes an oxide ion, and a sulfur atom becomes a sulfide ion. When an ionic compound is named, the name of the metallic ion is written before the name of the nonmetallic ion. Thus, Na_2S is sodium sulfide.

In this section, we learned that atoms gain stability by losing or gaining electrons. As a result of the formation of ionic bonds, atoms achieve a stable octet and energy level populations resembling those of the noble gases. In the next section, we shall look at another means by which atoms achieve a stable octet.

6-3 Covalent Bonding

In the last section, we discussed ionic bonding. However, the transfer of electrons from one atom to another does not adequately represent all bond types. For example, when two hydrogen atoms collide, there is no reason for one hydrogen atom to give up its electron to the other hydrogen atom. We believe that there is no electron transfer in this case. The electrons are *shared* between the two hydrogen atoms, and the bond is a **covalent bond**.

Each hydrogen atom has one valence electron (H·). When two hydrogen atoms collide, an electron pair is shared equally between the two hydrogen nuclei:

$$H\cdot + \cdot H \rightarrow H:H$$

The representation H : H is an **electron dot formula** and gives a simplified picture of the bonding.

The pair of electrons is now simultaneously attracted to the two hydrogen nuclei. This simultaneous attraction of the electron pair to the two nuclei produces a more stable state. The two atoms are held together because they share an electron pair between them. When the hydrogen atoms share a pair of electrons, each has become isoelectronic with the noble gas, helium. Because *one* pair of electrons (called the *shared pair*) is shared between the atoms, the bond is a **single covalent bond**. A **Lewis structure** resembles an electron dot formula, except that single lines are used to represent each shared pair of electrons, and dots are used to represent electrons that are not involved in bonding. Hence, the Lewis structure of H_2 is H—H.

In the past, we have discussed hydrogen as if it were normally found as individual atoms. In fact, a sample of hydrogen gas is actually made up of hydrogen molecules. Each hydrogen molecule consists of two hydrogen atoms bonded together. Thus, hydrogen gas consists of diatomic (two atom) H_2 molecules. The subscript indicates the number of atoms in one molecule of hydrogen. A hydrogen atom with a single unpaired electron is too reactive to remain unbonded for any length of time. If no other suitable type of atom is available for bonding, hydrogen atoms will bond to one another.

Suppose two fluorine atoms (2,7) come together. Will they form a bond? Each fluorine atom has seven valence electrons. Therefore, each fluorine atom requires *one more* electron to become isoelectronic with the noble gas, neon (2,8). When the fluorine atoms collide, each tries to gain an eighth valence electron, but neither fluorine atom can pull an electron from the other. Instead, they share a pair of electrons, enabling both atoms to become isoelectronic with the noble gas, neon:

$$:\overset{..}{\underset{..}{F}}\cdot \;+\; \cdot\overset{..}{\underset{..}{F}}: \;\rightarrow\; :\overset{..}{\underset{..}{F}}—\overset{..}{\underset{..}{F}}:$$

Thus, fluorine, like hydrogen, exists as diatomic (F_2) molecules.

In the same way that two fluorine atoms form a single covalent bond, two chlorine atoms form a single covalent bond, producing diatomic (Cl_2) molecules. The Lewis structure for a chlorine molecule is $:\overset{..}{\underset{..}{Cl}}—\overset{..}{\underset{..}{Cl}}:$. Bromine and iodine also belong to Group VII, and they form diatomic molecules (Br_2 and I_2).

We have learned so far that five elements exist as diatomic molecules rather than as individual atoms. They are hydrogen (H_2), fluorine (F_2), chlorine (Cl_2), bromine (Br_2), and iodine (I_2). The first three of these are gaseous elements. Bromine is one of the two elements which are liquids at room temperature (20-25°C). (The other liquid element is mercury.) Iodine is a solid element. Two other gaseous elements exist as diatomic molecules rather than as individual atoms, oxygen (O_2) and nitrogen (N_2). In fact, the only gaseous elements which exist as individual atoms are the noble gases. Thus, a total of seven elements exist as diatomic molecules rather than as individual atoms.

Practice Problem 6-4

Draw the Lewis structures for a bromine molecule and for an iodine molecule.

6-4 Polar Covalent Bonding and Electronegativity

In the previous sections we have discussed ionic bonding, in which electrons are transferred, and covalent bonding, in which electrons are shared equally. In this section, we shall discuss polar covalent bonding, in which electrons are shared unequally.

Polar Covalent Bonding

When a hydrogen atom and a chlorine atom unite, a hydrogen chloride molecule forms. A pair of electrons is shared between the two atoms and a type of covalent bond is formed:

$$H\cdot \: + \: \cdot \ddot{\underset{\cdot\cdot}{C}}l : \: \rightarrow \: H—\ddot{\underset{\cdot\cdot}{C}}l :$$

By sharing the pair of electrons, the hydrogen has become isoelectronic with the noble gas, helium. The chlorine has become isoelectronic with the noble gas, argon.

In the hydrogen chloride molecule, a pair of electrons is shared between two different types of atoms. Will the pair of electrons be shared equally? Will either the chlorine atom or the hydrogen atom have a stronger attraction for the shared pair of electrons?

Chemists have shown that the hydrogen chloride molecule is a *polar molecule*. It has a slightly negative (δ^-, read delta negative) and a slightly positive (δ^+, read delta positive) end. Further work has indicated that the chlorine end of the molecule is slightly negative and the hydrogen end of the molecule is slightly positive:

$$^{\delta^+}H \: :\ddot{\underset{\cdot\cdot}{C}}l :^{\delta^-} \quad \textbf{or} \quad \delta^+ \: \fbox{H \: Cl} \: \delta^-$$

The molecule as a whole is electrically neutral. It has an equal number of protons and electrons. However, the electron pair is unequally shared. The chlorine atom has a greater attraction for the shared pair of electrons than does the hydrogen atom. The chlorine atom does not attract the shared pair strongly enough to gain complete possession of it. Therefore, this is *not* an ionic bond. It is a covalent bond in which there is unequal sharing of electrons: a **polar covalent bond**.

In a polar covalent bond, the shared pair spends more of its time near one of the atoms than it does with the second atom. This makes the former atom slightly negative, and the other atom becomes slightly positive. Generally, polar covalent bonding occurs when atoms of two different elements share a pair of electrons. Is it possible to predict which end of the molecule will be slightly negative and which end of the molecule will be slightly positive?

Electronegativity

A quantitative measure of the electron-attracting ability of the atoms in a molecule is **electronegativity**. By measuring various properties such as ionization potentials and electron affinities of the atoms making up the molecule, how

**Figure 6-6 Linus Pauling (1901 –)
(Photo courtesy of The Bettman
Archive, Inc.)**

Linus Pauling was born in Portland, Oregon in 1901, the son of a druggist. He entered Oregon State College in 1917 and received his B.Sc. in chemical engineering in 1922. He was appointed a Teaching Fellow in Chemistry in the California Institute of Technology while a student there from 1922 to 1925. In 1925 he received his doctorate (*summa cum laude*) in chemistry, with minors in physics and mathematics.

Pauling's approach to research was marked by intuition and intelligent guesses. In 1922, he began the experimental determination of the structures of certain crystals and also started theoretical work on the nature of the chemical bond. He was one of the first persons to use quantum mechanics to explain the chemical bond. His work also included the areas of molecular structure determination, hydrogen bonding, metallic bonding, electronegativity, and the structure of proteins. He attempted to explain the chemical nature of sickle cell anemia and general anesthesia. Pauling is well known for his theory that large doses of Vitamin C can prevent or lessen the severity of the common cold.

He has published many books and articles. In 1931, he became the first recipient of the American Chemical Society Award in Pure Chemistry. He was awarded the 1954 Nobel Prize in Chemistry for his research into the nature of the chemical bond and the application of his bonding theory to the structural determination of complex substances. Pauling was awarded the Nobel Peace Prize in 1963 for his efforts on behalf of a nuclear test ban treaty. He became at that time only the second person to win the Nobel Prize twice. (Marie Curie was the first.) In 1981, he was still active in research.

polar the molecule is, and the energy required to break the bond, it is possible to construct a table of electronegativities. Numerical values assigned for electronegativities of the various elements are included in the periodic table at the back of this book. These values were calculated by the American chemist Linus Pauling (Fig. 6-6.) The electronegativity values are such that the bigger the number is, the greater is the tendency of an atom to attract a shared pair of electrons to itself.

Fluorine has been assigned the highest electronegativity (4.0). Fluorine has a high ionization potential, and it has a high electron affinity. That is, it takes a relatively large amount of energy to force a fluorine atom to lose an electron, but a fluorine atom is ready to accept an electron in order to change its energy level population from 2,7 to 2,8 and to become isoelectronic with neon. These two factors both indicate that in any bond between fluorine and another element, it will be more difficult to transfer an electron from fluorine to the other element than it will be to transfer an electron from the other element to fluorine.

Cesium and francium both have the smallest electronegativity (0.7). They both have low ionization potentials and it is relatively easy to transfer an electron from cesium or francium to another element.

In general, the elements with the lowest ionization potentials have the lowest electronegativities and the elements with the highest ionization potentials have the highest electronegativities. Thus, the variation of electronegativity parallels the variation of ionization potentials. As we move from left (metals) to right (nonmetals) across a period, the electronegativity increases. As we go from top to bottom in a family or group, the electronegativity decreases.

Another example of a polar covalent bond is the bond between chlorine and bromine in the molecule, BrCl. Each of these atoms is in Group VII and each has seven valence electrons. By sharing a pair of electrons each becomes isoelectronic with a noble gas:

$$:\ddot{\underset{..}{B}}r\cdot + \cdot\ddot{\underset{..}{C}}l: \rightarrow :\ddot{\underset{..}{B}}r—\ddot{\underset{..}{C}}l:$$

The electronegativity of chlorine is 3.0 and it is 2.8 for bromine. A chlorine atom is more electronegative than a bromine atom. The shared pair of electrons spends more time near the chlorine nucleus, and the chlorine end of the molecule becomes negative with respect to the bromine end:

$$^{\delta+}:\ddot{\underset{..}{B}}r—\ddot{\underset{..}{C}}l:^{\delta-}$$

The shared pair will spend more time near the Cl because less energy is required to transfer an electron from Br to Cl than is required to transfer an electron from Cl to Br.

Practice Problem 6-5

Draw a Lewis structure for BrF. Is this a polar or a nonpolar molecule? If it is polar, which end of the molecule is the negative end?

6-5 The Bonding Continuum

There is no sharp distinction between ionic and covalent bonding. In a chemical bond between atoms M and X, the polarity of the bond depends on the natures of M and of X. If they each have the same ability to attract electrons, the bond will be covalent and nonpolar. If X can attract electrons better than M, the bond will be polar covalent. If X attracts electrons so strongly that one can say the electron pair spends essentially all of its time in X, the bond is ionic, and there is an M^+ ion and an X^- ion. In fact, an ionic bond is simply an *extreme case* of polar covalent bonding. In these extreme cases, chemists find it easier to think of the bond as being 100% ionic, but they keep in mind that a 100% ionic bond is not always entirely realistic.

Electronegativities help us to predict which bonds are ionic and which bonds are covalent. Two elements of very different electronegativities such as Na (0.9) and Cl (3.0) are expected to form ionic bonds. Two elements of slightly different electronegativities such as C (2.5) and H (2.1) are expected to form only slightly polar covalent bonds. The greater the difference in electronegativity, the more polar the bond becomes. If the difference in electronegativity between two bonding atoms exceeds 1.7, it is better to consider the bond as being ionic.

Fig. 6-7 The Bonding Continuum

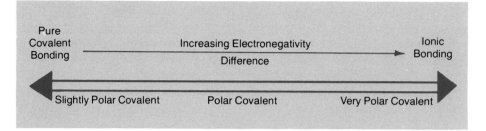

In any event, the transition between polar covalent bonding and ionic bonding is indefinite. It is better to think of a continuum with pure covalent (equal sharing) bonding at one end and ionic (electron transfer) bonding at the other end. In between is polar covalent bonding (Fig. 6-7).

One other point should be made in any comparison of ionic, polar covalent, and covalent bonding. It is the use of the word *molecule*. A molecule is any electrically neutral group of atoms that is bonded together tightly enough to be considered a single particle. We are using the word *bond* to describe the linkage between a pair of atoms. In the case of HCl, a hydrogen atom is bonded to a chlorine atom to form a molecule, and hydrogen chloride exists as molecules in the gaseous, liquid, or solid state. In the case of Cl_2, one chlorine atom is bonded to a second chlorine atom to form a molecule, and chlorine exists as molecules in the gaseous, liquid, or solid state.

However, the word *molecule* does not apply very well to ionic substances such as sodium chloride. When sodium reacts with chlorine, a sodium atom gives up its valence electron and becomes a sodium ion. A chlorine atom accepts the electron and becomes a chloride ion. In the gas phase, it is possible to have one positive sodium ion attracted to one negative chloride ion, and this could perhaps be called a molecule. However, ionic substances exist as solids (not gases) at room temperature. Ionic solids will be discussed in detail in Chapter 7. We can say that ionic solids consist of a stationary array or cluster of positive and negative ions held together by the attractive forces of oppositely charged ions. That is, solid sodium chloride does not consist of NaCl molecules. A crystal of sodium chloride consists of a large number of sodium ions and an equal number of chloride ions, none of which has a specific bonding partner. In the liquid phase, ionic substances consist of a fluid cluster of positive and negative ions in which each ion is free to move slowly throughout the liquid. Thus, liquid sodium chloride does not consist of NaCl molecules, either.

We can speak of molecules of covalently or polar covalently bonded substances. The formulas, Cl_2 and HCl, refer to a molecule of chlorine which is made up of two chlorine atoms, and to a molecule of hydrogen chloride which is made up of one hydrogen atom and one chlorine atom (Fig. 6-8). With the possible exception of the gas phase, we should not speak of molecules of ionically bonded substances. The formulas, NaCl and $CaCl_2$, merely tell us that for every sodium ion there is one chloride ion in sodium chloride and that for every calcium ion there are two chloride ions in calcium chloride.

Fig. 6-8 Models of Hydrogen Chloride (HCl) and Chlorine (Cl$_2$)

6-6 The Octet Rule

In this section we will consider some molecules made up of more than two atoms per molecule. These compounds will involve elements from the second period of the periodic table. We will determine the formula of each compound by using the octet rule.

The **octet rule** states that when atoms combine, the bonds are formed in such a way that each atom finishes with an octet of valence electrons. There is no clear explanation for an atom's stopping at an octet of valence electrons. In fact, there are some cases where an atom involved in bonding finishes with fewer than eight valence electrons. There are other cases where an atom finishes with more than eight valence electrons. However, for many molecules, there is a special stability associated with atoms having completed octets, and the octet rule is a useful generalization.

Suppose that an oxygen atom ($\cdot \ddot{O}$:) were to form a bond with one hydrogen atom (H$\cdot$):

$$ H\cdot + \cdot\ddot{O}: \rightarrow H-\ddot{O}: $$

By sharing a pair of electrons with the oxygen atom, the hydrogen atom has become isoelectronic with the noble gas, helium. However, the oxygen atom has not completed an octet of valence electrons. It still requires one more electron. An H—O molecule is reactive, and the oxygen atom has the ability to form a second bond to another hydrogen atom:

$$ H\cdot + H-\ddot{O}: \rightarrow H-\underset{\underset{H}{|}}{\ddot{O}}: $$

This compound, formed by the reaction of hydrogen and oxygen, is water, H$_2$O.

A nitrogen atom ($\cdot\ddot{\text{N}}\cdot$) has five valence electrons. It requires three more electrons to complete an octet, and we would expect it to bond to three hydrogen atoms:

$$3H\cdot \ + \ \cdot\ddot{\underset{\cdot}{\text{N}}}\cdot \ \rightarrow \ H-\underset{\underset{\displaystyle H}{|}}{\overset{\displaystyle \cdot\cdot}{\text{N}}}-H$$

The compound NH_3 is called ammonia. It is found in household cleaners and is used to make fertilizers.

A carbon atom ($\cdot\dot{\text{C}}\cdot$) has four valence electrons. It requires four more electrons to complete an octet, and we would expect it to bond to four hydrogen atoms:

$$4H\cdot \ + \ \cdot\dot{\underset{\cdot}{\text{C}}}\cdot \ \rightarrow \ H-\underset{\underset{\displaystyle H}{|}}{\overset{\overset{\displaystyle H}{|}}{\text{C}}}-H$$

The compound CH_4 is called methane.

We will finish this section by showing a method for writing the Lewis structure of a molecule whose formula is given. What is the Lewis structure of the molecule whose formula is N_2F_4? A nitrogen atom ($\cdot\ddot{\text{N}}\cdot$) has five valence electrons and requires three more. A fluorine atom ($\cdot\ddot{\ddot{\text{F}}}\colon$) has seven valence electrons and requires one more. We will attempt to draw the Lewis structure so that the four fluorine atoms and the two nitrogen atoms obey the octet rule. As a rule it is preferable to start with atoms which require the most electrons to complete their octets. In this case, the nitrogen atoms each require three electrons. We start by indicating one shared pair of electrons between the two nitrogen atoms:

$$\cdot\ddot{\underset{\cdot}{\text{N}}}\cdot \ + \ \cdot\ddot{\underset{\cdot}{\text{N}}}\cdot \ \rightarrow \ \cdot\ddot{\underset{\cdot}{\text{N}}}-\ddot{\underset{\cdot}{\text{N}}}\cdot$$

Now, each nitrogen atom requires two electrons, and can form two bonds (a total of four). Since each of the four fluorine atoms requires one electron and can form one bond, the Lewis structure can be completed:

$$\cdot\ddot{\underset{\cdot}{\text{N}}}-\ddot{\underset{\cdot}{\text{N}}}\cdot \ + \ 4\cdot\ddot{\ddot{\text{F}}}\colon \ \rightarrow \ \colon\ddot{\ddot{\text{F}}}-\underset{\underset{\displaystyle \colon\ddot{\ddot{\text{F}}}\colon}{|}}{\overset{\displaystyle \cdot\cdot}{\text{N}}}-\underset{\underset{\displaystyle \colon\ddot{\ddot{\text{F}}}\colon}{|}}{\overset{\displaystyle \cdot\cdot}{\text{N}}}-\ddot{\ddot{\text{F}}}\colon$$

In this structure each atom *does* obey the octet rule.

Practice Problem 6-6

Draw the Lewis structure of a molecule whose formula is H_2O_2.

6-7 Multiple Bonds

So far, we have drawn Lewis structures only for molecules having single covalent bonds. In this section, we consider molecules with bonds in which more than one pair of electrons are shared.

A carbon dioxide (CO_2) molecule has one carbon atom bonded to two oxygen atoms. The carbon atom ($\cdot\overset{\displaystyle\cdot}{C}\cdot$) requires four electrons, and the oxygen atoms ($\cdot\overset{\displaystyle\cdot\cdot}{\underset{\cdot}{O}}:$) each require two electrons. We start by indicating one shared pair between the carbon atom and an oxygen atom:

$$\cdot\overset{\cdot}{C}\cdot \;+\; \cdot\overset{\cdot\cdot}{\underset{\cdot}{O}}: \;\rightarrow\; \cdot\overset{\cdot}{C}\!-\!\overset{\cdot\cdot}{\underset{\cdot}{O}}:$$

We continue by indicating one shared pair between the carbon atom and a second oxygen atom:

$$\cdot\overset{\cdot}{C}\!-\!\overset{\cdot\cdot}{\underset{\cdot}{O}}: \;+\; \cdot\overset{\cdot\cdot}{\underset{\cdot}{O}}: \;\rightarrow\; :\overset{\cdot\cdot}{\underset{\cdot}{O}}\!-\!\overset{\cdot}{C}\!-\!\overset{\cdot\cdot}{\underset{\cdot}{O}}:$$

The carbon atom requires two more electrons, and each oxygen atom requires one more electron. At present, none of the atoms obeys the octet rule. However, if two pairs of electrons are shared between the carbon atom and each of the two oxygen atoms, the three atoms in the molecule will each obey the octet rule:

$$:\overset{\cdot\cdot}{\underset{\cdot}{O}}\!-\!\overset{\cdot}{C}\!-\!\overset{\cdot\cdot}{\underset{\cdot}{O}}: \;\rightarrow\; :\overset{\cdot\cdot}{O}\!=\!C\!=\!\overset{\cdot\cdot}{\underset{\cdot}{O}}$$

When two pairs of electrons are shared between two atoms, the result is a **double covalent bond**

Sample Problem 6-4

Draw the Lewis structure for formaldehyde, CH_2O, a compound used to preserve biological specimens.

SOLUTION
The carbon atom ($\cdot\overset{\cdot}{C}\cdot$) requires four electrons; the oxygen atom ($\cdot\overset{\cdot\cdot}{\underset{\cdot}{O}}:$) requires two electrons; and the hydrogen atoms ($\cdot H$) each require one electron. We will start by indicating one shared pair between the carbon atom and the atom which requires the next greatest number of electrons, oxygen:

$$\cdot\overset{\cdot}{C}\cdot \;+\; \cdot\overset{\cdot\cdot}{\underset{\cdot}{O}}: \;\rightarrow\; \cdot\overset{\cdot}{C}\!-\!\overset{\cdot\cdot}{\underset{\cdot}{O}}:$$

Since the carbon atom still requires the most electrons, we will bond each of the two hydrogen atoms to it:

$$\cdot\overset{\cdot}{C}\!-\!\overset{\cdot\cdot}{\underset{\cdot}{O}}: \;+\; 2\,H\cdot \;\rightarrow\; H\!-\!\overset{\displaystyle H}{\underset{\displaystyle |}{\overset{|}{C}}}\!-\!\overset{\cdot\cdot}{\underset{\cdot}{O}}:$$

This results in both the carbon atom and the oxygen atom being one electron short of an octet. This problem can be solved by having the carbon atom and the oxygen atom share two pairs of electrons:

$$H\!-\!\overset{\displaystyle H}{\underset{\displaystyle |}{\overset{|}{C}}}\!-\!\overset{\cdot\cdot}{\underset{\cdot}{O}}: \;\rightarrow\; H\!-\!\overset{\displaystyle H}{\underset{\displaystyle |}{\overset{|}{C}}}\!=\!\overset{\cdot\cdot}{\underset{\cdot}{O}}$$

Now the carbon atom and the oxygen atom both obey the octet rule.

Practice Problem 6-7

Draw a Lewis structure for carbon disulfide, CS_2.

The nitrogen molecule (N_2) is formed when two nitrogen atoms share electrons. If the two nitrogen atoms were to share a pair of electrons, neither of them would obey the octet rule:

$$:\dot{\ddot{N}}\cdot \; + \; \cdot\dot{\ddot{N}}: \; \rightarrow \; :\dot{\ddot{N}}—\dot{\ddot{N}}:$$

If two pairs of electrons were shared between the two nitrogen atoms, each atom would still have only seven valence electrons:

$$:\dot{N}\cdot \; + \; \cdot\dot{N}: \; \rightarrow \; :N\!\!=\!\!N:$$

However, if three pairs of electrons were shared between the two nitrogen atoms, each would obey the octet rule:

$$:\dot{N}\cdot \; + \; \cdot\dot{N}: \; \rightarrow \; :N\!\!\equiv\!\!N:$$

When three pairs of electrons are shared between two atoms, the result is a **triple covalent bond**

Sample Problem 6-5

Draw the Lewis structure for hydrogen cyanide, HCN, a poisonous gas which paralyzes the central nervous system and stops respiration.

SOLUTION

The carbon atom ($\cdot\dot{C}\cdot$) requires four electrons; the nitrogen atom ($:\dot{N}\cdot$) requires three electrons; and the hydrogen atom ($\cdot H$) requires one electron. We will select carbon as the central atom, and we will indicate one shared pair between the carbon atom and the nitrogen atom:

$$\cdot\dot{C}\cdot + \cdot\dot{N}: \; \rightarrow \; \cdot\dot{C}—\dot{N}:$$

Since the carbon atom still requires the most electrons, we will bond the hydrogen atom to it:

$$\cdot\dot{C}—\dot{N}: + H\cdot \; \rightarrow \; H—\dot{C}—\dot{N}:$$

This results in both the carbon atom's and the nitrogen atom's being two electrons short of an octet. It can be solved by having the carbon atom and the nitrogen atom share three pairs of electrons:

$$H—\dot{C}—\dot{N}: \; \rightarrow \; H—C\!\!\equiv\!\!N:$$

Now the carbon atom and the nitrogen atom both obey the octet rule.

Practice Problem 6-8

Draw the Lewis structure for the ethyne molecule, C_2H_2.

6-8 The Shapes of Molecules – VSEPR Theory

Molecules which are made up of one atom bonded to only one other atom are linear molecules. In Sections 6-3 and 6-4 we discussed some molecules of that type; however, in Sections 6-6 and 6-7 we discussed molecules which have other shapes. Lewis structures do not indicate the true shapes of molecules. In this section, we will use a simple, yet useful, theory to predict the shapes of some of the molecules that we have already discussed.

Shapes of Molecules with Single Bonds

Consider the methane molecule:

The carbon atom (the central atom) is surrounded by four shared pairs of electrons. These electrons make up an octet in what is called the valence shell of the carbon atom. The **valence shell** is the occupied energy level with the highest principal quantum number. The valence electrons of an atom occupy the valence shell.

The **Valence-Shell Electron-Pair Repulsion (VSEPR) Theory** proposes that the arrangement of atoms around a central atom in a molecule depends upon the repulsions between all of the electron pairs in the valence shell of the central atom. These valence shell electrons are regarded as occupying localized regions of space, called orbitals, which are located around the filled inner shells of the atom so that their average distance from each other is maximized. The basic postulate of VSEPR Theory is that electron pairs in the valence shell repel each other and therefore reside in orbitals which are as far apart as possible.

The most probable arrangements of two, three, and four electron pairs are collinear, trigonal planar, and tetrahedral, respectively (Fig. 6-9). In each of these arrangements, the electron pairs (residing in orbitals) are as far apart from each other as possible. Stated another way, the angles between the orbitals in each arrangement are maximized. The angle between two collinear orbitals is 180°; the angles between three trigonal planar orbitals are each 120°; and the angles between four tetrahedral orbitals are each 109.5°.

In the case of the carbon atom in methane, there are four pairs of valence-shell electrons occupying four orbitals. According to the basic postulate of VSEPR Theory, these *four* orbitals should be as far apart as possible, giving a tetrahedral arrangement of the four shared pairs of electrons. Thus, VSEPR Theory predicts that the four hydrogen atoms will be arranged tetrahedrally around the carbon atom in the methane molecule (Fig. 6-10, over).

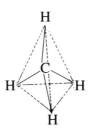

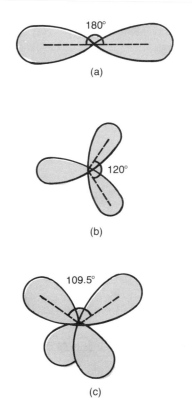

**Fig. 6-9 (a) Collinear Orbitals
(b) Trigonal Planar Orbitals
(c) Tetrahedral Orbitals**

Fig. 6-10 Models of Ammonia (NH₃) and Methane (CH₄)

There is a great deal of evidence to support this view of the structure of the methane molecule. For example, experiments indicate that all bond angles in methane are 109.5°.

Shapes of Molecules with Single Bonds and Lone Electron Pairs

Consider the ammonia molecule:

$$H—\overset{\displaystyle\cdot\cdot}{N}—H$$
$$|$$
$$H$$

The nitrogen atom (the central atom) is surrounded by four pairs of electrons. Three of the pairs are shared pairs, but the fourth is a nonbonding (lone) pair of electrons. How does the presence of a lone pair of electrons in the valence shell of nitrogen affect the shape of the ammonia molecule?

Because they are under the influence of only one nucleus, the two electrons of a lone pair occupy a bigger, more puffy orbital than the electrons of a shared pair which are attracted to two nuclei (Fig. 6-11). Thus, a lone-pair

Fig. 6-11 Representation of the Approximate Shapes of (a) a Shared-Pair Orbital and (b) an Unshared-Pair Orbital

(a)

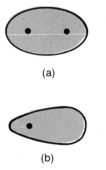

(b)

7-4 Hydrogen Bonding

We have learned that the forces of attraction between nonpolar molecules in a molecular solid are London dispersion forces. We have also learned that the forces of attraction between polar molecules in a molecular solid are the sum of London dispersion, dipole-dipole, and induction forces. Are these the only possible forces of attraction between the molecules in a molecular solid? In this section we learn of another force of attraction that is possible between the molecules in some molecular solids.

Bonding in Molecular Solids

Molecular solids composed of nonpolar molecules are held together by London dispersion forces. Within a group of related molecules, the London dispersion forces will increase as the number of electrons in the molecules increases. For example, the melting temperatures of the group CF_4, CCl_4, CBr_4, and CI_4 are $-184°C$, $-23°C$, $90°C$, and $171°C$, respectively. As the size of the molecules and the number of electrons increase from CF_4 to CI_4, more thermal energy (higher temperatures) must be used to overcome the intermolecular forces of attraction so that the solid can melt.

Molecular solids composed of polar molecules are held together by the sum of London dispersion, dipole-dipole, and induction forces (i.e., by van der Waals forces). Within a group of related molecules, the van der Waals forces will increase as the number of electrons in the molecules increases. For example, the melting temperatures of the group HCl, HBr, and HI are $-114°C$, $-87°C$, and $-51°C$. As the molecules in this series increase in size, higher temperatures must be used to overcome the intermolecular forces of attraction and melt the solid. Furthermore, we would expect that HF would melt at a temperature which is less than $-114°C$. In fact, however, it melts at $-84°C$ which is $30°C$ *higher* than $-114°C$. That is, in this group of molecules, the member having the fewest electrons does *not* have the lowest melting temperature. Before we look at an explanation for this, we will consider another group of related molecules.

Because the molecular sizes of the molecules in the group H_2O, H_2S, H_2Se, and H_2Te are increasing, we would expect a corresponding increase in melting temperatures. The last three members of the group *do* give the predicted trend of melting temperatures. H_2S melts at $-83°C$; H_2Se melts at $-64°C$; and H_2Te melts at $-49°C$. The H_2O should melt at a temperature which is less than $-83°C$. In fact, it melts at $0°C$ which is $83°C$ *higher* than $-83°C$. Once again the member having the fewest electrons does *not* have the lowest melting temperature.

Hydrogen Bonding

Why do HF and H_2O melt at temperatures that are higher than we would expect from the melting temperatures of related molecules? Solids such as HF and H_2O must be held together by intermolecular forces of attraction which are greater

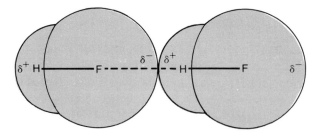

than van der Waals forces. What is the nature of these larger forces of attraction?

The Lewis structures of these two molecules are

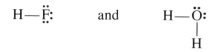

The H—F bond and the H—O bond are both polar convalent. In fact, the fluorine atom and the oxygen atom are the two most electronegative elements, and the H—F bond and the H—O bond are the two most polar bonds which involve hydrogen. In hydrogen fluoride, the slightly positive hydrogen atom of one molecule is chemically bonded to a fluorine atom, but it is also attracted to the slightly negative fluorine atom of another molecule (Fig. 7-8). This is a dipole-dipole attraction, but it is a large one because the bond in the hydrogen fluoride molecule is very polar. In water, the slightly positive hydrogen atom of one molecule is attracted to the slightly negative oxygen atom of another molecule. Again, this is a large dipole-dipole attraction, because the bonds in water are so polar. This attraction is called a **hydrogen bond** It is about one-tenth as strong as a covalent bond, but it is about ten times stronger than normal van der Waals forces. Hydrogen bonds occur only when hydrogen atoms are bonded to extremely electronegative elements such as fluorine, oxygen, or nitrogen. These three electronegative elements form covalent bonds with hydrogen atoms which are of such an extremely polar nature that the dipole-dipole attractions between neighbouring molecules are too large to be considered normal van der Waals forces. A hydrogen bond has been described as a hydrogen atom which is unequally shared between two highly electronegative atoms. However, the actual hydrogen bond is the attraction between the hydrogen atom of one molecule and a fluorine, oxygen, or nitrogen atom of a second molecule.

Hydrogen bonds do not involve the sharing of electrons; therefore, they are not a type of covalent bond. Nor do hydrogen bonds involve the attraction of ions for one another; therefore, they are not ionic bonds. Hydrogen bonds are examples of dipole-dipole attractions; thus, they are a type of van der Waals force. However, they are ten times stronger than normal van der Waals forces, and many chemists consider them to be in a category by themselves.

Nevertheless, hydrogen bonds do explain why it is more difficult to melt HF or H_2O than it is to melt larger, similar molecules. For example, a crystal of hydrogen fluoride consists of chains of hydrogen fluoride molecules all held

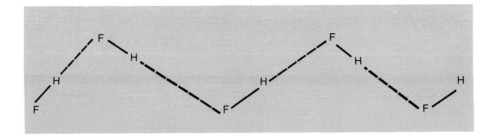

together by hydrogen bonds (Fig. 7-9). In order to melt the crystal, many of these hydrogen bonds must be broken. This requires more thermal energy (higher temperature) than is required to melt a crystal of hydrogen chloride, in which the intermolecular forces of attraction are normal van der Waals forces. Notice, however, that in a crystal of hydrogen iodide molecules, which are much larger than hydrogen fluoride molecules, the van der Waals forces are great enough that more heat is required to melt a crystal of hydrogen iodide than is required to melt a crystal of hydrogen fluoride.

Solid water consists of a three-dimensional network of molecules which are all held together by hydrogen bonds. This explains why ice is more difficult to melt than solid H_2S, solid H_2Se, or solid H_2Te. The structure of ice is discussed further in Chapter 11.

Hydrogen bonding is important in living organisms. All living organisms contain substances that are hydrogen bonded. The structure of proteins, the building blocks of animal tissue, is controlled by hydrogen bonding. Plant fibres are more rigid than animal tissue because of the greater amount of hydrogen bonding in plants.

7-5 Network Solids

We have discussed the forces of attraction that are present in atomic solids and molecular solids. In this section, we study the forces of attraction in network solids. Network solids have much higher melting points and are much harder than atomic solids and molecular solids. We begin with an element that forms network solids—carbon.

Carbon Network Solids

Carbon exists in two major forms, diamond and graphite. Different forms of the same element are known as **allotropes**. Diamond is one of the hardest known materials, while graphite is one of the softest. Why is this?

Let us look first at the facts about diamonds. Because diamonds are so hard, they are used in cutting tools—saws and drill bits. Of course, diamonds are also often used in jewelry.

When it is heated in air to about 900°C, diamond burns to produce carbon dioxide. In the absence of oxygen, diamond is converted to graphite at about 1800°C. Diamond is chemically unreactive, and it does not conduct electricity.

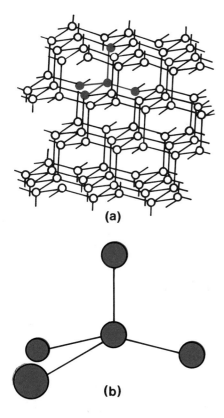

(a)

(b)

Fig. 7-10 (a) The Structure of a Portion of a Diamond Crystal. (The five darkened atoms are expanded and displayed alone in Fig. 7-9 (b)) (b) The Tetrahedral Arrangement of Four Carbon Atoms Around a Central Carbon Atom

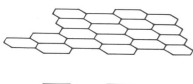

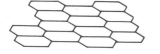

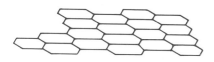

Fig. 7-11 The Layered Structure of a Portion of a Graphite Crystal

Carbon atoms each have four valence electrons, and the structure of diamond consists of carbon atoms which are each tetrahedrally bonded to four other carbon atoms by single covalent bonds (Fig. 7-10). A crystal of diamond can be considered to be a macromolecule (giant molecule) in which each carbon atom is bonded to four other carbon atoms. Diamond is thus a network solid. In any crystal of diamond, however, there are places where carbon atoms have not bonded to four other atoms as they should have done. These places are faults in the diamond crystal, and they are the cause of weak spots in the crystal. Nevertheless, a diamond crystal is one of the hardest of all materials because four covalent bonds per atom must be broken before carbon atoms in a diamond crystal will separate from one another.

The structure of diamond also accounts for its high melting temperature and its inability to conduct electricity. Diamond has a high melting temperature because the individual carbon atoms are held together by covalent bonds. These covalent bonds are far stronger than the van der Waals forces in atomic and in molecular solids. Thus, more energy must be used to break apart (melt) the particles in a crystal of diamond (or any network solid) than to break apart the particles in an atomic solid or in a molecular solid.

In a diamond crystal, none of the valence electrons of the carbon atoms are free to migrate. The valence electrons are shared between pairs of carbon atoms, forming covalent bonds. They are all locked in position in the diamond crystal. In a solid, electric charge is carried by electrons moving throughout the crystal. The lack of electron mobility within a diamond crystal explains the inability of diamond to conduct electricity.

Before turning to the other allotrope of carbon (graphite), we will briefly mention the other one of the first 20 elements which exists as a network solid—silicon. Silicon has a structure like that shown in Fig. 7-10. It is relatively inert and melts at 1410°C. In short, silicon is similar to diamond.

Like diamond, graphite has a high melting point (3500°C); however, here the important physical similarities end. Unlike diamond, graphite is a conductor of electricity, and it is a soft substance with a greasy feel. Furthermore, diamond is 1.6 times as dense as graphite.

Graphite's properties can be explained by its structure. Graphite exists as a layered structure (Fig. 7-11). Within a layer, each carbon atom is bonded to three other carbon atoms by strong covalent bonds. However, the layers are attracted to one another only by van der Waals forces. Thus, unlike the three-dimensional structure of diamond, graphite forms two-dimensional plates in which each carbon is bonded to three other carbon atoms. All these bond angles are 120°.

Three of the four valence electrons of each carbon atom in graphite are used in forming localized bonds with three other carbon atoms. Each carbon atom has a fourth valence electron involved in bonding, but this electron becomes part of a delocalized bond. One electron from each carbon atom is able to move from atom to atom throughout the two-dimensional plate as part of a system of delocalized bonds. For our purposes, a localized bond is one in which electrons are shared between two atoms, and a delocalized bond is one in which electrons are shared among a number of atoms. The movement of one electron per carbon atom throughout a layer of a graphite crystal explains why graphite is a good conductor of electricity.

The two-dimensional plates, held together only by van der Waals forces, are able to slip over one another. There are no covalent bonds between layers. It is the ability of the layers to slip over one another which makes graphite soft and slippery. A "lead" pencil is really a mixture of graphite and clay. A harder "lead" contains a larger proportion of clay. When a pencil is used to mark on a piece of paper, thin layers are rubbed off the graphite and are deposited on the paper.

Graphite may be soft, but it has a high melting temperature. In order for graphite to melt, not only must the layers separate, but also the atoms within a layer must separate. The atoms within a layer are held together by covalent bonds, and these bonds must break before the crystal can melt. Thus, we would expect it to be as difficult to melt graphite as to melt diamond.

Graphite is not as dense as diamond. Within a given layer, the carbon atoms are closer to one another (0.14 nm) than carbon atoms are in diamond (0.15 nm). However, the spacing between carbon layers in graphite is 0.34 nm. Thus, there are relatively wide spaces between the carbon layers in graphite; this explains its lower density.

Because of graphite's high melting temperature and its ability to conduct electricity, it can be used to make electrodes for electric furnaces. Because it is slippery, it can be used as a dry lubricant in machines that are subjected to high temperatures. Graphite is also used in some nuclear reactors to slow neutrons enough to cause more nuclear reactions.

Silica: Another Network Solid

A common compound which forms a network solid is silicon dioxide, SiO_2. This compound is commonly called silica, and along with other silicon-oxygen compounds, it makes up about 87% of the earth's crust. Silica forms a regular network solid which is often called quartz. In quartz, each silicon is tetrahedrally bonded to four oxygen atoms, each of which is also bonded to another silicon atom (Fig. 7-12). Quartz is a hard substance and has a high melting point, just as we would expect.

When quartz is melted (at approximately 1600°C) and then cooled rapidly, an amorphous solid called quartz glass or silica glass results. The silicon-oxygen network remains largely intact during melting; however, many silicon-oxygen bonds are broken, and the regular crystal order of the quartz is lost. If the molten quartz is cooled rapidly, the atoms are unable to regain their crystalline order, and an irregular, amorphous glass results. A picture of an amorphous, volcanic glass is shown in Fig. 7-13 (overleaf).

Thus, network solids are very hard, difficult to melt, and poor conductors of electricity. The atoms which make up these solids are covalently bonded to one another. We have seen that carbon and silicon are elements that form network solids. Silicon dioxide is a compound that forms a network solid.

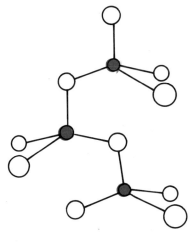

Fig. 7-12 The Structure of a Portion of a Quartz Crystal. (The blue spheres represent silicon atoms, and the white spheres represent oxygen atoms.)

Fig. 7-13 An Amorphous, Volcanic
Glass

7-6 Metallic Solids

So far, we have studied atomic solids, molecular solids, and network solids. Atomic solids and molecular solids tend to be fairly soft, easily melted, and poor conductors of electricity. Network solids are also usually poor conductors of electricity; however, they are harder and have higher melting points than atomic solids or molecular solids. Now let us see how the properties of these three types of solids compare with those of the next type of solids—metallic solids.

Seven of the first twenty elements are metals. Metals have a metallic lustre. They are good conductors of heat and electricity. They can be drawn into wires—they are ductile. They can be hammered into sheets without cracking—they are malleable. What explanation can be provided for these properties of metals?

As a group, metals have small numbers of valence electrons. Therefore, metals have outer energy levels which are less than one-half filled. Also, metals are readily ionized. Their valence electrons are not tightly held. We will use these factors to develop a theory of attractive forces within a metallic solid.

Because metals conduct electricity so well, we would expect that the valence electrons are delocalized throughout the crystal. The facts that metal atoms do not hold their valence electrons tightly and that metal atoms have outer energy levels which are less than half-filled add to this expectation. Thus, we can think of a metallic solid as being an array of positive ions in a "sea" of mobile electrons.

Let us apply this idea to sodium metal. In a crystal of sodium, each atom has one valence electron. The valence electrons (one from each sodium atom) are able to migrate throughout the crystal. Everywhere a valence electron moves, it finds itself between two sodium nuclei with outer energy levels able to accommodate it. The positive sodium nuclei are not attracted to one another; they are all attracted to the cloud of electrons. This cloud of electrons serves as the ''glue'' which holds the nuclei together (Fig. 7-14).

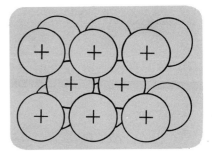

Fig. 7-14 The Structure of a Portion of a Sodium Crystal. (The shaded area represents the electron cloud.)

Since beryllium, magnesium, and calcium all have two valence electrons, they can each contribute two electrons per atom to the electron cloud. Their Group I equivalents (lithium, sodium, and potassium) have only one valence electron to contribute. Therefore, since the Group II metals have a thicker electron ''glue'', we might expect them to be more difficult to melt than their Group I equivalents. The thicker electron ''glue'' also makes Group II metals more difficult to boil and harder than their Group I equivalents. For example, sodium melts at 98°C and boils at 892°C, but magnesium melts at 650°C and boils at 1107°C. Furthermore, magnesium is harder than sodium.

A **metallic bond** is the attraction between a cloud of mobile electrons and the positive metallic ions arranged in the cloud. It is the mobility of the electrons that allows metals to conduct electricity. The mobility of the electrons also explains the ductility and malleability of metals. That is, one plane of ions in a metallic crystal can slip over another, and, as it does so, the electron cloud merely distorts to maintain bonding. Metals are also good heat conductors because of the mobile electrons. When one end of a metallic crystal is warmed, the electrons in that region acquire large amounts of kinetic energy. These electrons move rapidly through the crystal and give extra energy to the atoms in the cooler part of the crystal. The mobile electrons are also able to absorb and re-emit light of all wavelengths. Therefore, metals are good reflectors of light, which explains why they have a lustre.

While metallic solids are not as hard as network solids, they are harder than molecular solids or atomic solids. Furthermore, within a period, the strength of a metallic bond increases as the number of valence electrons possessed by the metal atom increases. As we go from left to right in a period, the increased number of valence electrons means there are more electrons in the ''glue'', and there is also a greater attraction of the electron ''glue'' for the nucleus because there are more protons in the nucleus.

7-7 The Crystal Shapes of Metals

Just as molecules, such as methane, have definite shapes, so do the positive ions in a metallic crystal have a definite arrangement. For example, lithium, sodium, the other alkali metals, and iron have a body-centered cubic (BCC) structure (Fig. 7-15, over). In this structure every atom (i.e., every positive ion, according to the theory of metallic bonding) has eight nearest neighbours, and every atom is in the centre of a cube. Fig. 7-15 shows only a portion of a BCC structure. The BCC structure extends uniformly in three dimensions: every atom is surrounded by eight neighbours and is in the centre of a cube.

Fig. 7-15 Body-Centered Cubic Structure

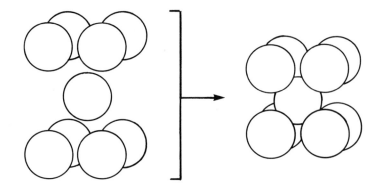

Beryllium and magnesium have a hexagonal closest-packed (HCP) structure. If we examine Fig. 7-16, we notice that the shaded atom in the exploded view to the left is surrounded by six neighbours in the same plane, three neighbours above, and three below. Thus, the central atom in Fig. 7-16 has 12 neighbours. This is the greatest number of neighbours possible, so it is called a closest-packing system. Every atom in an HCP structure has 12 neighbours. HCP crystals are more dense than BCC crystals because each atom in an HCP has more neighbours packed around it than does each atom in a BCC structure. The middle layer of the exploded view in Fig. 7-16 shows why the term *hexagonal* is used. The shaded atom is surrounded by six atoms arranged at the corners of a regular hexagon.

Fig. 7-16 Hexagonal Closest-Packing

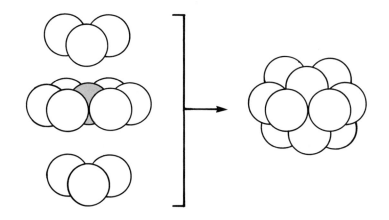

Aluminum has a cubic closest-packed (CCP) structure. This is also called face-centered cubic (FCC). In Fig. 7-17, the layers shown in the exploded view at the top centre can be used to generate two structures. Structure (a) shows how the term, face-centered cubic, is derived. This structure is a cube with an atom located in the center of each side or face. However, structure (b) is equally correct, and if we rotate this structure, we observe that a structure which is very similar to Fig. 7-16 results. In fact, the only difference is that the top layer of three atoms has been rotated through 60°. Thus, in structure (b), the central

Fig. 7-17 Cubic Closest-Packing

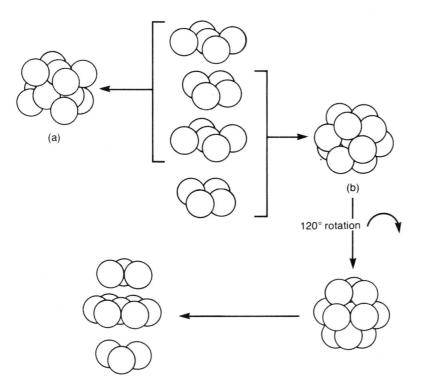

(a)

(b)

120° rotation

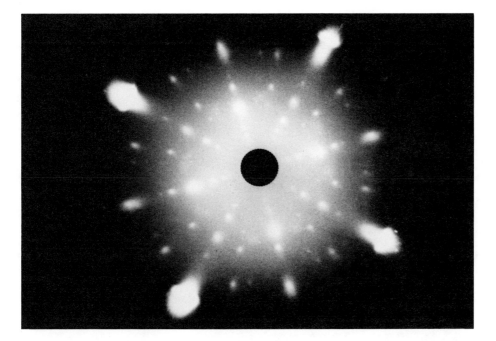

Fig. 7-18 An X-ray Diffraction Photograph of a Metallic Crystal with Face-centered cubic (or Cubic closest-packed) Structure. The metal is palladium, Element 46. The center hole (black in photo) shows the direction of the X-ray beam.

atom is surrounded by 12 neighbours. If this structure were extended uniformly in three dimensions, every atom would have 12 neighbours, and it is a closest-packing system. Nearly all pure metals crystallize in one of the three patterns described in this section.

7-8 Alloys

An **alloy** is a substance which has metallic properties and which contains more than one element. Alloys are made because they have desirable properties. For example, stainless steel is mainly iron, but, whereas iron corrodes rapidly, stainless steel resists corrosion. The low melting point of Wood's metal makes it useful in fuse plugs and in sprinkler heads. The pipes of a sprinkler system are filled with air under pressure. When a fire melts the Wood's metal, the sprinkler head breaks, and the air rushes out of the pipes. Water takes the place of the air in the pipes and then sprays on the fire through the broken sprinkler head. Some common alloys are listed in Table 7-1.

Alloys are often harder than pure metals because the impurity forms localized and rigid bonds which prevent the layers from slipping over one another easily. Electrical conductivity depends on the ability of the mobile electrons to flow smoothly through the metal. Therefore, impurities in a metal may affect its ability to conduct electricity.

Types of Alloys

There are three types of alloys: simple mixtures, solid solutions, and intermetallic compounds. Solid solutions may be substitutional solid solutions or interstitial solid solutions.

TABLE 7-1 Some Common Alloys

ALLOY	CONSTITUENT METALS (Composition by Mass)	IMPORTANT PROPERTY	USE
Brass	Cu (67%), Zn (33%)	Resists corrosion	Marine hardware
Stainless Steel	Fe (80.6%), Cr (18%), Ni (1%), C (0.4%)	Resists corrosion	Cutlery
Wood's Metal	Bi (50%), Pb (25%), Sn (12.5%), Cd (12.5%)	Low melting point (70°C)	Sprinkler heads
Solder	Pb (67%), Sn (33%)	Low melting point (275°C)	Plumbing
Dental Alloy	Ag (70%), Sn (26%) Cu (3%), Zn (1%)	Easily moulded when mixed with equal mass of mercury	Dental fillings
18 K Yellow Gold	Au (75%), Ag (12.5%), Cu (12.5%)	Harder than pure gold	Jewelry
18 K White Gold	Au (75%), Ni (16.5%), Zn (5%), Cu (3.5%)	Harder than pure gold and has a different colour than pure gold	Jewelry
Pewter	Sn (85.5%), Cu (6.8%), Bi (6%), Sb (1.7%)	Resists tarnish	Utensils

Solder is a *simple mixture*. The lead and the tin are not soluble in one another. Thus, solder consists of tiny crystals of pure lead mixed with tiny crystals of pure tin.

However, when chromium and nickel form an alloy, a true solution results. Nickel crystallizes in a CCP structure, and chromium atoms replace some of the nickel atoms in the CCP structure. Thus, the chromium atoms have taken up some of the positions in the crystal structure of the nickel. This is called a *substitutional solid solution*.

Steel is a good example of an *interstitial solid solution*. In steel, the smaller carbon atoms do not replace any iron atoms in the crystal structure. Instead, the carbon atoms pack in the holes or interstices which exist in the crystal structure (Fig. 7-19). The carbon atoms prevent the iron atoms from sliding over one another as readily as they do in pure iron by forming rigid, localized bonds with iron atoms. Therefore, steel is harder than pure iron. A number of small atoms, such as boron, carbon, and nitrogen, can be used to form interstitial solid solutions.

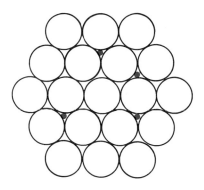

Fig. 7-19 Interstitial Solid Solution

Intermetallic compounds are alloys which are homogeneous like solid solutions. However, unlike solid solutions, they appear to have definite compositions. For example, copper and aluminum form a compound which is called duralumin. The formula for this compound is $CuAl_2$. The formulas of intermetallic compounds cannot be predicted by the rules of bonding presented in Chapter 6.

Dental filling is an interesting alloy which contains intermetallic compounds. Dental filling is made by mixing equal masses of dental alloy (Table 7-1) and mercury. Any alloy which contains mercury is called an amalgam, and dental filling is often called dental amalgam. The intermetallic compounds found in dental amalgam are Ag_2Hg_3, Sn_8Hg, and Ag_3Sn. When the mercury is mixed with the dental alloy, a paste forms. This paste can be packed into a cavity in a tooth. When the paste hardens, a strong filling which resists scratching and corrosion results.

7-9 Ionic Solids

Ionic solids result from the reaction of a metal and a nonmetal. The best known compound formed from a metal and a nonmetal is sodium chloride, so let us consider solid sodium chloride. Chlorine is so much more electronegative than sodium that sodium chloride is best considered to be ionic. When sodium reacts with chlorine, the sodium atom gives up its outer electron to the chlorine atom:

$$Na\cdot \rightarrow Na^+ + 1e^-$$

$$:\ddot{\underset{..}{C}}l\cdot + 1e^- \rightarrow :\ddot{\underset{..}{C}}l:^-$$

$$Na^+ + Cl^- \rightarrow NaCl$$

In the gas phase, it is possible to get one positive sodium ion attracted to one negative chloride ion. However, solid sodium chloride is a cluster of ions (Fig. 7-20). Each sodium ion is surrounded by six chloride ions and each chloride ion is surrounded by six sodium ions. It is impossible to say that a

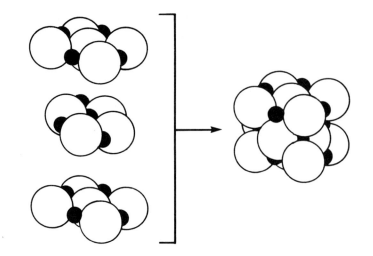

sodium ion is bonded to only one of the six surrounding chloride ions, and it is impossible to say that a chloride ion is bonded to only one of the six surrounding sodium ions. In fact, the formula NaCl merely tells us that for every positive sodium ion there is a chloride ion in the sodium chloride crystal. In the same way, the formula $CaCl_2$ indicates that in a crystal of ionic calcium chloride there are twice as many chloride ions as there are calcium ions.

Any ionic crystal can be considered to be an array of positive and negative ions, arranged in such a way that every positive ion has only negative neighbours and vice versa. There are no distinct molecules in an ionic solid. Ionic crystals are stable because each ion in the crystal is surrounded by a number of neighbouring ions of opposite charge.

Like network solids and many metals, ionic solids have high melting points. For example, sodium chloride melts at 801°C, and calcium chloride melts at 772°C. However, ionic compounds are structurally different from metals, network solids, and molecular solids.

Ionic solids, unlike metals, do not conduct electricity. There are no mobile electrons in an ionic solid. Every electron in an ionic solid belongs to an ion and is unable to move to any other ion. However, molten ionic solids are able to conduct electricity, although not as well as metals. The electric charge is carried through a molten ionic compound by slow-moving positive and negative ions. Also, unlike metals, ionic solids are brittle. Rather than bend, an ionic crystal shatters if it is subjected to a stress.

Ionic solids are generally harder than molecular solids. The attractions between ions of opposite charge in an ionic solid are stronger than the van der Waals forces which hold the molecules together in a molecular solid. As well, molecular solids melt to form liquids which do not conduct electricity.

Ionic solids are generally softer than network solids. Network solids are held together by covalent bonds which tend to make them more difficult to break apart than ionic solids.

When ionic solids dissolve in water, they form solutions which conduct electricity. The process of dissolving ionic solids in water is considered in Chapter 9. When molecular solids dissolve in water, they form solutions which may or may not conduct electricity. Metallic solids and network solids do not dissolve in water.

Summary

In summary, ionic solids are hard and have high melting points. They do not conduct electricity; however, they can be melted to form liquids which do conduct electricity. When they dissolve in water, they produce solutions which conduct electricity. An ionic solid consists of positive and negative ions arranged so that each ion is surrounded by ions of opposite charge. The attraction that these oppositely charged ions have for one another gives the ionic solid its stability. The word *molecule* has little meaning in ionic solids since each ion has a number of oppositely charged ions surrounding it, and there are no distinct molecules in the solid.

A Final Word

In this chapter, we discussed the types of solids. We learned of the forces of attraction between the particles in each type of solid. We also learned some of the characteristic properties of each type of solid. A summary of the information contained in this chapter is presented in Table 7-2.

Now that you have finished reading this chapter, you should reread the Key Objectives to make sure that you have learned the most important points of the chapter. In addition, you should learn the meaning of each important term found in the chapter.

TABLE **7-2 Types of Solids**

TYPE OF SOLID	EXAMPLES	PARTICLES MAKING UP SOLID	FORCE OF ATTRACTION BETWEEN PARTICLES	RELATIVE MELTING POINT	HARDNESS	ELECTRICAL CONDUCTIVITY
Atomic	helium neon	atoms	London dispersion	low	soft	poor
Molecular	Cl_2 HCl H_2O	molecules	van der Waals sometimes hydrogen bonding	low	usually soft	poor
Network	diamond quartz	atoms	covalent bonds	very high	hard	poor
Metallic	sodium magnesium	positive ions in electron cloud	metallic bonds	moderate to high	soft to hard	good
Ionic	NaCl $CaCl_2$	positive and negative ions	ionic bonds	high	hard	poor

Fig. 7-21 A Photomicrograph (× 600) of a 1060 steel (0.60% C). The shaded regions are austenite (0.6% C) in FCC (or CCP) Fe. They are surrounded by white regions, which are α-ferrite (0.02%) in BCC Fe.
Steel is an interstitial solid solution.

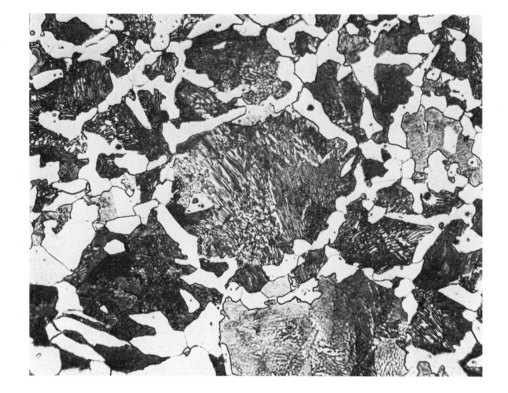

Key Terms

What is the meaning of each of the following terms?

crystalline solid   van der Waals forces
amorphous solid   hydrogen bond
London dispersion forces   allotrope
dipole-dipole forces   metallic bond
induction forces   alloy

Questions

1. Which elements form ionic solids?
2. Which of the first twenty elements form network solids?
3. What is the difference between a crystalline solid and an amorphous solid? Give an example of each.
4. Describe the forces of attraction in an atomic solid. Upon what factor does the strength of these forces depend?
5. What are the characteristics of an atomic solid?
6. How do dipole-dipole forces differ from induction forces?
7. Which of the noble gases would you expect to have the highest melting point? Explain your answer.
8. Which types of solids contain particles held together primarily by van der Waals forces?
9. Which should have the higher melting point, Br_2 or I_2? Why?

Radon
- most e-

I_2 - most e-

10.

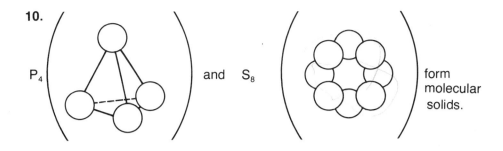

P_4 ( ) and S_8 ( ) form molecular solids.

Which one should have the higher melting point? Why?

11. Why is it easier to solidify C_3H_8 than CH_4? Br_2 than Cl_2?
12. Which would you expect to form a solid with a higher melting point,

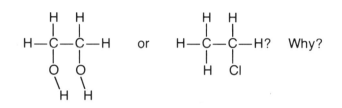

or $\quad$ Why?

13. Why does HF have a higher melting point than HCl, even though CF_4 has a lower melting point than CCl_4?

electronegativity is closer to HF doesn't take as long

14. Explain why H_2S melts at $-83°C$, whereas H_2O melts at $0°C$.
15. How do hydrogen bonds differ from the other types of van der Waals forces?
16. How do the two allotropes of carbon resemble one another? How do they differ?
17. Why is diamond more dense than graphite?
18. Explain why graphite is a very soft substance even though it has a high melting point.
19. CO_2 changes from a solid to a gas (sublimes) at $-78.5°C$, while SiO_2 melts at about $1700°C$ and vaporizes at about $2200°C$. Account for these differences in terms of their structures.
20. Would you expect SiO_2 to be ductile?
21. How do you account for the fact that the network solid silicon carbide (carborundum) is a very high-melting, hard substance?
22. How do quartz crystals differ from quartz glass?
23. Which element has the higher melting point, Na or Al? Why?
24. What is the difference between an interstitial and a substitutional solid solution?
25. Why are alloys often harder than pure metals?
26. List three properties of metals, and explain these properties in terms of metallic bonding.
27. What is meant by the term, delocalized electrons? What type of solid contains delocalized electrons?
28. Describe the packing structures of cubic closest-packed, hexagonal closest-packed, and body-centered cubic crystals.
29. What is the number of nearest neighbours in a closest-packed crystal?

e⁻ can move

30. Why do metals conduct electricity, while ionic solids do not?
31. Why are metallic crystals malleable, whereas ionic crystals are brittle?
32. NaF and MgO have the same crystal structure and similar interionic distances. Why has MgO a higher melting point than NaF?
33. A student interpreted the formula of CaF_2 to mean that the crystal was made up of calcium atoms and fluorine molecules. How would you explain that this interpretation is incorrect?
34. Predict the order of increasing melting points for the following chlorine-containing substances: Cl_2, NaCl, and CCl_4. Explain your prediction.
35. What kind of attractive force must be overcome to melt the following substances: lithium chloride, ice, solid argon, and silicon dioxide?
36. What type of bonding exists in following substances: solid Ne, Cu, and diamond?
37. What experiments would help you decide whether a white substance was an ionic, network, or molecular solid?
38. Both solid Kr and solid Cu have a face-centered cubic structure. What are the differences between the two solids? Explain these differences.
39. Why is aluminum able to conduct heat better than quartz glass?
40. On a separate piece of paper, construct and complete Table 7-3.

TABLE 7-3

| TYPE OF SOLID | EXAMPLE | FORCES OF ATTRACTION | HARDNESS | MELTING POINT (*High or Low*) | ELECTRICAL CONDUCTIVITY | | SOLUBILITY IN WATER |
					Of Solid	*Of Liquid*	
		London dispersion only					
					poor	good	
metallic							
	I_2						
			hard	high	poor	poor	

41. To which class of solid does each of the following belong: NO_2, $BaCl_2$, CBr_4, SiO_2, Zn, He, Hg, HBr, Kr, and I_2?
42. Which of Na, Si, He, KF, and HF, in the solid phase, would be an example of
   a) a solid in which the atoms are covalently bonded together in a network?
   b) a solid with strong hydrogen bonds?
   c) a solid which is a good conductor of electricity?
   d) a substance which does not conduct electricity except in the liquid state?
   e) a solid held together only by London dispersion forces?
43. Using the data from Table 7-4, discuss what seem to be the forces of attraction in each of the five substances. Remember that you are describing the solid phase of each substance whether it is a solid at room temperature or not.
44. Aluminum fluoride is probably an ionic compound. What is its formula? Describe a crystal of aluminum fluoride in terms of the relative numbers of its ions.

TABLE 7-4

| SUBSTANCE | M.P. (°C) | B.P. (°C) | ELECTRICAL CONDUCTIVITY | | SOLUBILITY IN WATER |
			Of Solid	Of Liquid	
A	776	1500	poor	good	soluble
B	−39	356	good	good	insoluble
C	−190	−42	poor	poor	low solubility
D	961	1950	good	good	insoluble
E	1420	2355	poor	poor	insoluble

45. Describe London dispersion forces, dipole-dipole forces, induction forces, hydrogen bonding, and metallic bonding. Give an example of a solid that is held together mainly by London dispersion forces. Give an example of a solid that is held together mainly by hydrogen bonding.

46. Hydrogen peroxide, H_2O_2, melts at −0.4°C and boils at 151°C. Use these data to support a suggestion that hydrogen bonding is important in H_2O_2.

47. Explain why a steel cable is strong even though it is made up of neutral atoms packed together.

8 Nomenclature and Formula Writing

In Chapter 3 we learned the symbols of the elements, and we discovered that atoms of one element combine with atoms of other elements in small whole-number ratios. In other words, the atoms of an element appear to have a fixed combining power for the atoms of another element. Combining powers are important properties of elements, because they determine the ratios in which atoms combine.

Millions of compounds are known. Chemists use thousands of them routinely during their careers. Obviously, chemists must know the formulas of the substances they handle, and they must agree on a standard system for naming all these materials. Universality of communication requires this. It follows that students of chemistry must also know the language of chemistry— nomenclature and formula writing. In this chapter we shall therefore use the concept of combining powers of atoms to predict formulas for compounds such as those shown in Fig. 8-1. Then we shall develop simple, systematic names that are related to the formulas of compounds.

Key Objectives

When you have finished studying this chapter, you should be able to
1. given the formulas of positive and negative ions, write the formulas of the compounds formed by combinations of these ions.
2. given the formula of a substance, write its name.
3. given the name of a substance, write its formula.

8-1 Oxidation Numbers

As we learned in Chapter 6, when two or more atoms unite to form a compound, they form either ionic or covalent bonds. Atoms of some elements have a tendency to lose electrons and thereby acquire a positive charge. Atoms of other elements have a tendency to gain electrons and thereby acquire a

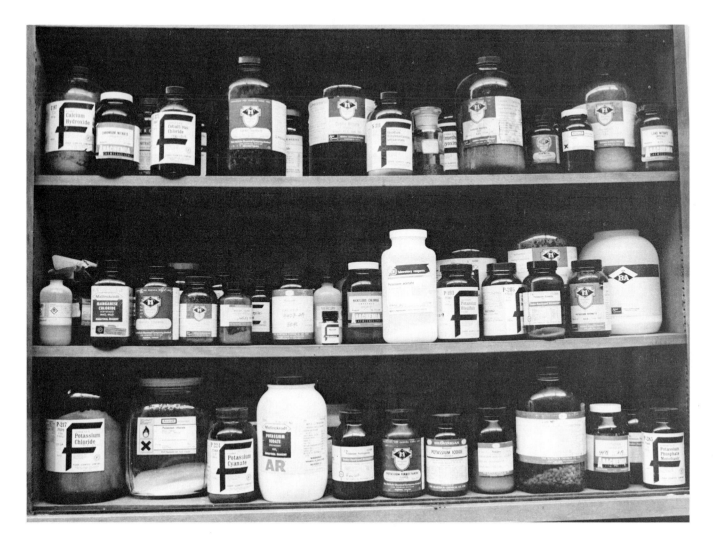

Fig. 8-1 A Variety of Compounds in a
Chemical Stockroom

negative charge. In ionic compounds the atoms have full positive and negative charges (e.g., Na^+Cl^-). In polar covalent compounds the atoms have only small positive and negative charges (e.g.,

$$^{\delta^+} H—O^{\delta^-}$$
$$|$$
$$H\ _{\delta^+}$$

Chemists use oxidation numbers to keep track of the *positive* or *negative character* of atoms or ions. When electrons are removed completely or shifted partially away from an atom during a chemical reaction, the atom is given a more positive oxidation number. When electrons are gained or shifted toward an atom during a reaction, the atom is given a more negative oxidation number. The actual numerical value of the oxidation number depends on the number of electrons shifted partially or transferred completely. In NaCl, for example, the oxidation number of Na is +1, because one electron has been transferred from it. The oxidation number of Cl is −1, because one electron has been transferred to it from the sodium. In a covalent substance such as H—Cl the hydrogen atom has an oxidation number of +1 due to a shift (but not a transfer) of its valence electron toward the more electronegative chlorine atom. The chlorine atom has an oxidation number of −1 due to a shift of one electron toward it. In H−O the oxygen atom is more electronegative than a hydrogen atom. The

H

oxidation number of each hydrogen atom is +1 due to a shift of its valence electron toward the oxygen atom. The oxidation number of the oxygen atom is −2 due to a shift of two electrons (one from each hydrogen atom) toward it.

Oxidation numbers may be deduced from energy level populations, but it is easier, by using the periodic table, to learn symbols of elements and formulas for ions, and the oxidation numbers that go with them. Let's see how this is done.

Free Elements

Consider the formation of a molecule of H_2, O_2, or N_2 from their individual atoms. We would write the equations as

$$H\cdot + \cdot H \rightarrow H\colon H$$

$$:\ddot{O}\cdot + \cdot\ddot{O}: \rightarrow :\ddot{O}::\ddot{O}:$$

$$:\dot{N}\cdot + \cdot\dot{N}: \rightarrow :N\vdots N:$$

In each case, the molecule is made up of *identical* atoms (H, O, or N). Each hydrogen atom in a molecule of hydrogen has the *same* tendency to attract the shared valence electrons toward itself. Neither atom can attract shared electrons from the other, so that the shared electrons are shared equally. Thus, there is no shift of electrons from one hydrogen atom to the other. Both atoms of the molecule therefore have a charge of zero, just as they do in the isolated state.

Similarly, the four shared electrons in an oxygen molecule and the six shared electrons in a nitrogen molecule are shared equally. Since there is no transfer of electrons, all atoms again have a charge of zero.

These results allow us to state a general rule: *The oxidation numbers of atoms of elements in the free state are always zero*. Thus, for He, Na, F_2, and As_4, the oxidation numbers are all zero.

Elements in Ionic Compounds

Table 8-1 lists the oxidation numbers of the ions of some of the common elements in the format of a periodic table. Note that ions of the metals (and of hydrogen) in Group I of the periodic table all have oxidation numbers of +1, since the atoms all have one valence electron which they can lose to form the ion. Similarly, in compounds, the elements of Group II have oxidation numbers of +2, and the elements of Group III usually have oxidation numbers of +3. In other words, the oxidation number of a metal ion is usually the same as its group number.

The ions of the halogens (Group VII elements) have oxidation numbers of -1, since these atoms all have seven valence electrons and can gain one more electron to complete a stable octet, forming a negative ion. Similarly, the ions of Group VI elements usually have oxidation numbers of -2.

Some metal atoms can have several different oxidation numbers. For example, a tin atom can lose either four electrons to form a Sn^{4+} ion with an oxidation number of $+4$, or it can lose only two electrons to form a Sn^{2+} ion with an oxidation number of $+2$. Similarly, an arsenic atom can lose either three or five electrons to form ions with oxidation numbers of $+3$ or $+5$, respectively.

In summary, *the oxidation number of an ion is the same as its charge*. For example, the Mg^{2+} ion has an oxidation number of $+2$; for Al^{3+} the oxidation number is $+3$; and for S^{2-} it is -2. Note that the superscript "2+", which is part of the symbol Mg^{2+}, is itself a symbol which indicates the number of "+" charges on the ion, while the oxidation number is written as "+2", because it is a number, not a symbol.

Sample Problem 8-1

Using a periodic table instead of Table 8-1, give the oxidation number of each element in **a**) BaO; **b**) GaBr$_3$.

SOLUTION
a) Since Ba is in Group II, it loses two electrons to form Ba^{2+}. Therefore, the oxidation number of Ba is $+2$. Since O is in Group VI, it gains two electrons to form O^{2-}. Therefore, the oxidation number of O is -2.
b) Since Ga is in Group III, it loses three electrons to form Ga^{3+}. Therefore, the oxidation number of Ga is $+3$. Since Br is in Group VII, it gains one electron to form Br^-. Therefore, the oxidation number of Br is -1.

TABLE **8-1.** **Oxidation Numbers of the Ions of Some Common Elements**

I	II										III	IV	V	VI	VII	O
H(+1)																
Li(+1)	Be(+2)			TRANSITION METALS							B(+3)		N(−3)	O(−2)	F(−1)	
Na(+1)	Mg(+2)										Al(+3)		P(−3)	S(−2)	Cl(−1)	
K(+1)	Ca(+2)			Cr(+2) Cr(+3) Cr(+6)		Fe(+2) Fe(+3)	Co(+2) Co(+3)	Ni(+2) Ni(+3)	Cu(+1) Cu(+2)	Zn(+2)	Ga(+3)				Br(−1)	
Rb(+1)	Sr(+2)								Ag(+1)	Cd(+2)		Sn(+2) Sn(+4)			I(−1)	
Cs(+1)	Ba(+2)								Au(+1) Au(+3)	Hg(+1) Hg(+2)		Pb(+2) Pb(+4)				

Practice Problem 8-1

Using a periodic table instead of Table 8-1, give the oxidation number of each element in CsI, $BaCl_2$, and Al_2S_3.

Elements in Covalent Substances

In covalent substances, the more electronegative element is assigned a negative oxidation number, and the less electronegative element is assigned a positive oxidation number. In HCl, the H atom shares its one electron with the chlorine atom, and the chlorine shares one of its electrons with the hydrogen atom. Because the chlorine atom is more electronegative, there is a *shift* of electron density towards the chlorine atom. There is *not* a complete transfer of an electron from the hydrogen atom to the chlorine atom, because the bond still retains some covalent character. However, for purposes of assigning oxidation numbers, the electron is counted *as if* it were completely transferred from the hydrogen atom to the chlorine atom. Thus, the chlorine atom is assigned an oxidation number of -1. The hydrogen is then assigned an oxidation number of $+1$. In H_2O, each hydrogen atom shares one electron with the oxygen atom and thereby acquires an oxidation number of $+1$, because hydrogen is less electronegative than oxygen. Two electrons (one from each hydrogen atom), have been shifted toward the oxygen atom, and its oxidation number is therefore -2. Similarly, it is easy to show that in NH_3 the oxidation numbers of N and H are -3 and $+1$, respectively.

Thus, whether a given compound is ionic or covalent, the same method is used to determine the oxidation numbers of its atoms. This situation arises because electrons are counted *as if* they had transferred completely from one atom to another, even if they are only shifted partially.

Sample Problem 8-2

What are the oxidation numbers of each atom in the covalent substances
a) H_2S; **b)** PCl_3; **c)** P_4?

SOLUTION
a) In H_2S, each hydrogen atom shares one electron with the sulfur atom and thereby acquires an oxidation number of $+1$, because hydrogen is less electronegative than sulfur. Two electrons (one from each hydrogen atom), have been shifted toward the sulfur atom, and its oxidation number is therefore -2.
b) In PCl_3 the phosphorus atom shares three of its electrons (one with each chlorine atom), and its oxidation number is therefore $+3$, because phosphorus is less electronegative than chlorine. One electron has been shifted to each chlorine atom, and the oxidation number of each chlorine atom is therefore -1.
c) The oxidation number of P in P_4 must be zero, because all the atoms in the molecule are identical (P_4 is the formula of elemental phosphorus).

Practice Problem 8-2

What are the oxidation numbers of each atom in each of the following:
a) Ag; **b)** Cl_2; **c)** CH_4; **d)** PF_5?

Polyatomic Ions

A polyatomic ion is an ion which contains two or more atoms. The most common positively charged polyatomic ion is NH_4^+. It is found in compounds such as ammonium nitrate (NH_4NO_3) and ammonium phosphate [$(NH_4)_3PO_4$], both of which are important ingredients in fertilizers. Common negatively charged polyatomic ions are OH^- and SO_4^{2-}. The hydroxide ion, OH^-, is found in sodium hydroxide ($NaOH$), a component of household drain cleaners. The sulfate ion, SO_4^{2-}, is found in calcium sulfate ($CaSO_4$). Both gypsum and plaster of Paris consist of calcium sulfate combined with different numbers of water molecules. Table 8-2 is a listing of common negatively charged polyatomic ions. Their oxidation numbers are the same as their charge.

TABLE 8-2. **Oxidation Numbers and Names of Some Negative Polyatomic Ions.**

OXIDATION NUMBER = -1			
Ion	*Name*	*Ion*	*Name*
CN^-	cyanide	HSO_4^-	hydrogen sulfate
$C_2H_3O_2^-$	acetate	$H_2PO_3^-$	dihydrogen phosphite
ClO^-	hypochlorite	$H_2PO_4^-$	dihydrogen phosphate
ClO_2^-	chlorite	MnO_4^-	permanganate
ClO_3^-	chlorate	NO_2^-	nitrite
ClO_4^-	perchlorate	NO_3^-	nitrate
HCO_3^-	hydrogen carbonate	OCN^-	cyanate
$HC_2O_4^-$	hydrogen oxalate	OH^-	hydroxide
HSO_3^-	hydrogen sulfite	SCN^-	thiocyanate

OXIDATION NUMBER = -2			
Ion	*Name*	*Ion*	*Name*
CO_3^{2-}	carbonate	HPO_4^{2-}	hydrogen phosphate
$C_2O_4^{2-}$	oxalate	O_2^{2-}	peroxide
CrO_4^{2-}	chromate	SO_3^{2-}	sulfite
$Cr_2O_7^{2-}$	dichromate	SO_4^{2-}	sulfate
HPO_3^{2-}	hydrogen phosphite	$S_2O_3^{2-}$	thiosulfate

OXIDATION NUMBER = -3			
Ion	*Name*	*Ion*	*Name*
AsO_3^{3-}	arsenite		
AsO_4^{3-}	arsenate	PO_4^{3-}	phosphate

The presence of a charge on a polyatomic ion means that electron(s) have been gained or lost. A superscript "+", as in NH_4^+, indicates that the NH_4 unit has one electron less than the total contributed by the one nitrogen and four hydrogen atoms. The charge on the whole unit is $+1$. Similarly, a superscript "2−", as in SO_4^{2-}, means that the SO_4 unit has gained two extra electrons, and the charge on the whole unit is -2.

8-2 Writing Formulas

Knowing the oxidation numbers of elements and ions can help us remember or predict the formulas of these compounds.

When we meet a compound containing an unfamiliar element, we can use a rule known as the zero sum rule. The *zero sum rule* states that the sum of the positive oxidation numbers and the negative oxidation numbers of the elements in a compound must be zero. Thus, in the compound, AlF_3, aluminum has an oxidation number of $+3$, and each fluorine has an oxidation number of -1. The sum of the oxidation numbers is zero. In PbO_2, each oxygen has an oxidation number of -2, so lead has an oxidation number of $+4$. Again, the sum of the oxidation numbers is zero.

Sample Problem 8-3

Write the formulas of the compounds of bromide ion (Br^-) with potassium ion (K^+), magnesium ion (Mg^{2+}), and aluminum ion (Al^{3+}).

SOLUTION
Since potassium ion has an oxidation number of $+1$ and bromide ion has an oxidation number of -1, the formula of this compound is KBr.

$$KBr \quad +1 + (-1) = 0$$

However, magnesium ion has an oxidation number of $+2$, and two bromide ions will be required since each has an oxidation number of -1. The formula of this compound is $MgBr_2$, and the subscript 2 indicates that there are two bromide ions for every magnesium ion in the compound.

$$MgBr_2 \quad +2 + 2(-1) = 0$$

Finally, aluminum ion has an oxidation number of $+3$ and three bromide ions will be required for every aluminum ion. The formula of this compound is $AlBr_3$.

$$AlBr_3 \quad +3 + 3(-1) = 0$$

Practice Problem 8-3

Write the formulas of the compounds of iodide ion (I^-) with K^+, Mg^{2+}, and Al^{3+}.

Sample Problem 8-4

Write the formulas of the compounds of sulfide ion (S^{2-}) with K^+, Mg^{2+}, and Al^{3+}.

SOLUTION
Potassium ion has an oxidation number of $+1$, but sulfide ion has an oxidation number of -2. Thus, two potassium ions will be required to balance one sulfide ion. The formula of this compound is K_2S. The subscript 2 indicates that there are two potassium ions for every sulfide ion in the compound.

$$K_2S \quad 2(+1) + (-2) = 0$$

However, magnesium ion has an oxidation number (+2) which balances the oxidation number of the sulfide ion (−2). Magnesium sulfide is simply MgS.

$$MgS \quad +2 + (-2) = 0$$

Finally, aluminum ion has an oxidation number of +3 and two aluminum ions have a combined oxidation number of +6. Sulfide ion has an oxidation number of −2, and three sulfide ions have a combined oxidation number of −6. In the case of aluminum sulfide, the simplest way to ensure that the sum of the positive oxidation numbers will equal the sum of the negative oxidation numbers is to use the formula Al_2S_3. There must be two aluminum ions for three sulfide ions.

$$Al_2S_3 \quad 2(+3) + 3(-2) = 0$$

Practice Problem 8-4

Write the formulas of the compounds of selenide ion (Se^{2-}) with K^+, Mg^{2+}, and Al^{3+}.

Table 8-1 lists 36 positive monatomic ions. In addition, we know the formula for one positive polyatomic ion (NH_4^+). Table 8-1 also lists eight negative monatomic ions, and 31 negative polyatomic ions are listed in Table 8-2. The 37 positive ions can (in theory, at least) react with each of the 39 negative ions to form a total of $37 \times 39 = 1443$ possible compounds. Most of these are stable compounds, and you now have enough information to write the formulas resulting from each of the 1443 combinations.

Sample Problem 8-5

Write the formulas of the compounds of **a)** NH_4^+ and Cl^-, **b)** Na^+ and CO_3^{2-}, and **c)** Ba^{2+} and SO_4^{2-}.

SOLUTION
a) Ammonium has an oxidation number of +1 and chloride ion has an oxidation number of −1. The formula of this compound is NH_4Cl.

$$NH_4Cl \quad +1 + (-1) = 0$$

b) Sodium ion has an oxidation number of +1, but carbonate ion has an oxidation number of −2. Thus there must be two sodium ions for every carbonate ion and this is indicated by a subscript 2 following the Na. The formula is Na_2CO_3.

$$Na_2CO_3 \quad 2(+1) + (-2) = 0$$

c) Barium ion has an oxidation number of +2 and sulfate ion has an oxidation number of −2. The formula of this compound is $BaSO_4$.

$$BaSO_4 \quad +2 + (-2) = 0$$

Practice Problem 8-5

Write the formulas of the compounds of **a)** NH_4^+ and NO_3^-, **b)** Ag^+ and PO_4^{3-}, and **c)** Al^{3+} and PO_4^{3-}.

In writing the formulas of compounds which include more than one unit of a given polyatomic ion the formula of that polyatomic ion is enclosed in parentheses, and the number of units of the polyatomic ion is indicated with a subscript. Sample Problem 8-6 illustrates this point.

Sample Problem 8-6

Write the formulas of the compounds of: **a)** Ca^{2+} and NO_3^- , **b)** NH_4^+ and PO_4^{3-} , and **c)** Al^{3+} and SO_4^{2-} .

SOLUTION

a) Two nitrate ions (each with oxidation number of -1) are required for each calcium ion ($+2$). Thus, the formula for nitrate ion is enclosed in parentheses, and a subscript 2 is used. The formula is $Ca(NO_3)_2$.

$$Ca(NO_3)_2 \quad +2 + 2(-1) = 0$$

$Ca(NO_3)_2$ may be read "Ca onto NO_3 taken twice." The word *onto* implies that more than one unit of a polyatomic ion follows. The word *taken* implies that more than one unit of a polyatomic ion has preceded. In practice, chemists often shorten the reading to "Ca, NO_3 taken twice."

b) Three ammonium ions (each $+1$) are required for each phosphate ion (-3). The formula for ammonium ion is enclosed in parentheses, and a subscript 3 is used. The formula is $(NH_4)_3PO_4$. It is read "NH_4 taken three times, PO_4."

$$(NH_4)_3PO_4 \quad 3(+1) + (-3) = 0$$

c) Two aluminum ions (each $+3$) are required for three sulfate ions (each -2). The formula for sulfate ion is enclosed in parentheses and a subscript 3 is used. Furthermore, a subscript 2 follows the aluminum. The formula is $Al_2(SO_4)_3$. It is read "Al two onto SO_4 taken three times," or "Al two, SO_4 taken three times."

$$Al_2(SO_4)_3 \quad 2(+3) + 3(-2) = 0$$

Practice Problem 8-6

Write the formulas of the compounds of **a)** Al^{3+} and NO_3^-, **b)** NH_4^+ and SO_3^{2-}, and **c)** Al^{3+} and SO_3^{2-} .

8-3 Naming Chemical Compounds Containing Only Two Elements

In the last section, we learned how to use oxidation numbers to write chemical formulas. A compound is identified by its chemical formula. For this reason, chemists use formulas to refer to various substances. For example, HCl is the formula which refers to a specific compound. But each compound also has a name to distinguish it from other compounds. Thus, the compound represented by the formula H_2O is called "water." Such a name is called a *trivial* name.

There is no way that such a name could be figured out from the formula. Other compounds with trivial names are NH_3 (ammonia) and $C_{12}H_{22}O_{11}$ (sugar). These names arose in the early days of chemistry when names were invented on the spot as compounds were discovered. As the number of known compounds began to increase, it quickly became apparent that there must be a *systematic* method of nomenclature which uniquely describes each compound. Thus, although the trivial name of NaCl is "salt," its systematic name is "sodium chloride." The latter name certainly gives a better indication of the make-up of the compound. In this section we shall describe the method of deriving systematic names for compounds. Since many compounds are composed of ions, or can be considered as if they were composed of ions, we shall first examine the means of naming monatomic ions and the compounds that are formed by combinations of these ions.

Positive Monatomic Ions

The name of a positive monatomic ion is the same as the name of the element. Thus, Li^+ is lithium (ion), Mg^{2+} is magnesium (ion), and Al^{3+} is aluminum (ion).

The atoms of some metals form more than one stable ion. For example, tin forms the ions Sn^{2+} and Sn^{4+}; iron forms the ions Fe^{2+} and Fe^{3+}; and copper forms the ions Cu^+ and Cu^{2+} (Table 8-1). In such cases a Roman numeral in parentheses is added immediately after the name of the element to indicate the oxidation state of the element. Thus, Sn^{2+} is tin(II) and Sn^{4+} is tin(IV); Fe^{2+} is iron(II) and Fe^{3+} is iron(III); Cu^+ is copper(I) and Cu^{2+} is copper(II). This system of nomenclature is called the *Stock system*, after the German chemist A. Stock, who first proposed it. Roman numerals are not used if the positive ion has only one possible oxidation state, e.g., ions of elements of Groups I, II, and III.

TABLE **8-3**   **Names of Some Positive Ions that use the Suffixes *-ous* and *-ic***

ELEMENT	OXIDATION NUMBER	OLD SYSTEM	STOCK SYSTEM
Au	+1	aur*ous*	gold(I)
Au	+3	aur*ic*	gold(III)
Co	+2	cobalt*ous*	cobalt(II)
Co	+3	cobalt*ic*	cobalt(III)
Cu	+1	cupr*ous*	copper(I)
Cu	+2	cupr*ic*	copper(II)
Fe	+2	ferr*ous*	iron(II)
Fe	+3	ferr*ic*	iron(III)
Hg	+1	mercur*ous*	mercury(I)
Hg	+2	mercur*ic*	mercury(II)
Sn	+2	stann*ous*	tin(II)
Sn	+4	stann*ic*	tin(IV)

An older method of naming such ions was to use the suffixes -*ous* and -*ic*. For the ion of lower oxidation number, the suffix -*ous* was added to the stem of the name of the element. For the ion of higher oxidation number, the suffix -*ic* was used. Thus, Sn^{2+} was stann*ous* ion and Sn^{4+} was stann*ic* ion; Fe^{2+} was ferr*ous* ion and Fe^{3+} was ferr*ic* ion; while Cu^+ was cupr*ous* ion and Cu^{2+} was cupr*ic* ion. The system had the disadvantage that a given suffix does not consistently represent the same oxidation number. For example, the suffix -*ic* stands for an oxidation number of +4 in stannic ion, +3 in ferric ion, and +2 in cupric ion. Furthermore, the system does not work at all for ions which may have more than two oxidation numbers (chromium, for example, may have oxidation numbers of +2, +3, and +6). Because this system is still used by chemists, it is (unfortunately) necessary for students to learn it. This older system is illustrated in Table 8-3 (on previous page).

Negative Monatomic Ions

The name of a negative monatomic ion is formed by adding the suffix -*ide* to the stem (the first part) of the name of the element. The stems of some common elements are listed in Table 8-4.

TABLE **8-4. Stems (boldface) of Some Common Elements**

hydrogen	
carbon	**sulf**ur
nitrogen	**chlor**ine
oxygen	**selen**ium
fluorine	**brom**ine
phosphorus	**iod**ine

Binary Compounds Containing a Metal and a Nonmetal

A *binary compound* is one which contains only two elements. The systematic name of a binary compound consists of two words, the name of the positive ion and the name of the negative ion. Usually the more positive, more metallic element is written first (NaCl, not ClNa). Thus, NaCl is sodium chloride; CaO is calcium oxide; FeS is iron(II) sulfide or ferrous sulfide; and $FeCl_3$ is iron(III) chloride or ferric chloride.

Sample Problem 8-7

Name each of the following compounds: $BaCl_2$, $FeBr_3$, SrI_2.

SOLUTION
The first part of the name is the name of the first element in the formula. The second part of the name is the stem of the element followed by the suffix -*ide*. Therefore the name of $BaCl_2$ is barium chloride; for $FeBr_3$ it is iron(III) bromide or ferric bromide; and for SrI_2 the name is strontium iodide.

Practice Problem 8-7

Name each of the following compounds: Li_2O, BeF_2, MgO, Ca_3N_2.

Binary Compounds Containing Hydrogen and Another Element

Compounds of hydrogen and a nonmetal from Groups VI and VII are named by writing the word hydrogen followed by the stem of the name of the nonmetal to which the ending -*ide* has been added. Thus, HCl is hydrogen chloride and H_2S is hydrogen sulfide. Of course, H_2O has the trivial name water.

In compounds of hydrogen and a metal, the hydrogen is usually the more electronegative element. Therefore, the symbol for the metal is written first in the formula (e.g., NaH). The names are formed according to the usual rules for binary compounds of a metal and a nonmetal (e.g., sodium hydride).

The Group IV element carbon forms many compounds with hydrogen. These are called *hydrocarbons* and they are discussed in Chapter 16.

Nonsystematic or trivial names are normally used for compounds containing hydrogen and a Group V element. For example, NH_3 is called ammonia, PH_3 is called phosphine, AsH_3 is called arsine, and SbH_3 is called stibine.

Binary Compounds Containing Two Nonmetals

Binary compounds containing two nonmetals are named by using yet another naming system. In this system the name of each element is preceded by a prefix which indicates the number of atoms of the element. The prefixes are listed in Table 8-5. Normally the prefix *mono-* is omitted from the name of the first element. The absence of a prefix indicates the number one. Since the formula of a binary compound is written with the less electronegative atom first, the name of a binary compound of two nonmetals is formed according to the pattern

prefix + element name   prefix + element stem + -*ide*.

Thus, As_2S_3 is called diarsenic trisulfide; NO_2 is nitrogen dioxide; N_2O_5 is dinitrogen pentoxide; and CCl_4 is carbon tetrachloride.

TABLE 8-5 Commonly Used Numerical Prefixes.

NUMBER	PREFIX	NUMBER	PREFIX
1	mono-	6	hexa-
2	di-	7	hepta-
3	tri-	8	octa-
4	tetra-	9	nona-
5	penta-	10	deca-

Note: The final ''a'' or ''o'' of a prefix is omitted if the name of the atom or ion being counted begins with an ''a'' or an ''o.''

In cases where there is no ambiguity, the Stock system can be used. Thus, As_2S_3 can be called arsenic(III) sulfide; N_2O_5 is nitrogen(V) oxide; and CCl_4 could be called carbon(IV) chloride (but the name is not used because there is no other stable chloride of carbon). Both NO_2 and N_2O_4 have nitrogen in the $+4$ oxidation state. Therefore the Stock system cannot be used in these two cases because of the ambiguity.

Sample Problem 8-8

Name the compounds represented by the following formulas:
a) NO; b) P_2S_5; c) SCl_2; d) HI.

SOLUTION
a) There is one atom of each element. The appropriate prefix is therefore *mono-*. But the prefix is omitted before the "nitrogen" and its final "o" is omitted before "oxide." The correct name is therefore nitrogen monoxide.
b) The numbers are 2 and 5, so the prefixes are *di-* and *penta-*. The name is diphosphorus pentasulfide.
c) The numbers are 1 and 2, so the prefixes are *mono-* (omitted) and *di-*. The name is sulfur dichloride.
d) Compounds of hydrogen and a nonmetal are named in the same manner as are compounds of metals and nonmetals. The name is therefore hydrogen iodide.

Practice Problem 8-8

Name the compounds represented by the following formulas: CF_4, $AsCl_5$, PBr_3, HBr.

8-4 Naming Compounds Composed of More Than Two Elements

Many compounds consist of a polyatomic ion and a metal ion, another polyatomic ion, or hydrogen. As you might expect, the names of such compounds are formed by writing first the name of the positive portion of the compound, followed by the name of the negative ion. Whereas the names of all monatomic negative ions end in *-ide* (e.g., chloride, oxide), the names of negative polyatomic ions generally end in *-ate* or *-ite*. The names and formulas of some common negative polyatomic ions are given in Table 8-2. Fortunately, only one common positive polyatomic ion is found in pure compounds, and that is NH_4^+, ammonium ion.

Of the ions listed in Table 8-2, only three do not have the general *-ate* and *-ite* endings: cyanide, hydroxide, and peroxide. Only two do not contain oxygen: CN^- and SCN^-. Two ions (SCN^- and $S_2O_3^{2-}$) can be considered as being formed from OCN^- and SO_4^{2-} by replacing an oxygen atom with a sulfur atom. For these the prefix *thio-* is placed before the names cyanate and sulfate.

Eight of the ions listed in Table 8-2 can be considered as being formed by the combination of H^+ with a different negative ion. E.g., HSO_4^- can be considered as being formed by the combination of H^+ with SO_4^{2-} according to the reaction

$$H^+ + SO_4^{2-} \rightarrow HSO_4^-$$

The formulas of these ions all begin with the symbol "H." These ions are named by placing the word "hydrogen" before the name of the other ion. Thus, HSO_4^- is called the hydrogen sulfate ion; HCO_3^- is the hydrogen carbonate ion; and HPO_4^{2-} is the hydrogen phosphate ion. The presence of two hydrogen atoms is indicated by the prefix "*di-*," as in $H_2PO_4^-$, dihydrogen phosphate ion. It is important when referring to these ions to state that these are ions, in order to avoid ambiguity. For example, HCO_3^- is the hydrogen carbonate ion, but, as we shall see in the next section, H_2CO_3 is called hydrogen carbonate.

Some simple principles will help you to remember the names of the oxygen-containing ions. If there are only two oxygen-containing ions of an element (e.g., SO_4^{2-} and SO_3^{2-}), the ion with the greater number of oxygen atoms has a name ending in *-ate*, while the ion with the smaller number of oxygen atoms has a name ending in *-ite* (e.g., sulfate and sulfite). If there are four oxygen-containing ions (e.g., ClO^-, ClO_2^-, ClO_3^-, ClO_4^-), the two ions with the fewest oxygen atoms have names ending in *-ite*, and the two with the greatest number of oxygen atoms have names ending in *-ate*. The ion with the most oxygens is distinguished by the prefix *per-*, and the one with the fewest oxygen atoms is given the prefix *hypo-* (e.g., hypochlorite, chlorite, chlorate, and perchlorate). Table 8-6 summarizes these principles.

TABLE 8-6   Nomenclature of Polyatomic Oxygen-Containing Ions

NOMENCLATURE	GROUP V	GROUP VI	GROUP VII	EXAMPLES
hypo_____ite			ClO^-	hypochlorite
_____ite	NO_2^-	SO_3^{2-}	ClO_2^-	nitrite, sulfite, chlorite
_____ate	NO_3^-	SO_4^{2-}	ClO_3^-	nitrate, sulfate, chlorate
per_____ate			ClO_4^-	perchlorate

Sample Problem 8-9

Name the compounds represented by the following formulas:
a) $KClO_3$; b) NH_4I; c) $Ba(BrO_3)_2$; d) $CuSO_3$; e) Cu_2SO_4.

SOLUTION
a) We know that ClO_3^- is an ion called chlorate. Therefore, this is potassium chlorate.
b) We know that NH_4^+ is an ion called ammonium. Therefore, this is ammonium iodide.
c) We know that ClO_3^- is an ion called chlorate. Since bromine is in the same group as chlorine, we would expect BrO_3^- to be called bromate. The compound is therefore barium bromate.

d) We know that SO_3^{2-} is an ion called sulfite. There is one sulfite ion with an oxidation number of -2. There is also one copper ion. Since the sum of the positive and negative oxidation numbers must equal zero, the oxidation number of the copper ion must be $+2$. Therefore, this is copper(II) sulfite. The name copper sulfite is incorrect, because it does not specify which of the two possible oxidation states of copper is present.

e) We know that SO_4^{2-} is an ion called sulfate. There is one sulfate ion with an oxidation number of -2. There are also two copper ions, and the zero sum rule requires that their total oxidation number equal $+2$. Each copper ion has an oxidation number of $+1$, and the compound is copper(I) sulfate (not copper sulfate!).

Practice Problem 8-9

Name the compounds represented by the following formulas:
K_3PO_4, $Ca(ClO_4)_2$, $Al(OH)_3$, $SrCO_3$, NH_4NO_3, $Fe(C_2H_3O_2)_3$.

8-5 Nomenclature of Acids

A compound of hydrogen and a nonmetal from Groups VI and VII is named by writing the word *hydrogen* followed by the stem of the name of the nonmetal to which the ending *-ide* has been added. Solutions of these compounds dissolved in water (aqueous solutions) are acids. They are named by using the prefix *hydro-*, the stem of the name of the nonmetal, and the ending *-ic*, followed by the word *acid*. Thus, a solution of HCl dissolved in water is called hydrochloric acid, a solution of HBr in water is called hydrobromic acid, and a solution of H_2S in water is called hydrosulfuric acid. The names of some common binary acids are listed in Table 8-7.

TABLE 8-7 Names of Some Common Binary Acids

FORMULA	NAME OF ACID
HF	hydrofluoric acid
HCl	hydrochloric acid
HBr	hydrobromic acid
HI	hydriodic* acid
H_2S	hydrosulfuric acid
H_2Se	hydroselenic acid

A compound composed of hydrogen and a negative polyatomic ion from Table 8-2 is named by writing the word *hydrogen* followed by the name of the polyatomic ion. Thus, H_2SO_4 is hydrogen sulfate, HNO_2 is hydrogen nitrite, and H_3PO_4 is hydrogen phosphate. Aqueous solutions made by dissolving compounds of hydrogen and negative polyatomic ions in water are also acids.

---

*The "o" of the prefix *hydro-* is dropped for ease of pronunciation.

Their solutions are given special names. The name of the aqueous solution is formed by dropping the word *hydrogen*, as well as the suffix from the name of the negative ion. The suffix is replaced with a new one, plus the word *acid*. The suffix *-ite* becomes *-ous acid*, and the suffix *-ate* becomes *-ic acid*. Thus, an aqueous solution of H_2SO_4 is sulfuric acid; an aqueous solution of $HClO_4$ is perchloric acid; and an aqueous solution of HNO_2 is nitrous acid. The only common exceptions are the acids containing phosphorus—for these the stem is not *phosp-*, but *phosphor-*, as in H_3PO_4, phosphoric acid. The nomenclature of aqueous solutions of oxygen-containing acids is summarized in Table 8-8.

TABLE 8-8 Nomenclature of Aqueous Solutions of Oxygen-Containing Acids

NOMENCLATURE	GROUP V	GROUP VI	GROUP VII	EXAMPLES
hypo_____ous acid			HClO	hypochlorous acid
_____ous acid	HNO_2			nitrous acid
		H_2SO_3		sulfurous acid
			$HClO_2$	chlorous acid
_____ic acid	HNO_3			nitric acid
		H_2SO_4		sulfuric acid
			$HClO_3$	chloric acid
per_____ic acid			$HClO_4$	perchloric acid

Aqueous solutions of acids formed from negative ions whose names end in *-ide* are named in the same way as binary acids. Thus we have HCN, hydrocyanic acid. (H_2O_2 is such a weak acid that even in aqueous solution it is called hydrogen peroxide.)

Sample Problem 8-10

Name the following oxyacids of iodine, both in the pure state and in aqueous solution: **a)** HIO; **b)** HIO_2; **c)** HIO_3; **d)** HIO_4.

SOLUTION
a) The IO^- ion contains the smallest number of oxygen atoms. It is called hypoiodite ion. The pure compound is hydrogen hypoiodite. The aqueous solution is then called hypoiodous acid.
b) The IO_2^- ion contains the next smallest number of oxygen atoms. It is therefore the iodite ion. The pure compound is then called hydrogen iodite; its aqueous solution is iodous acid.
c) The IO_3^- ion contains the second largest number of oxygen atoms. Its name is iodate ion, so the pure compound is called hydrogen iodate, and its aqueous solution is iodic acid.
d) The IO_4^- ion contains the largest number of oxygen atoms. It is therefore the periodate ion. The pure compound is hydrogen periodate, and the aqueous solution is called periodic acid.

Practice Problem 8-10

Name the aqueous solutions of the following compounds:
$HC_2H_3O_2$, H_2CO_3, $HMnO_4$, $H_2C_2O_4$, H_3AsO_4.

arsenate.

Practice Problem 8-11

Draw a large table similar to Table 8-9. Fill in each blank with the formula and name of the compound that results when the positive ion at the left is combined with the negative ion at the top.

TABLE 8-9 Names and Formulas of Compounds

	OH^-	F^-	$C_2H_3O_2^-$	O^{2-}	$C_2O_4^{2-}$	$S_2O_3^{2-}$	PO_3^{3-}
H^+							
Na^+							
NH_4^+							
Ag^+							
Cu^{2+}							
Ca^{2+}							
Ni^{2+}							
Zn^{2+}							
Hg^{2+}							
Al^{3+}							

Practice Problem 8-12

Give formulas for the following compounds: hydrogen bromide, hydriodic acid, carbon tetrabromide, sulfur trioxide, potassium oxalate, iron(III) nitrate, iron (III) sulfite, cobalt(II) chlorate, cobalt(II) oxalate, tin(IV) nitrite, and tin(IV) sulfite.

8-6 Introduction to Chemical Equations

Now that we can write chemical formulas, we can use them to write chemical equations. A chemical equation is a shorthand method for describing a chemical change. The symbols and formulas are used to indicate the substances involved in the change. In order to balance an equation, we must know what substances react and what substances are formed, and we must know the formulas of all substances in the reaction.

When water is decomposed, hydrogen and oxygen are formed:

$$H_2O \rightarrow H_2 + O_2$$

The formula for the reactant is on the left, and the formulas for the products are on the right. The arrow is read as "yields" and the plus sign is read as "and." When a plus sign appears on the left side, it implies "reacts with."

The above equation does not obey the Law of Conservation of Mass. Two atoms of oxygen in the O_2 molecule could not be formed from one water molecule containing only one oxygen atom. The proper coefficients (numbers) must be placed in front of each formula:

$$2 H_2O \rightarrow 2 H_2 + O_2$$

The equation is read, "two water molecules yield two hydrogen molecules and one oxygen molecule." Remember that subscripts in a correct formula cannot be changed in order to make an equation balance. Substances have a definite atomic composition.

The symbol for heat is Δ.

$$2 KClO_3 \xrightarrow{\Delta} 2 KCl + 3 O_2(g)$$

The (g) indicates that a gas (in this case, oxygen) is given off in a reaction. The above equation is read, "two potassium chlorate formula units yield (when heated) two potassium chloride formula units and three molecules of gaseous oxygen." As was stated in Chapter 6, the word *molecule* does not have much meaning in the case of ionic solids such as potassium chlorate and potassium chloride (or any compound which contains the ammonium ion or a metal ion). Therefore, we referred to potassium chlorate and potassium chloride formula units rather than molecules.

An (ℓ) indicates a pure liquid, (s) indicates a solid, and (aq) indicates an aqueous solution (i.e., a substance dissolved in water). For example, a formula unit of silver nitrate dissolved in water reacts with a formula unit of sodium chloride dissolved in water to yield a formula unit of solid silver chloride and a formula unit of sodium nitrate dissolved in water. This information can be conveyed by the chemical equation

$$AgNO_3 \text{ (aq)} + NaCl \text{ (aq)} \rightarrow AgCl \text{ (s)} + NaNO_3 \text{ (aq)}$$

Sample Problem 8-11

What is meant by the following chemical equation?

$$CaCO_3 \text{ (s)} \xrightarrow{\Delta} CaO \text{ (s)} + CO_2 \text{ (g)}$$

SOLUTION
This equation means that one formula unit of solid calcium carbonate yields (when heated) one formula unit of solid calcium oxide and one molecule of gaseous carbon dioxide.

Practice Problem 8-13

If CH_4 is methane, what is meant by the following chemical equation?

$$CH_4 \text{ (g)} + 2 O_2 \text{ (g)} \rightarrow CO_2 \text{ (g)} + 2 H_2O \text{ (g)}$$

A Final Word

In this chapter we have learned how to write the formulas and the names of chemical compounds. We have also learned the meaning of a simple chemical equation. The information that is contained in this chapter is an essential foundation for further studies in chemistry. A knowledge of nomenclature and formula writing is as important to a student of chemistry as a knowledge of vocabulary is to a student of a second language.

Now that you have finished reading this chapter, you should reread the Key Objectives to make sure that you have learned the most important points of the chapter. This chapter can best be learned through practice. The best way to do this is to complete the exercises and answer the questions at the end of the chapter.

Questions

1. Indicate the oxidation number of the underlined ion in each of the following species: **a)** $\underline{Zn}^{2+}$; **b)** Ba$\underline{S}$; **c)** Ca$\underline{SO_3}$; **d)** NaO$\underline{H}$; **e)** H$\underline{N}$O$_3$.

2. Indicate the oxidation number of the underlined ion in each of the following species: **a)** $\underline{Br}O_3^-$; **b)** Na$_2$$\underline{S}_2O_3$; **c)** (NH$_4$)$_2$$\underline{Cr}_2O_7$; **d)** KC$_2$$\underline{H}_3O_2$; **e)** Sr$\underline{S}$.

3. Give the oxidation number of each element in the following: **a)** Br$\overline{F}_5$; **b)** S$_8$; **c)** SiCl$_4$; **d)** SCl$_2$; **e)** SbCl$_5$.

4. Give the oxidation number of each element in the following: **a)** P$_4$O$_{10}$; **b)** AsH$_3$; **c)** O$_3$; **d)** GeCl$_4$; **e)** SF$_6$.

5. Write formulas for the compounds formed by all possible combinations of Cs$^+$, Ba^{2+}, and Ga^{3+} with I$^-$, S^{2-}, and P^{3-} (nine possibilities).

6. Write formulas for all possible combinations of Rb$^+$, Sr^{2+}, Ga^{3+}, Pb^{4+}, and Bi^{5+} with Br$^-$, S^{2-}, and N^{3-}. (There are fifteen possibilities, but not all of them actually exist.)

7. Write formulas for all possible combinations of NH$_4^+$, Ca^{2+}, Al^{3+}, and Sn^{4+} with CN$^-$, CO$_3^{2-}$, and PO$_4^{3-}$ (Not all of the compounds represented will actually exist.)

8. Write formulas for all possible combinations of K$^+$, Mg^{2+}, and B^{3+} with C$_2$H$_3$O$_2^-$, C$_2$O$_4^{2-}$, and PO$_3^{3-}$.

9. Name each of the following compounds: LiH, NH$_3$, FeS, SnBr$_4$, Hg$_2$Cl$_2$, N$_2$S$_5$, N$_2$O, and Al$_2$O$_3$.

10. Name each of the following compounds: NaCl, Li$_2$S, PH$_3$, BaF$_2$, BeO, Mg$_3$N$_2$, GaI$_3$, Al$_2$S$_3$, and BN.

11. What is the oxidation number of the metal in each of the following compounds: SrCl$_2$, YbI$_3$, TlOCN, V$_2$O$_5$, and Y(OH)$_3$?

12. What is the oxidation number of the polyatomic ion in each of the following compounds: Na$_2$MoO$_4$, Mg(IO$_3$)$_2$, CaSiO$_3$, Al(C$_2$H$_5$O)$_3$, and Li$_2$B$_4$O$_7$?

13. Give formulas and Stock system names for all possible combinations of Au$^+$, Co^{2+}, Fe^{3+}, and Pb^{4+} with ClO$^-$, CrO$_4^{2-}$, and AsO$_4^{3-}$ (Not all of the represented compounds actually exist.)

14. Use the Stock system to rename the following compounds: **a)** ferrous sulfate; **b)** cobaltic sulfide; **c)** mercurous iodate; **d)** stannic iodide.

15. Name the following compounds according to the Stock system of nomenclature: $CuClO_2$, $Hg_2Cr_2O_7$, Tl_3PO_4, $Cu(HCO_3)_2$, $Fe(ClO_3)_2$, $Hg_3(PO_3)_2$, $Au(ClO_4)_3$, $Co_2(Cr_2O_7)_3$, $FeAsO_4$.

16. Use the Stock system to rename the following compounds: **a)** cobaltous nitrate; **b)** mercuric selenide; **c)** stannous fluoride; **d)** ferric chloride.

17. Name each of the following compounds: $(NH_4)_2Cr_2O_7$, $Cu(NO_3)_2$, $Ba(HCO_3)_2$, CaC_2O_4, $Pb(C_2H_3O_2)_2$, and $Al_2(S_2O_3)_3$.

18. Write the name of the aqueous solution of each of the following: H_2SO_4, HCl, HNO_3, $HC_2H_3O_2$, H_3PO_4, and $HClO_4$.

19. What is the formula for lithium sulfide? Potassium iodide? Magnesium bromide? Magnesium sulfide? Aluminum sulfide? Aluminum chloride?

20. What is the formula for iron(III) chloride? Iron(II) oxide? Cobalt(II) bromide? Tin(IV) chloride?

21. What is the formula for magnesium hydroxide? Iron(III) carbonate? Carbon tetrabromide? Diphosphorus pentasulfide? Nitrogen(V) sulfide?

22. What is the formula for permanganic acid? Oxalic acid? Ammonium chromate? Sodium perchlorate? Potassium thiosulfate? Aluminum sulfite?

23. Write formulas for the following compounds: **a)** stannous chloride; **b)** ferric sulfate; **c)** vanadium(II) bromide; **d)** tin(IV) oxide; **e)** gold(III) cyanide.

24. Write formulas for the following compounds: **a)** aluminum acetate; **b)** sodium oxide; **c)** potassium permanganate; **d)** barium sulfite; **e)** silicon tetrachloride; **f)** calcium hydrogen carbonate; **g)** silver phosphate; **h)** ferrous arsenate; **i)** ferric sulfate; **j)** iron(III) phosphite.

25. What do the following equations mean?
    a) $CaO(s) + H_2O(\ell) \rightarrow Ca(OH)_2(s)$
    b) $C_3H_8(g) + 5\,O_2(g) \rightarrow 3\,CO_2(g) + 4\,H_2O(g)$ (C_3H_8 is propane)
    c) $AgNO_3(aq) + NaCl(aq) \rightarrow AgCl(s) + NaNO_3(aq)$
    d) $Na_2SO_4(aq) + BaCl_2(aq) \rightarrow BaSO_4(s) + 2\,NaCl(aq)$

26. What is meant by the following equations?
    a) $2CO(g) + O_2(g) \rightarrow 2CO_2(g)$
    b) $PCl_3(\ell) + Cl_2(g) \rightarrow PCl_5(g)$
    c) $AgNO_3(aq) + HCl(aq) \rightarrow AgCl(s) + HNO_3(aq)$
    d) $2NaHCO_3(aq) + H_2SO_4(aq) \rightarrow Na_2SO_4(aq) + 2H_2O(\ell) + 2CO_2(g)$

The Liquid Phase and Solutions

Why would a mountain climber find it difficult to cook an egg in boiling water at the top of Mount Robson (Fig. 9-1), the highest peak in the Canadian Rockies (3.95 km high)? Why isn't gasoline soluble in water? What is acid rain? Why is it sometimes called "the rain of death"? You will find the answers to these questions as you study the liquid phase and solutions.

In this chapter we begin with a discussion of the liquid phase. We propose a structure which explains the observed properties of liquids. Various types of solutions and the factors that affect solubility are considered. We describe solutions of electrolytes and extend the discussion to include various aspects of the chemistry of acids and bases, finishing with a brief description of the concept of pH.

Key Objectives

When you have completed studying this chapter, you should be able to
1. explain the physical properties of liquids in terms of their structure and forces of attraction.
2. explain what is meant by a physical equilibrium, using a liquid-vapour equilibrium as an example.
3. describe the processes occurring during the dissolving of a nonelectrolyte.
4. describe the processes occurring during the dissolving of an electrolyte.
5. explain the effects of molecular polarity on the solubility of a particular solute in a particular solvent.
6. distinguish between dissociation and ionization, and give an example of each.

PART ONE: The Liquid Phase

9-1 The Structure of Liquids

The structure of liquids is not as well known as that of either gases or solids. At ordinary temperatures and pressures the particles in a liquid are generally not as close to each other as those of a solid, but they are much closer together than the particles of a gas.

Fig 9-1 Mount Robson (Tourism British Columbia Photograph)

We are able to see from Fig. 9-2 that in liquids the molecules are close together but are packed with no apparent order. There appear to be empty spaces throughout the liquid. However, these empty spaces are not fixed in the same locations all the time, because the molecules are moving about continuously in a random manner.

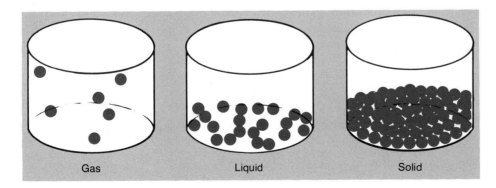

Gas   Liquid   Solid

Fig. 9-2 Comparison of the Structures of the States of Matter

9-2 Attractive Forces in the Liquid Phase

In the liquid state a number of forces of attraction tend to keep the molecules close together. These forces are called intermolecular forces, since they occur between molecules. Van der Waals forces and hydrogen bonding, which is an extreme form of van der Waals forces, have been described in Chapter 7. These forces account for attractions between molecules in the liquid phase.

For molecules such as hydrogen, the halogens, the noble gases, and symmetrical (nonpolar) molecules like carbon tetrachloride and carbon dioxide, the main intermolecular forces of attraction in the liquid phase are London dispersion forces. For polar molecules such as hydrogen chloride and hydrogen bromide, the attractions include dipole-dipole, induction, and London dispersion forces.

Another type of intermolecular force (hydrogen bonding) is not as common as the other types, but it is much stronger. This form of attraction normally involves molecules in which hydrogen is attached to either fluorine, oxygen or nitrogen. Examples of molecules exhibiting hydrogen bonding are hydrogen fluoride, water, and ammonia. Hydrogen bonding can impart abnormal properties to liquids. For instance, if we consider the boiling points of hydrogen compounds of nonmetals in Group VI (Table 9-1, Fig. 9-3), the trend would cause us to predict that water should boil near $-80°C$. Instead, we find that water does not boil until $100°C$.

TABLE 9-1 Boiling Points of Hydrogen Compounds of Group VI Elements

COMPOUND	BOILING POINT (°C)
H_2Te	−2.3
H_2Se	−41.3
H_2S	−60.3
H_2O	100.0

Fig. 9-3 Boiling Points of Hydrogen Compounds of Group VI Elements

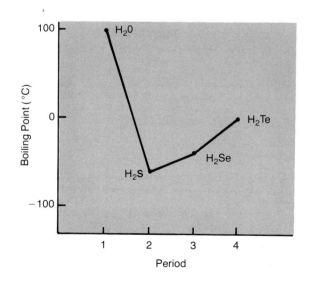

Of the types of intermolecular forces, hydrogen bonding is the strongest, followed by dipole-dipole attractions, and finally by London dispersion forces. The forces between molecules in a liquid are weaker than those of ionic and covalent bonds which hold ions and atoms together.

9-3 Physical Properties of Liquids

We can explain some of the physical properties of liquids by considering the structure of, and attractive forces within, liquids.

The densities of liquids are ordinarily much greater than those of gases. For example, the density of liquid water at $100°C$ and standard atmospheric pressure is 9.58×10^2 kg/m³. Water vapour under the same conditions has a predicted density of 5.88×10^{-1} kg/m³. Thus, the density of this liquid is 1630 times greater than that of the gas. This confirms that the molecules in the liquid state must be much closer together.

Empty spaces in the liquid phase give molecules some freedom to move past one another. This explains why liquids flow readily and take the shapes of their containers. The empty spaces in liquids allow the molecules in this phase to diffuse (mix together), but not as readily as do the molecules in the gas phase. Gases have much more empty space; this enables them to mix uniformly almost instantly. Since there are relatively few open spaces between molecules in a liquid (the molecules being so close together), it is much more difficult to compress a liquid than to compress a gas. Liquids expand much less when heated than do gases. This is because there are stronger forces of attraction to overcome in liquids when the molecules are separated from each other by heating.

The volume resulting from mixing two different liquids together is not necessarily the sum of the original volumes. For example, when 50 mL of ethyl alcohol is mixed with 50 mL of water the volume of the resulting solution is 96 mL. This decrease in volume upon mixing is mainly due to strong intermolecular forces (hydrogen bonds) between the two different liquids.

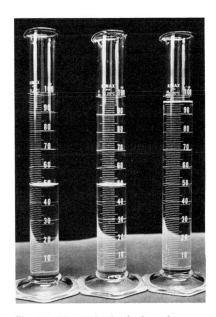
Fig. 9-4 When 50 mL of ethanol are mixed with 50 mL of water, the volume of the resulting mixture is only 96 mL.

9-4 Freezing a Liquid

If a liquid is cooled, its molecules will slow down and lose kinetic energy. With further cooling, the molecules will move even more slowly and will experience stronger forces of attraction as they come into closer contact with one another. Eventually, a temperature is reached at which the liquid releases heat energy and changes phase to become a solid. This temperature is known as the **freezing point** of the liquid.

The freezing point of any liquid is characteristic of that particular liquid. A pure liquid will freeze at a specific temperature. If an impurity is present, the liquid will freeze at a lower temperature. For example, ethylene glycol is added to the water in a car radiator to prevent damage to the radiator during cold weather. The ethylene glycol impurity lowers the freezing point of the water. Enough ethylene glycol is used so that the water will not freeze, even during the coldest expected weather. The radiator damage that could be caused by the expansion of water during freezing is thus avoided.

9-5 A Liquid in an Open Container

If a liquid in an open container is allowed to stand for a few days, the level of the liquid in the container decreases. The liquid is evaporating. People who complain of dry air caused by central heating often use dishes of water as humidifiers. The evaporation of the water adds moisture to the air and increases the humidity. Evaporation of a liquid involves the escape of surface molecules which are moving fast enough to overcome the intermolecular forces of attraction and enter the gas phase. This process of evaporation can be made to occur faster by heating the liquid. This causes an increase in the kinetic energy of the molecules. Thus, since the molecules are moving faster, more molecules possess enough energy to escape into the gas phase.

With further heating tiny bubbles form in the liquid and rise to the surface of the liquid (Fig. 9-5). The atmospheric pressure on the surface of the liquid is transmitted undiminished and equally in all directions throughout the liquid. Thus, the pressure in all parts of the liquid equals atmospheric pressure. When the temperature of the liquid is high enough so that the pressure inside the bubble (vapour pressure) equals the atmospheric pressure, the bubble is able to rise to the surface. That is, the pressure inside the bubble is large enough to prevent the outside pressure from collapsing the bubble. When the vapour bubbles reach the surface of the liquid they break and allow the vapour to escape into the air. This process is called **boiling** and the temperature at which it occurs is called the **boiling point** of the liquid.

The temperature of a boiling liquid will remain constant as long as the pressure on the surface of the liquid stays the same. The temperature at which a liquid boils therefore depends upon the pressure on the surface of the liquid. Water has a boiling point of 100°C when the pressure on its surface is standard atmospheric pressure (101.3 kPa), which is the approximate average atmospheric pressure at sea level. Atmospheric pressure decreases as the height above sea level increases. Water boils at a lower temperature on a mountain top than at sea level because the pressure on its surface is less.

p_1 = pressure on liquid surface

p_2 = pressure within vapour bubble = vapour pressure of liquid

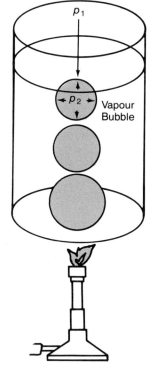

Fig. 9-5 A Boiling Liquid

9-6 A Liquid in a Closed Container

Are there differences between a liquid in an open container and a liquid in a closed container? One obvious difference is that the liquid in the closed container may not completely evaporate because the vapour is confined to the container.

Evaporation will begin to occur as it did in the open container, but in the closed container, the vapour will have to remain above the liquid surface. As more liquid evaporates to become a gas, more of the vapour is confined above the surface of the liquid. As the number of molecules in the vapour state increases, it becomes more likely that some of them will collide with molecules on the surface of the liquid and enter the liquid phase once again.

This change of state from a gas to a liquid is known as condensation. Eventually the rate at which molecules are leaving the liquid phase to enter the gas phase is equal to the rate at which molecules are leaving the gas phase to enter the liquid phase once again (Fig. 9-6). This condition is known as a physical equilibrium, because the physical changes of evaporation and condensation are occurring at *equal rates*. This example is called liquid-vapour equilibrium.

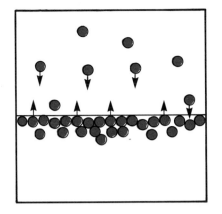

Fig. 9-6 Liquid-Vapour Equilibrium

A liquid-vapour equilibrium is a *dynamic* state since both evaporation and condensation continue to occur. Since they occur at equal rates, there is no further change in the number of molecules in the liquid or gas phase. For such a change to occur the temperature would have to be altered.

If the temperature of the liquid were raised the number of molecules that entered the gas phase would increase. More molecules would leave the liquid at the higher temperature because they would be moving faster and they would possess enough energy to escape from the surface of the liquid.

Another aspect of the liquid-vapour equilibrium is that the molecules in the vapour phase are colliding with the walls of the container and are exerting pressure on those walls. This pressure exerted by a vapour in equilibrium with its liquid is called the **vapour pressure** of the liquid. The vapour pressure depends upon the number of molecules colliding with the walls of the container and on the average force of the collisions. At constant temperature the average force of the collisions is constant. Therefore the vapour pressure is a measure of the tendency for molecules to leave the liquid and enter the vapour phase. If two liquids have different vapour pressures at the same temperature, the molecules of the liquid with the higher vapour pressure have a greater tendency to escape from the liquid phase.

Vapour pressure is a physical property of a particular liquid and is related to the intermolecular forces of attraction in the liquid. At 20°C, for instance, the vapour pressure of ether is about 25 times as great as the vapour pressure of water. Ether molecules have a much greater tendency than water molecules to escape the liquid phase, because the intermolecular forces of attraction are London dispersion forces (weak) in ether and hydrogen bonding (strong) in water.

As the temperature of a liquid increases, its vapour pressure also increases (Fig. 9-7, overleaf). This is because more molecules have enough energy to enter the vapour phase. These molecules move faster because of the higher temperature. Their collisions with the walls of the container are more energetic and more frequent, causing a higher vapour pressure.

The operation of a pressure cooker makes use of some of the concepts we have studied in this chapter. The pressure inside a pressure cooker builds up to a higher pressure than the pressure outside the cooker. This means that as heat is

Fig. 9-7 Effect of Temperature on the Vapour Pressure of Liquids

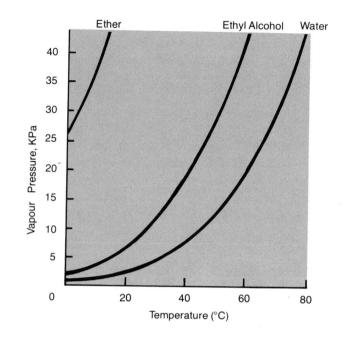

added to the pressure cooker, the vapour pressure and the temperature of the water will be greater than if the water were boiling in an open container. In an open container, the pressure on the surface of the water is atmospheric pressure (101.3 kPa), and the water boils at 100°C. In the pressure cooker, however, the temperature of the water can rise above 100°C, because the water will not boil until its vapour pressure equals the operating pressure of the cooker. Thus it is possible to cook foods faster in a pressure cooker because the temperature of the boiling water is higher than normal.

9-7 Distillation

Liquids may contain impurities such as dissolved solids or other liquids. An apparatus resembling Fig. 9-8 may be used to separate water or other liquids from nonvolatile impurities (substances with very low vapour pressures and little tendency to evaporate). When the distilling flask is heated, the liquid boils. The vapour travels down the inner glass tube of the condenser, which is cooled by cold water flowing along the outside of this tube. The vapour condenses on the cold surface to form a liquid which runs down the tube and is collected. This purified liquid is referred to as the *distillate*. The process is known as *distillation*.

Another type of distillation, called *vacuum distillation*, is used by chemists to purify substances which may be unstable, and decompose at the higher temperatures of a regular distillation. Air is removed from above the liquid in the distilling flask to reduce the pressure. Since the pressure above the liquid is lowered, the compound in question boils at a lower, safer temperature at which it does not decompose.

Fig. 9-8 Apparatus for Distillation

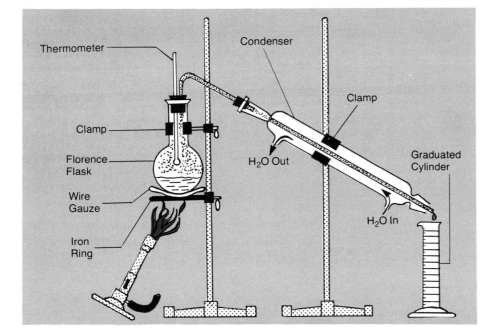

In Part One of this chapter, we have discussed the structure of pure liquids and the forces that hold the molecules together in the liquid state. We have used this information to explain the physical properties of pure liquids. In Part Two, we discuss the nature and properties of homogeneous mixtures made by dissolving substances in liquids.

PART TWO: Solutions

9-8 General Features of a Solution

When a lump of sugar is placed in a cup of tea, the sugar disappears, but it remains chemically unchanged. We know that the sugar is unchanged when it mixes with the water of the tea because we can still taste it. This is an example of a solution. The sugar has dissolved in the hot water of the tea.

A **solution** is a homogeneous (the same throughout) mixure of two or more substances. The particles in a solution are of molecular size. These particles are scattered randomly throughout the solution and are in continuous motion. The composition of a solution can vary within certain limits. You can dissolve one lump, two lumps, or three lumps of sugar in a cup of tea, but you cannot dissolve a box of sugar cubes in one cup of tea. When the sugar dissolves in the tea, the sugar molecules are distributed randomly and evenly throughout the cup of tea. Once the tea has been stirred, the uniform sweetness of the tea tells us that the solution is homogeneous.

In some ways, the tea example is confusing. Tea itself is a solution of many substances dissolved in water. Therefore, let us think of sugar dissolved in pure water. Two words that we should define are solvent and solute. Generally we refer to the substance that is present in larger quantity as the **solvent**. The **solute** is the substance present in smaller quantity which is dissolved in the solvent. In our example, water is the solvent and sugar is the solute. The sugar dissolves in the water. However, we are allowed to interchange the terms whenever it is convenient. In solutions where one substance is a liquid and the other substance is a gas or a solid, the liquid is usually called the solvent.

Solutions are often referred to as dilute or concentrated. A **dilute** solution is one which contains a relatively small amount of solute compared to the amount of solvent. A **concentrated** solution contains a relatively large amount of solute. These terms are used qualitatively. We will learn how to express the concentration of a solute quantitatively in a later chapter.

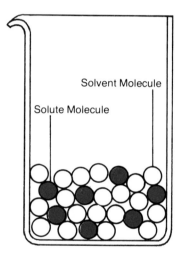

Fig. 9-9 A Liquid Solution (E.g., Sugar in Water)

9-9 Why Solutions Are Important

Solutions are important for many reasons. Many useful products of the chemical industry involve chemical reactions in which the reacting substances are dissolved in various solvents. In fact, many chemical reactions take place at an acceptable rate only when the reacting substances are in solutions. Medicines such as cough syrups and antacids are frequently taken in solution.

Chemists work mainly with liquid solutions, rather than with gaseous or solid solutions. In particular, the liquid solvent most often used is water. Water is an excellent solvent. Solutions made by dissolving solutes in water are called **aqueous solutions**.

Water is one of our most abundant chemicals. Two-thirds of our body mass is water, and our life processes depend on reactions in water. Important chemicals such as hormones and nutrients are transported throughout the human body dissolved in the bloodstream, which is composed mainly of water.

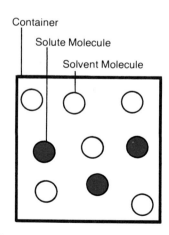

Fig. 9-10 A Gaseous Solution (E.g., Air—Oxygen in Nitrogen)

9-10 Types of Solution

Liquid solutions are made by dissolving solids, liquids, or gases in liquids. Sugar in water is an example of a solution of a solid dissolved in a liquid (Fig. 9-9). Salt water is another example of a common type of solution. Much of our discussion of solutions will deal with aqueous solutions. Other aqueous solutions include alcohol dissolved in water (liquid in a liquid) and oxygen dissolved in water (gas in a liquid).

A solution of alcohol in water is an example of a liquid dissolved in another liquid. Alcohol and water mix in any proportion. They are said to be miscible (easily mixed) in all proportions. However, some combinations of liquids do not mix to any great extent. Gasoline floats on top of water, but it will not dissolve very well in the water. Gasoline and water are practically immiscible.

Gaseous solutions are made by dissolving a gas in another gas (Fig. 9-10). All gases mix in all proportions to produce homogeneous solutions. Air itself is a solution of oxygen and many other gases dissolved in nitrogen. There are, however, few common examples of gaseous solutions involving liquids and solids as solutes.

A solid solution is formed when one solid substance is mixed with another solid substance to produce a homogeneous mixture (Fig. 9-11). Many alloys are solid solutions. For example, brass is a solid solution in which zinc atoms have been mixed homogeneously into the solid crystal of copper atoms.

Table 9-2 contains other examples of the various types of solutions with their uses. Since there are three states of matter there are nine possible solute-solvent combinations.

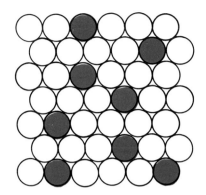

Fig. 9-11 A Solid Solution (E.g., Brass—Zinc in Copper)

TABLE 9-2 Examples of Solutions

SOLVENT	SOLUTE	EXAMPLE	USE
liquid	liquid	ethylene glycol in water	antifreeze
liquid	solid	ammonium nitrate in water	ice pack
liquid	gas	carbon dioxide in water	carbonated beverages
gas	gas	oxygen in helium	deep sea diving
gas	liquid	gasoline in air	automobile engines
gas	solid	p-dichlorobenzene in air	mothballs
solid	solid	copper in gold	jewelry
solid	liquid	mercury in dental alloy	dental amalgams
solid	gas	hydrogen in palladium	gas stove lighter

9-11 The Solution Process

Consider the dissolving of sugar crystals in water. Once the sugar crystals are placed in the water, sugar molecules from the surface of the crystals are attracted by water molecules, become dislodged, and move into spaces between other water molecules. This process is called *dissolving*.

The circled areas of the sugar molecule (Fig. 9-12) show polar oxygen-hydrogen bonds and represent areas of the molecule which attract polar water

Fig. 9-12 Structure of Sucrose (Sugar) Molecule

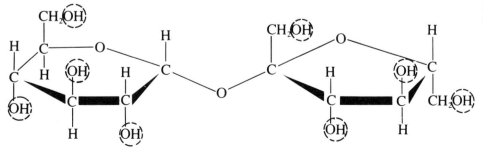

molecules. For instance, the slightly positive hydrogen atoms in the circled areas could attract the slightly negative oxygen atom in water, or the slightly negative oxygen atoms in the circled areas could attract the slightly positive hydrogen atoms in water. As the sugar molecules leave the surface of the sugar crystals, the crystals become smaller and the amount of sugar dissolved in the water becomes larger.

However, an opposing process soon begins. The positive ends of polar oxygen-hydrogen bonds in sugar molecules (the hydrogen atoms) are attracted to the negative ends of oxygen-hydrogen bonds in other sugar molecules (the oxygen atoms). Thus when sugar molecules in the solution collide with undissolved sugar crystals, they are attracted to and stick to the surface of the crystals. This process is called *crystallization* (Fig. 9-13). The dissolved sugar molecules are crystallizing.

Fig. 9-13 In the crystallization of sugar, dissolved sugar molecules (shown as ovals) are attracted to the undissolved sugar crystal.

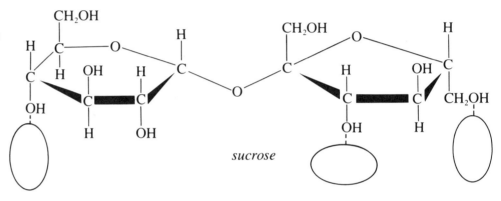

sucrose

As more and more sugar molecules dissolve, more sugar molecules crystallize. Finally a state of balance or equilibrium occurs:

$$\text{solute} + \text{solvent} \xrightleftharpoons[\text{crystallizing}]{\text{dissolving}} \text{solution}$$

The rate at which sugar molecules dissolve equals the rate at which sugar molecules crystallize. Solution equilibrium has been reached. This is called a state of **dynamic equilibrium** because two opposing processes (dissolving and crystallizing) occur at equal rates. At this point the solution is said to be *saturated* with sugar (Fig. 9-14).

A simple model can help us to understand a dynamic equilibrium. Suppose two rooms are connected by an open door. Ten students are in each room. Each student is allowed to go from one room to the other as long as a student in the other room will trade places. At all times there are ten students in each room but they are not always the same students. Some students are going from one room to the other, and other students are going in the opposite direction. In the same way, in a saturated solution, some sugar molecules are dissolving while other sugar molecules are crystallizing. However, there is always the same amount of sugar in the solution.

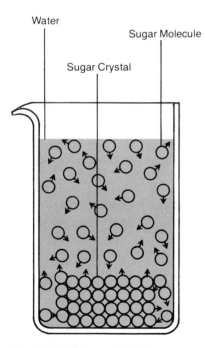

Water

Sugar Molecule

Sugar Crystal

Fig. 9-14 A Saturated Solution

A **saturated solution** contains the maximum amount of solute that can remain dissolved in a given amount of solvent at a particular temperature. In a saturated solution, the rate at which the solute molecules dissolve equals the rate at which the solute molecules crystallize. A solution equilibrium is reached. Usually, a solution is saturated if undissolved solute remains visible no matter how hard the solution is stirred, or how long the solution sits.

Sometimes a saturated solution may be heated to dissolve extra solid and then carefully cooled to the original temperature without reappearance of the extra solid. This solution is not stable because a small crystal or agitation of the solution may cause crystallization to occur. A solution which contains more dissolved solute than it would if it were saturated is said to be a **supersaturated solution**

If the solution is *unsaturated*, all of the solute molecules will be dissolved. There will be no solution equilibrium because there will be no opposing processes of dissolving and crystallizing. An **unsaturated solution** contains less than the maximum amount of solute that can dissolve in a given amount of solvent at a particular temperature.

During the solution process there are really three processes occurring simultaneously. The solute particles must separate from each other. This process is *endothermic* (heat is absorbed). The solvent molecules must separate from each other, and this is also endothermic. Solute particles attract solvent molecules. Energy is released, and this process is therefore *exothermic* (Fig. 9-15). An overall solution process could be exothermic, with heat released, and an accompanying rise in temperature of the solution. However, a solution process could also be endothermic with heat absorbed, and an accompanying decrease in the temperature of the solution. Whether the solution process is exothermic or endothermic depends upon the magnitude of the three heat terms involved. In general, when a solid dissolves in a liquid the overall process is endothermic:

$$\text{solute} + \text{solvent} + \text{energy} \rightarrow \text{solution}$$

A practical use is made of the fact that the dissolving of most solids in a liquid is endothermic. Ammonium nitrate, NH_4NO_3, absorbs heat when it dissolves in water. It is used to make ice packs. The solid ammonium nitrate is placed in a thin-walled plastic bag. This bag is sealed inside a thicker plastic

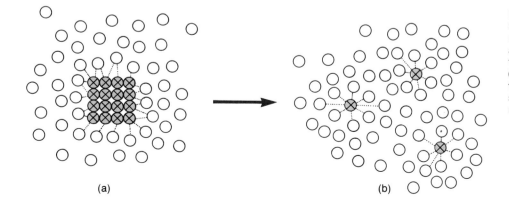

(a)   (b)

Fig. 9-15 The Formation of a Solution
(a) Solvent molecules, $\bigcirc$, attract solute particles, $\otimes$, on the surface.
(b)Solute particles removed from the surface become surrounded by solvent molecules.

and a pressure of 101.3 kPa:

$$2H_2(g) + O_2(g) \rightarrow 2H_2O(\ell) + 572 \text{ kJ (heat)}$$

This reaction consists of hydrogen molecules and oxygen molecules reacting to produce water molecules plus energy. A chemical change has taken place, and a new substance, water, has been formed. This new substance has properties which differ from those of either hydrogen or oxygen. Hydrogen and oxygen are referred to as the **reactants** or starting materials, and water is the **product** or substance formed as a result of the reaction.

Conservation of Mass and Charge

No atoms are lost, destroyed, or created during this reaction. There are the same number of oxygen and hydrogen atoms after the reaction as before. Chemical reactions obey the Law of Conservation of Mass, as we learned in Chapter 3. The total mass of the reactants equals the total mass of the products.

The total number of electrons and protons in all the atoms after this chemical reaction is the same as before the reaction. Thus, the number of positive and negative charges remains constant. That is, charge is conserved.

Conservation of Energy

Energy is also conserved during a chemical reaction. The total amount of energy (kinetic plus potential) after the chemical reaction equals the total amount of energy before the reaction if energy is not allowed to enter or to leave the system. From the equation, we see that this reaction is **exothermic**, since heat energy (572 kJ) is released. The energy term appears on the product side of the equation. If heat energy is absorbed, a reaction is **endothermic**. The amount of heat released in this reaction (572 kJ) is the amount of heat given off when two moles of liquid water are formed, under certain conditions of temperature (25°C) and pressure (101.3 kPa), from two moles of hydrogen gas reacting with one mole of oxygen gas. An extremely small amount of energy would be released when only two molecules of water are formed. The masses of chemicals influence the amount of heat lost or gained. If one mole of water had been formed, then only 286 kJ of heat energy would have been given off. The state of matter of the product is also important and should be mentioned in the chemical equation. For instance, if two moles of gaseous water had been formed then 484 kJ of heat energy would have been released. The difference between 572 kJ and 484 kJ is the amount of energy required to change two moles of liquid water at 25°C to two moles of gaseous water at 25°C.

A Closer Look at a Chemical Reaction

If there is no change in the total amount of mass, charge or energy during a chemical reaction, then what exactly *does* happen? To answer this, let us take a closer look at the chemical reaction under discussion:

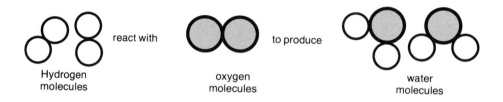

Hydrogen molecules react with oxygen molecules to produce water molecules

The reactant molecules are undergoing translational, vibrational, and rotational motion. These types of motion were discussed in Chapter 3. Kinetic energy is associated with these motions. These molecules also possess potential energy stored in the chemical bonds. This energy is a result of the attractive forces between the bonded atoms. The potential energy stored in chemical bonds is referred to as **chemical energy**.

When hydrogen is mixed with oxygen, nothing happens. If a spark, a flame, or another source of energy is added to the mixture, however, the reaction may be explosive. Chemical reactions often need an initial "energy kick" to get them going. In an endothermic reaction, energy must be supplied continuously to keep the reaction going. This energy may be heat absorbed from the surroundings. However, for the endothermic reaction

$$CaCO_3(s) + heat \rightarrow CaO(s) + CO_2(g)$$

heat energy must be provided continuously from a source such as a Bunsen burner.

In an exothermic reaction, no further energy is required after the initial energy kick. As water molecules are formed, energy is released, supplying the energy needed to keep the reaction going. Why is energy needed to start the reaction and to keep it going? Energy is required to break chemical bonds—the hydrogen-hydrogen bonds and the oxygen-oxygen bonds. We are now able to see what causes the energy effects in chemical reactions. Energy effects in chemical reactions are a result of the rearrangement of atoms during a reaction—the breaking of chemical bonds and the formation of chemical bonds. Energy is required to break bonds, and energy is released when bonds are formed. Whether a reaction will be exothermic or endothermic depends upon the relative energies of the bond-breaking and bond-making events.

Since energy is given off during the formation of water from hydrogen and oxygen, the potential energy of the product (water) must be less than that of the reactants (hydrogen and oxygen). Because energy is conserved in chemical reactions, and because the potential energy of the products is less than that of the reactants, the kinetic energy of the products must be greater than that of the reactants. The temperature will increase during the reaction, since temperature is a measure of the kinetic energy of the molecules.

The energy released in chemical reactions may be in the form of heat energy, as in the formation of water. Heat energy is also released when coal or oil is burned. The energy released may also be electrical, as in a battery, or in the form of light, as in fireflies. Sometimes more than one form of energy is released during a reaction.

What information regarding a chemical reaction is not conveyed by a balanced chemical equation? A chemical equation does not tell us the steps by which reactants are converted into products. A chemical reaction requires a collision between reactant particles. These particles must have sufficient energy and the proper orientation at the time of collision in order to break the chemical bonds of the reactants and form the chemical bonds of the products. Because it is unlikely that more than two reactant particles will simultaneously collide, chemical reactions normally involve a series of simple reaction steps. Each of these simple reaction steps includes not more than two reactant particles. A balanced chemical equation does not tell us at what rate a chemical reaction occurs. The rate of a chemical reaction is a measure of the amount of products formed in a given amount of time. Some chemical reactions proceed slowly, taking days or weeks. An example is the production of alcohol by fermentation. Other chemical reactions, such as acid-base neutralizations, take place extremely quickly.

Factors Affecting the Rate of a Chemical Reaction

Increasing the temperature of the reactants is one way of increasing the rate of a chemical reaction. Thus, we use high temperatures to reduce the time it takes to cook food. In storing food, we wish to slow down the chemical reactions leading to food spoilage. This is accomplished by storing the food at low temperatures.

Another method of increasing the rate of a chemical reaction is to use a catalyst. A **catalyst** is a chemical which speeds up a reaction and can be recovered unchanged when the reaction is complete. When oxygen is prepared by heating potassium chlorate, manganese dioxide is added to speed up the reaction. A catalyst lowers the initial amount of energy required to start a chemical reaction. Catalysts are essential in many industrial processes. Examples are petroleum refining and the production of sulfuric acid, ammonia, and plastics. Biological catalysts (enzymes) are essential for maintaining the life processes in our bodies.

The rate of a chemical reaction may also be increased by increasing the concentration of the reactants and the surface area of reactants. The effect of surface area is sometimes shown quite dramatically in saw mills and flour mills. The large amount of surface area provided by the finely divided particles in a mill can increase the rate of a combustion reaction to the extent that an explosion may occur.

Reversible Chemical Reactions

Not all chemical reactions proceed with the reactants being completely converted into products. Some chemical reactions are reversible. That is, the products can react to produce the original reactants. Eventually the rate at which reactants produce products becomes equal to the rate at which products produce the original reactants. When this occurs, a state of chemical equilibrium exists, and the chemical equation is written with arrows in both directions. For example, the Haber process for the industrial production of ammonia involves the reversible reaction

$$N_2(g) + 3H_2(g) \rightleftharpoons 2NH_3(g)$$

Fig. 10-1 Seltzer Tablet giving off Gas in Water

At equilibrium, the rate at which N_2 and H_2 react to produce NH_3 is equal to the rate at which NH_3 reacts to produce N_2 and H_2.

10-2 Recognizing a Chemical Reaction

What type of evidence indicates that a chemical reaction is occurring? One or more of the following is usually observed:

1. *Change in temperature (heat effect)*

A chemical reaction may be accompanied by a decrease in temperature (absorption of heat) or by an increase in temperature (release of heat):

$$HCl(aq) + NaOH(aq) \rightarrow NaCl(aq) + H_2O(\ell) + heat$$

2. *Evolution of a gas*

Some chemical reactions produce a gas as a product. If the reaction occurs in a liquid solution, tiny bubbles of the gas can be seen escaping from the liquid:

$$CaCO_3(s) + 2HCl(aq) \rightarrow CaCl_2(aq) + H_2O(\ell) + CO_2(g)$$

3. *Formation of a precipitate*

When some liquid solutions are mixed together, one of the products may be practically insoluble. This solid product will fall to the bottom of the solution and is referred to as a *precipitate:*

$$AgNO_3(aq) + NaCl(aq) \rightarrow NaNO_3(aq) + AgCl(s)$$

4. *Change in colour*

If the solvent is colourless, the intensity of the colour of a solution depends upon the concentration of the solute. If this solute takes part in a chemical reaction, there will be a change in the intensity of the colour of this solution as the reaction proceeds. In other reactions a new colour may appear if one of the products is coloured:

$$Cu(NO_3)_2(aq) + Zn(s) \rightarrow Zn(NO_3)_2(aq) + Cu(s)$$
$$\text{blue} \qquad\qquad \text{colourless}$$
$$[\text{due to } Cu^{2+}(aq)]$$

5. *Formation of an odour*

One of the products of a chemical reaction may have an odour which is noticeably different from that of the reactants:

$$FeS(s) + 2HCl(aq) \rightarrow FeCl_2(aq) + H_2S(g)$$
$$\text{odour of}$$
$$\text{rotten eggs}$$

10-3 Types of Reactions

It is not easy to classify all chemical reactions precisely. Nevertheless, most reactions can be classified under one of the following four major categories:

Addition reactions, or direct combinations, are reactions in which atoms and molecules join together directly to produce larger molecules. Equations for addition reactions are usually of the type

$$A + B \rightarrow AB$$

Some examples of addition reactions are
a) formation of sulfur dioxide by combustion of sulfur:

$$S + O_2 \rightarrow SO_2$$

b) reaction of zinc and sulfur to form zinc sulfide:

$$Zn + S \rightarrow ZnS$$

c) formation of calcium hydroxide when calcium oxide reacts with water:

$$CaO + H_2O \rightarrow Ca(OH)_2$$

Decomposition reactions are just the opposite of addition reactions. Equations for decomposition reactions are usually of the type

$$AB \rightarrow A + B$$

Some examples are
a) decomposition of carbonic acid:

$$H_2CO_3 \rightarrow H_2O + CO_2$$

b) formation of oxygen by heating mercury(II) oxide:

$$2\,HgO \xrightarrow{\triangle} 2\,Hg + O_2$$

c) preparation of oxygen by heating potassium chlorate:

$$2KClO_3 \xrightarrow{\triangle} 2KCl + 3\,O_2$$

Displacement or **substitution** reactions involve a change of partners. In these reactions one atom or group of atoms in a molecule is replaced by another atom or group of atoms, according to the general equation

$$A + BC \rightarrow AC + B$$

Some examples are
a) zinc metal and copper sulfate react to form copper metal and zinc sulfate:

$$Zn + CuSO_4 \rightarrow ZnSO_4 + Cu$$

b) magnesium reacts with hydrogen chloride to liberate hydrogen:

$$Mg + 2\,HCl \rightarrow MgCl_2 + H_2$$

c) chlorine displaces bromine from calcium bromide:

$$Cl_2 + CaBr_2 \rightarrow Br_2 + CaCl_2$$

Double displacement or **metathetic** reactions involve a joint exchange of partners, according to the general equation

$$AB + CD \rightarrow BC + AD$$

Some examples are

a) neutralization of sodium hydroxide with hydrochloric acid:

$$NaOH + HCl \rightarrow NaCl + H_2O$$

b) formation of hydrogen sulfide by the action of hydrochloric acid on iron(II) sulfide:

$$FeS + 2HCl \rightarrow H_2S + FeCl_2$$

c) precipitation of barium sulfate when solutions of barium chloride and ammonium sulfate are mixed:

$$BaCl_2 + (NH_4)_2SO_4 \rightarrow BaSO_4 + 2NH_4Cl$$

10-4 Balancing Chemical Equations

In Section 8-6 you learned the basic principle involved in writing a chemical equation: the Law of Conservation of Mass must be obeyed. That is, there must be as many atoms of each type on the left-hand side as on the right-hand side when the equation is balanced.

Before an equation can be balanced, the formulas of all the reactants and products must first be known. Only then can a start be made at placing the proper coefficients in front of each formula in order to balance the numbers of atoms on each side of the equation. Usually the procedure that works best is
a) balance all atoms other than oxygen and hydrogen.
b) balance oxygen.
c) balance hydrogen.

Let us put the principles into operation by balancing the following equations:
a) $SF_4 + H_2O \rightarrow SO_2 + HF$
b) $Al + H_2SO_4 \rightarrow Al_2(SO_4)_3 + H_2$
c) $Ca(OH)_2 + H_3PO_4 \rightarrow Ca_3(PO_4)_2 + H_2O$

Equation (a) $\qquad SF_4 + H_2O \rightarrow SO_2 + HF$

Step 1. Balance atoms other than oxygen and hydrogen. Since sulfur is balanced at the moment, we shall start by balancing fluorine. With four fluorine atoms on the left, there must be four fluorine atoms, or 4HF, on the right. Note that, in balancing the number of fluorine atoms, the coefficient goes in front of the formula (e.g., 4HF), as will always be the practice. This indicates four molecules of hydrogen fluoride, each containing one fluorine atom. If the coefficient were placed in error after the fluorine as a subscript in the formula, we would have HF_4. This does not represent hydrogen fluoride; rather, it represents a nonexistent compound! Thus, by putting the coefficients in front of the formula, we make sure that no new reactants or products are falsely indicated as a result of balancing the chemical equation.

$$\underline{1} \, SF_4 + H_2O \rightarrow SO_2 + \underline{4} \, HF$$

We shall temporarily underline the coefficients to remind ourselves that they are temporarily fixed and should not be changed unless absolutely necessary.

The "1" in front of the SF_4 is not absolutely necessary, but it is a convenience during the balancing process.

Step 2. Balance sulfur. Now that we have fixed one sulfur atom on the left, we need one sulfur atom, or 1 SO_2, on the right:

$$\underline{1}\ SF_4 + H_2O \rightarrow \underline{1}\ SO_2 + \underline{4}\ HF$$

Step 3. Balance oxygen. With two oxygen atoms fixed on the right, we therefore need two oxygen atoms, or 2 H_2O, on the left:

$$\underline{1}\ SF_4 + \underline{2}\ H_2O \rightarrow \underline{1}\ SO_2 + \underline{4}\ HF$$

Step 4. Balance hydrogen. Since all coefficients are fixed, hydrogen should be balanced. A check shows four hydrogen atoms (2 H_2O) on the left and four hydrogen atoms (4 HF) on the right. The balanced equation is therefore

$$SF_4 + 2\ H_2O \rightarrow SO_2 + 4\ HF$$

Notice that coefficients of 1 are omitted from the balanced equation. If there is no coefficient in front of a formula, the coefficient is assumed to be 1.

Equation (b) $\qquad Al + H_2SO_4 \rightarrow Al_2(SO_4)_3 + H_2$

Step 1. Balance atoms other than oxygen and hydrogen. Since aluminum appears first in the equation, start with aluminum:

$$\underline{2}\ Al + H_2SO_4 \rightarrow \underline{1}\ Al_2(SO_4)_3 + H_2$$

Step 2. Balance sulfur:

$$\underline{2}\ Al + \underline{3}\ H_2SO_4 \rightarrow \underline{1}\ Al_2(SO_4)_3 + H_2$$

Step 3. Balance oxygen. Oxygen is already balanced with 12 atoms on each side of the equation.

Step 4. Balance hydrogen:

$$\underline{2}\ Al + \underline{3}\ H_2SO_4 \rightarrow \underline{1}\ Al_2(SO_4)_3 + \underline{3}\ H_2$$

All atoms are now balanced. The final equation is

$$2\ Al + 3\ H_2SO_4 \rightarrow Al_2(SO_4)_3 + 3\ H_2$$

Equation (c) $\qquad Ca(OH)_2 + H_3PO_4 \rightarrow Ca_3(PO_4)_2 + H_2O$

Step 1. Balance atoms other than oxygen and hydrogen. Start with calcium:

$$\underline{3}\ Ca(OH)_2 + H_3PO_4 \rightarrow \underline{1}\ Ca_3(PO_4)_2 + H_2O$$

Step 2. Balance phosphorus:

$$\underline{3}\ Ca(OH)_2 + \underline{2}\ H_3PO_4 \rightarrow \underline{1}\ Ca_3(PO_4)_2 + H_2O$$

Step 3. Balance oxygen. There are $6 + 8 = 14$ oxygen atoms on the left and only eight [in the $Ca_3(PO_4)_2$] have been fixed on the right as a result of balancing calcium and phosphorus. The six remaining oxygen atoms must be present as 6 H_2O:

$$\underline{3}\ Ca(OH)_2 + \underline{2}\ H_3PO_4 \rightarrow \underline{1}\ Ca_3(PO_4)_2 + \underline{6}\ H_2O$$

Step 4. Balance hydrogen. Hydrogen atoms are already balanced with six atoms on each side. The balanced equation is therefore

$$3 \text{ Ca(OH)}_2 + 2 \text{ H}_3\text{PO}_4 \rightarrow \text{Ca}_3(\text{PO}_4)_2 + 6 \text{ H}_2\text{O}$$

Sample Problem 10-1

Write balanced equations to represent
a) the combustion of acetylene gas, C_2H_2, to form carbon dioxide and water.
b) the removal of carbon dioxide from the air in a spacecraft by its reaction with lithium hydroxide according to the unbalanced equation

$$\text{CO}_2 + \text{LiOH} \rightarrow \text{Li}_2\text{CO}_3 + \text{H}_2\text{O}$$

c) the preparation of carbon dioxide gas by the action of sulfuric acid on sodium hydrogen carbonate according to the unbalanced equation

$$\text{NaHCO}_3 + \text{H}_2\text{SO}_4 \rightarrow \text{CO}_2 + \text{Na}_2\text{SO}_4 + \text{H}_2\text{O}$$

SOLUTIONS
a) The unbalanced equation is

$$\text{C}_2\text{H}_2 + \text{O}_2 \rightarrow \text{CO}_2 + \text{H}_2\text{O}$$

Balance C: $\underline{1} \text{ C}_2\text{H}_2 + \text{O}_2 \rightarrow \underline{2} \text{ CO}_2 + \text{H}_2\text{O}$

Balance O: We can not balance oxygen at this point because we have not yet fixed the number of oxygen atoms on either side. In balancing carbon atoms, however, we have fixed the number of hydrogen atoms on the left.

Balance H: $\underline{1} \text{ C}_2\text{H}_2 + \text{O}_2 \rightarrow \underline{2} \text{ CO}_2 + \underline{1} \text{ H}_2\text{O}$

Now balance O: $\underline{1} \text{ C}_2\text{H}_2 + \frac{5}{2} \text{ O}_2 \rightarrow \underline{2} \text{ CO}_2 + \underline{1} \text{ H}_2\text{O}$

Multiply both sides by 2 to get rid of fractions.

$$\underline{2} \text{ C}_2\text{H}_2 + \underline{5} \text{ O}_2 \rightarrow \underline{4} \text{ CO}_2 + \underline{2} \text{ H}_2\text{O}$$

The balanced equation is

$$2 \text{ C}_2\text{H}_2 + 5 \text{ O}_2 \rightarrow 4 \text{ CO}_2 + 2 \text{ H}_2\text{O}$$

This problem illustrates the fact that it is possible to have fractional coefficients during the balancing process. Both sides of the equation must be multiplied by an appropriate factor to get the final balanced equation with whole number coefficients.

b)
$$\text{CO}_2 + \text{LiOH} \rightarrow \text{Li}_2\text{CO}_3 + \text{H}_2\text{O}$$

Balance C: Already balanced.

Balance Li: $\underline{1} \text{ CO}_2 + \underline{2} \text{ LiOH} \rightarrow \underline{1} \text{ Li}_2\text{CO}_3 + \text{H}_2\text{O}$

Balance O: $\underline{1} \text{ CO}_2 + \underline{2} \text{ LiOH} \rightarrow \underline{1} \text{ Li}_2\text{CO}_3 + \underline{1} \text{ H}_2\text{O}$

Balance H: H is now balanced with two atoms on each side.

The balanced equation is

$$\text{CO}_2 + 2 \text{ LiOH} \rightarrow \text{Li}_2\text{CO}_3 + \text{H}_2\text{O}$$

c) $$NaHCO_3 + H_2SO_4 \rightarrow CO_2 + Na_2SO_4 + H_2O$$

Balance Na: $\underline{2}\ NaHCO_3 + H_2SO_4 \rightarrow CO_2 + \underline{1}\ Na_2SO_4 + H_2O$

Balance C: $\underline{2}\ NaHCO_3 + H_2SO_4 \rightarrow \underline{2}\ CO_2 + \underline{1}\ Na_2SO_4 + H_2O$

Balance S: $\underline{2}\ NaHCO_3 + \underline{1}\ H_2SO_4 \rightarrow \underline{2}\ CO_2 + \underline{1}\ Na_2SO_4 + H_2O$

Balance O: $\underline{2}\ NaHCO_3 + \underline{1}\ H_2SO_4 \rightarrow \underline{2}\ CO_2 + \underline{1}\ Na_2SO_4 + \underline{2}\ H_2O$

Balance H: Balanced.

The balanced equation is

$$2\ NaHCO_3 + H_2SO_4 \rightarrow 2\ CO_2 + Na_2SO_4 + 2\ H_2O$$

Practice Problem 10-1

Write balanced equations to represent
a) the combustion of methane, CH_4, to form carbon dioxide and water vapour.
b) the combustion of the rocket fuel, B_5H_9, which burns to form B_2O_3 and water vapour.
c) the formation of ammonium sulfate particles in the upper atmosphere according to the unbalanced equation

$$NH_3 + SO_3 + H_2O \rightarrow (NH_4)_2SO_4$$

10-5 Reactions Involving Electron Transfer

Chemical reactions can be classified into two major types according to another criterion:

1) Reactions which do not involve transfer of electrons from one atom to another.

2) Reactions which do involve transfer of electrons from one atom to another.

Double displacement reactions do not generally involve electron transfers. Addition, decomposition, and displacement reactions, however, frequently do involve transfer of electrons between atoms.

The following reactions, for example, all involve electron transfers:

$$2\ Mg + O_2 \rightarrow 2\ MgO \text{ (addition)}$$
$$2\ HgO \rightarrow 2\ Hg + O_2 \text{ (decomposition)}$$
$$2\ Na + 2\ H_2O \rightarrow 2\ NaOH + H_2 \text{ (displacement)}$$
$$Cl_2 + 2\ NaBr \rightarrow Br_2 + 2\ NaCl \text{ (displacement)}$$

How do we know that electrons are being transferred between atoms? We calculate the oxidation numbers of the atoms involved (Section 8-1). When an atom loses electrons during a reaction, its oxidation number becomes more positive. When an atom gains electrons, its oxidation number becomes less positive (more negative).

Sample Problem 10-2

In which of the following reactions is electron transfer involved?
a) $H_2 + Br_2 \rightarrow 2\,HBr$
b) $2\,Na_3PO_4 + 3\,BaCl_2 \rightarrow Ba_3(PO_4)_2 + 6\,NaCl$
c) $Zn + 2\,HCl \rightarrow ZnCl_2 + H_2$
d) $C + 2\,H_2 \rightarrow CH_4$

SOLUTION
a) The oxidation numbers are indicated above each atom in the equation

$$\overset{0}{H_2} + \overset{0}{Br_2} \rightarrow 2\,\overset{+1\,-1}{HBr}$$

Both H and Br change oxidation state, so electron transfer must be involved.

b) The oxidation numbers are indicated above each atom or ion:

$$2\,\overset{+1\;\;-3}{Na_3PO_4} + 3\,\overset{+2\,-1}{BaCl_2} \rightarrow \overset{+2\;\;-3}{Ba_3(PO_4)_2} + 6\,\overset{+1\,-1}{NaCl}$$

No atoms change oxidation state, so electron transfer is not involved. This is a double displacement reaction.

c)
$$\overset{0}{Zn} + 2\,\overset{+1\,-1}{HCl} \rightarrow \overset{+2\,-1}{ZnCl_2} + \overset{0}{H_2}$$

Both Zn and H change oxidation state, so electron transfer is involved.

d)
$$\overset{0}{C} + 2\,\overset{0}{H_2} \rightarrow \overset{-4\,+1}{CH_4}$$

Both C and H change oxidation state, so electron transfer is involved.

Practice Problem 10-2

In which of the following reactions is electron transfer involved?
a) $P_4 + 5\,O_2 \rightarrow P_4O_{10}$
b) $Ba + 2\,H_2O \rightarrow Ba(OH)_2 + H_2$
c) $(NH_4)_2SO_4 + Pb(NO_3)_2 \rightarrow 2\,NH_4NO_3 + PbSO_4$

The loss of electrons from an atom, with a consequent increase in oxidation number, is called **oxidation**. The substance which loses the electrons is said to be **oxidized**, and the substance which removes them is called the **oxidizing agent**.

The gain of electrons by an atom, with a consequent decrease in oxidation number, is called **reduction**. The substance which gains the electrons is said to be **reduced**, and the substance which supplies them is called the **reducing agent**.

Oxidation and reduction always occur together. If one atom is oxidized during a chemical reaction, some other atom must be reduced. If an atom loses electrons, they must be accepted by another atom. Hence reactions which involve electron transfer are usually called **oxidation-reduction** reactions or simply **redox** reactions.

The definitions of oxidation and reduction are frequently remembered by the sentence, "LEO the lion says GER." The capitalized letters stand for "Loss of Electrons is Oxidation; Gain of Electrons is Reduction." Their relationship to oxidation numbers may be remembered by a simple diagram:

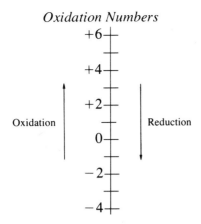

Oxidation Numbers

If the oxidation number of an atom goes up on the scale, the atom is oxidized. If the oxidation number goes down the scale, the atom is reduced.

In the reaction between magnesium and oxygen, the oxidation number of magnesium increases from 0 to +2. Magnesium, with only two valence electrons, tends to donate them to some other atom in order to achieve a stable octet. In losing these electrons, the magnesium atoms are oxidized. Each oxygen atom, having six valence electrons, will accept the two electrons to achieve an octet, and is reduced in the process. The oxidation number of oxygen is decreased from 0 to −2. These statements can be summarized as

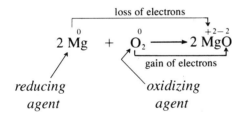

When mercury(II) oxide is decomposed to oxygen and mercury, the oxide ions transfer electrons to the mercury(II) ions:

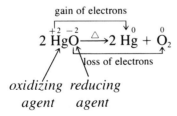

When sodium reacts with water to form hydrogen and sodium hydroxide, sodium atoms transfer electrons to hydrogen atoms:

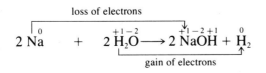

Finally, the reaction between chlorine and sodium bromide can be summarized as

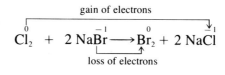

A closer look at these equations shows that the total number of electrons lost equals the total number of electrons gained. We also conclude that the reducing agent is oxidized and the oxidizing agent is reduced.

Sample Problem 10-3

In each of the following redox reactions, indicate the oxidizing agent, the reducing agent, the substance oxidized, the substance reduced, and diagram the gain and loss of electrons in each reaction.

a) $4 NH_3 + 7 O_2 \rightarrow 4 NO_2 + 6 H_2O$
b) $5 CO + I_2O_5 \rightarrow 5 CO_2 + I_2$

SOLUTION

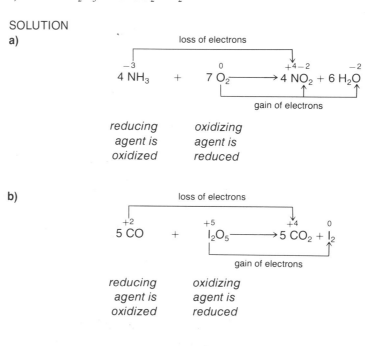

Practice Problem 10-3

In each of the following redox reactions, indicate the oxidizing agent, the reducing agent, the substance oxidized, the substance reduced, and diagram the gain and loss of electrons in each reaction.

a) $Ni + HgCl_2 \rightarrow Hg + NiCl_2$
b) $Mg + 2 HCl \rightarrow MgCl_2 + H_2$

10-6 Electricity From Oxidation-Reduction Reactions

What happens when a piece of zinc metal is immersed in a solution of copper(II) sulfate? The copper(II) sulfate solution consists of hydrated sulfate ions and blue hydrated copper(II) ions:

$$CuSO_4(s) \rightarrow Cu^{2+}(aq) + SO_4^{2-}(aq)$$

Very quickly the zinc metal becomes coated with metallic copper. The zinc strip gradually dissolves, flakes of metallic copper accumulate at the bottom of the container, and the blue colour of the solution gradually fades away.

A reaction has occurred between the zinc atoms and the copper ions:

$$Zn(s) + Cu^{2+}(aq) \rightarrow Zn^{2+}(aq) + Cu(s)$$

The sulfate ions are spectator ions and serve simply to balance the positive charge of the metal ions. Each zinc atom has lost two electrons to form a zinc ion, and each copper ion has gained two electrons to form a copper atom:

$$\text{Oxidation: } Zn \rightarrow Zn^{2+} + 2e^-$$
$$\text{Reduction: } Cu^{2+} + 2e^- \rightarrow Cu$$

The copper ions have accepted electrons from the zinc atoms at the surface of the zinc strip immersed in the copper sulfate solution. It is not possible to detect a flow of electrons because the electrons are transferred directly from the zinc atoms to the copper ions.

Practice Problem 10-4

When a copper wire is immersed in a colourless solution of silver nitrate, the solution gradually turns blue and silver crystals begin to grow on the wire. Explain what is happening in terms of oxidation, reduction, and transfer of electrons.

The reaction between zinc and copper(II) sulfate occurs spontaneously. If the zinc atoms and copper ions could be kept separate from each other, the electrons could be forced to flow through an external wire. Since a flow of electrons constitutes an electric current, we would then have an **electrochemical cell:** a device for converting chemical energy into electrical energy.

A simple device which separates the reactants consists of a container divided into two compartments by a porous barrier (Fig. 10-2, over). One compartment contains a zinc strip immersed in a solution of zinc sulfate; the other contains a copper strip immersed in a solution of copper(II) sulfate. These metal strips, which are immersed in the solutions, are called **electrodes**.

At the zinc electrode, zinc atoms tend to go into solution as zinc ions, leaving their electrons behind on the metal. When a wire is connected between the two electrodes, the electrons, which repel each other, can travel through the wire to the copper electrode. At that point copper ions in the other compartment can remove electrons from the surface of the copper electrode and become

Fig. 10-2 An Electrochemical Cell

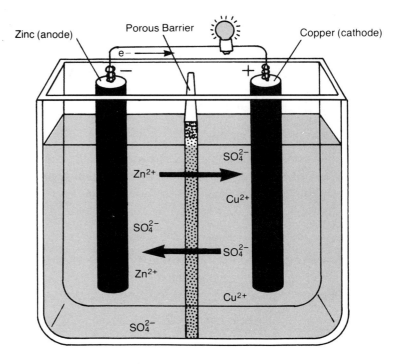

reduced to copper atoms. Again the reaction has occurred between the zinc atoms and the copper ions:

$$Zn(s) + Cu^{2+}(aq) \rightarrow Zn^{2+}(aq) + Cu(s)$$

However, this time it is possible to detect the flow of electrons because the electrons are transferred from the zinc atoms to the copper ions via a wire. This flow of electrons (electric current) through the wire constitutes the **external circuit** and can be used to light a bulb or do other useful work.

We should also realize that as surplus zinc ions are formed in one compartment, sulfate ions will tend to diffuse through the porous barrier into that compartment from the other side. The sulfate ions do this in order to balance out the excess positive charge created as zinc ions are produced. As copper ions are removed by reduction in the other compartment, zinc ions will tend to diffuse *in* from the opposite side of the porous barrier to replace the positive charge that has been removed. This migration of ions in opposite directions through the porous barrier constitutes what is known as the **internal circuit**.

In any electrochemical cell, oxidation takes place at the **anode**. In this cell, the zinc electrode is the anode. Anions (negative ions) migrate toward the anode. In this case, sulfate ions migrate toward the zinc electrode. Reduction takes place at the **cathode**. In this cell, the copper electrode is the cathode. Cations (positive ions) migrate *toward* the cathode. In this case, zinc ions migrate *toward* the copper electrode.

Many useful types of cells have been developed to make use of indirect electron transfer. Among these are lead storage batteries found in cars; dry cells used in flashlights; nickel-cadmium cells used in calculators; and fuel cells used in spacecraft.

Practice Problem 10-5

Draw a diagram of a cell that can be used to obtain electrical energy from the spontaneous reaction

$$Cu(s) + 2\,AgNO_3(aq) \rightarrow Cu(NO_3)_2(aq) + 2\,Ag(s)$$

Label the anode and the cathode, and indicate the direction of flow of electrons in the external circuit and of ions in the internal circuit. Write the equations for the reactions occurring at each electrode.

10-7 Oxidation-Reduction Reactions From Electricity

In 1800 William Nicholson and Sir Antony Carlyle connected platinum wires to the terminals of a battery and immersed the ends of the wire in a container of water. They found that hydrogen was evolved at one wire and oxygen was evolved at the other wire. This showed that an electric current could be used to produce a chemical reaction. The use of an electric current to produce a chemical change is called **electrolysis**. Electrolysis is used in industry to prepare chemicals such as chlorine, fluorine, and sodium hydroxide. As in the case of an electrochemical cell, the conductors immersed in the liquid are called electrodes and the liquid itself is called an electrolyte.

A device which uses electrical energy to bring about a chemical change is called an **electrolytic cell**. The electric current can be provided by an automobile battery, a dry cell, or any other suitable source such as a direct current (DC) generator. Wires lead from the positive and negative terminals of

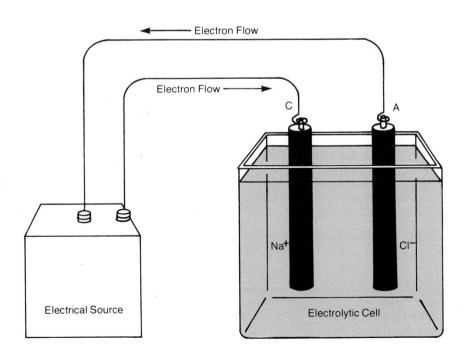

Fig. 10-3 An Electrolytic Cell

Electron Flow

Electron Flow

C

A

Na⁺

Cl⁻

Electrical Source

Electrolytic Cell

the source to two electrodes immersed in an electrolyte containing positive and negative ions (Fig. 10-3). These electrodes are inert. That is, they do not react during the cell operation. Platinum or carbon electrodes are commonly used.

Consider a cell containing molten sodium chloride (Fig. 10-3). Electrons flow from the negative electrode of the source to electrode C. Electrode C becomes negatively charged, and positive sodium ions migrate toward it. Each sodium ion gains one electron from electrode C, becoming a sodium atom:

$$\text{Reduction: } Na^+ + e^- \rightarrow Na\cdot$$

This gain of electrons by sodium ions constitutes a reduction, and the electrode (C) at which reduction occurs is the cathode.

Meanwhile, electrons are removed from electrode A by the positive terminal of the electrical source. Electrode A acquires a positive charge, and the negative Cl^- ions migrate toward it. Each Cl^- ion gives up one electron to electrode A, becoming a chlorine atom:

$$\text{Oxidation: } :\overset{..}{\underset{..}{Cl}}:^- \rightarrow :\overset{..}{\underset{..}{Cl}}\cdot + 1e^-$$

Two chlorine atoms combine to form a chlorine molecule:

$$2 :\overset{..}{\underset{..}{Cl}}\cdot \rightarrow Cl_2$$

The overall reaction at electrode A is

$$2\,Cl^- \rightarrow Cl_2 + 2e^-$$

This loss of electrons by chloride ions constitutes an oxidation, and the electrode (A) at which oxidation occurs is the anode.

The equation representing the sum of the anode and cathode reactions is

$$\begin{array}{l} 2\,Na^+ + 2e^- \rightarrow 2\,Na \\ \underline{2\,Cl^- \rightarrow Cl_2 + 2e^-} \\ 2\,Na^+ + 2\,Cl^- \rightarrow 2\,Na + Cl_2 \end{array}$$

or $\qquad$ $2\,NaCl \xrightarrow{\text{electrolysis}} 2\,Na + Cl_2$

Thus an electric current has succeeded in decomposing a substance into simpler components.

The current in the external circuit consists of the flow of electrons through the wires. Within the electrolytic cell the current (internal circuit) is carried by ions migrating to and from the two electrodes. Positive ions (cations) migrate to the cathode and negative ions (anions) migrate to the anode.

Sample Problem 10-4

Describe the construction and operation of an electrolytic cell which uses molten copper(II) chloride as an electrolyte.

SOLUTION

The cell would consist of two electrodes dipped into the molten copper(II) chloride and connected to an electrical source. At the electrode connected to the negative terminal of the source (the cathode) the reaction is

$$\text{Reduction: } Cu^{2+} + 2e^- \rightarrow Cu$$

Thus copper metal would be deposited on the cathode. At the anode the reaction is

$$\text{Oxidation: } 2\ Cl^- \rightarrow Cl_2 + 2e^-$$

Chlorine gas is liberated at the anode. The overall reaction is

$$Cu^{2+} + 2\ Cl^- \xrightarrow{\ \ \text{electrolysis}\ \ } Cu + Cl_2$$

Electrons travel from the anode to the cathode in the external circuit. In the internal circuit Cu^{2+} ions migrate to the cathode, and Cl^- ions move toward the anode.

Practice Problem 10-6

Describe schematically an electrolytic cell which uses molten aluminum bromide as the electrolyte. Write equations for the reactions which occur at the electrodes and for the overall reaction. Indicate the motion of particles in the external and internal circuits.

10-8 Fuel Cells

General Features of Fuel Cells

Fuel cells are electrochemical cells that convert chemical energy directly into electrical energy. They must be supplied continuously with the chemicals which provide the chemical energy. These chemicals must be prevented from reacting directly, for this would lead to a kind of chemical short circuit. The result would be heat energy but no electrical energy. Fuel cells consist of two electrodes: the fuel electrode (anode) at which fuel such as hydrogen, methanol, or hydrazine is oxidized, and the oxygen or air electrode (cathode) at which reduction of molecular oxygen takes place.

The Hydrogen-Oxygen Fuel Cell

The hydrogen-oxygen fuel cell has been used in the Gemini and Apollo space programs to produce water and electricity. In a hydrogen-oxygen fuel cell (Fig. 10-4, over), the two electrodes consist of porous carbon impregnated with catalysts such as palladium or platinum. The electrodes are immersed in a solution of sodium hydroxide which supplies OH^- ions. The reaction at the anode is

$$2\ H_2(g) + 4\ OH^-(aq) \rightarrow 4\ H_2O(\ell)) + 4e^-$$

The released electrons travel to the cathode, where the reaction is

$$O_2(g) + 2\ H_2O(\ell) + 4e^- \rightarrow 4\ OH^-(aq)$$

The overall reaction is

$$2\ H_2(g) + O_2(g) \rightarrow 2\ H_2O(\ell)$$

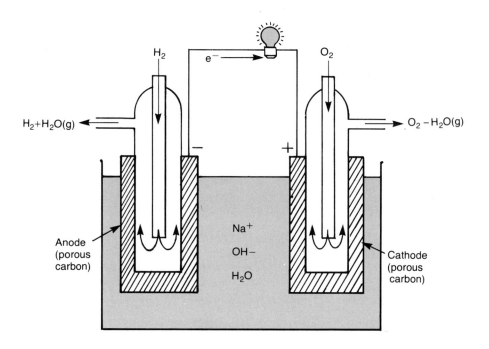

Fig. 10-4 A Hydrogen-Oxygen Fuel Cell

Efficiency and Advantages of Fuel Cells

Fuel cells are important because they are an efficient means of converting chemical energy into electrical energy. When coal or oil is burned to generate electricity, the chemical energy stored in the chemical bonds is converted to thermal (heat) energy. This heat is converted to the mechanical energy used to run electrical generators. The process of burning coal or oil to produce electricity is no more than 50% efficient. Fuel cells, by converting chemical energy directly into electrical energy, can be as much as 80% efficient. In addition to their high efficiency, fuel cells offer the following advantages: no significant air or water pollution, quiet operation, few moving parts, high reliability, and unattended operation.

Possible Uses of Fuel Cells

Fuel cells have many possible uses. Some of these include providing electricity to remote communication systems, weather and oceanographic stations, and offshore platforms. Other applications involve powering submarines, automobiles, and mass transit vehicles. Fuel cells may also be used to provide emergency and auxiliary power for hospitals and other buildings.

Problems With Fuel Cells

Widespread use of fuel cells is hampered by their relatively high cost of operation, which is caused mainly by the expensive electrodes and catalysts required. Another difficulty is the short period of operation caused by the short lifetime of the electrodes. Finally, fuel cells are rather heavy and bulky for the amount of energy they are able to provide.

A Final Word

At the beginning of this chapter, we learned about the nature of chemical reactions. The energy absorbed or released during a chemical reaction is due to the net effect of the bond-breaking and bond-making processes as reactants become products. The rate of a chemical reaction is usually affected by the concentration (or surface area) of the reactants, the temperature, and the use of catalysts. We learned that some chemical reactions are reversible and attain a state of chemical equilibrium. A chemical reaction can be recognized by such signs as a change of temperature, the evolution of a gas, the formation of a precipitate, a change in colour, or the formation of an odour.

We examined the four major types of reactions: addition, decomposition, displacement, and double displacement. We learned how to balance chemical equations by inspection.

Finally, we examined chemical reactions involving electron transfer (oxidation-reduction). Such reactions can be used to produce electricity (electrochemical cells and fuel cells). Also, electricity can be used to bring about oxidation-reduction reactions (electrolytic cells).

Now that you have finished reading this chapter, you should reread the Key Objectives to make sure that you have learned the most important points of the chapter. In addition, you should learn the meaning of each important term found in the chapter.

Key Terms

What is the meaning of each of the following terms?

reactant	reduction
product	reduced
exothermic	reducing agent
endothermic	oxidation-reduction reaction
chemical energy	electrochemical cell
catalyst	electrode
addition reaction	external circuit
decomposition reaction	internal circuit
displacement reaction	anode
double displacement reaction	cathode
oxidation	electrolysis
oxidized	electrolytic cell
oxidizing agent	fuel cell

Questions

1. Explain what is meant by the following terms: addition reaction; decomposition reaction; displacement reaction; double displacement reaction. Give an example of each type.
2. Classify each of the following reactions as addition, decomposition, displacement, or double displacement reactions:

a) $CaCO_3 \rightarrow CaO + CO_2$
b) $K_2SO_4 + Ba(NO_3)_2 \rightarrow BaSO_4 + 2\ KNO_3$
c) $2\ H_2 + O_2 \rightarrow 2\ H_2O$
d) $CaC_2 + 2\ H_2O \rightarrow C_2H_2 + Ca(OH)_2$
e) $2\ Al + 6\ HCl \rightarrow 2\ AlCl_3 + 3\ H_2$

3. Balance the following equations:
   a) $Fe_3O_4 + H_2 \rightarrow Fe + H_2O$
   b) $Ga + H_2SO_4 \rightarrow H_2 + Ga_2(SO_4)_3$
   c) $Fe_2O_3 + C \rightarrow Fe + CO$
   d) $Ca(OH)_2 + HCl \rightarrow CaCl_2 + H_2O$
   e) $P_4 + O_2 \rightarrow P_2O_5$

4. What is an oxidizing agent? A reducing agent? How would you expect electronegativity to be related to oxidizing and reducing power?

5. In which of the following reactions is electron transfer involved?
   a) $2\ Ca + O_2 \rightarrow 2\ CaO$
   b) $CaO + H_2O \rightarrow Ca(OH)_2$
   c) $Ca + 2\ H_2O \rightarrow Ca(OH)_2 + H_2$

6. In each of the following oxidation-reduction reactions, indicate the oxidizing agent, the reducing agent, the substance oxidized, the substance reduced, and the number of electrons transferred by one atom of the reducing agent:
   a) $2\ Fe + O_2 \rightarrow 2\ FeO$
   b) $2\ Fe + 3\ Br_2 \rightarrow 2\ FeBr_3$
   c) $Fe + 2\ HCl \rightarrow FeCl_2 + H_2$

7. A chlorine atom has a much higher ionization potential than a sodium atom. What does this mean in terms of the behaviour of the two elements?

8. What is the difference, if any, between hydrogen chloride and hydrochloric acid?

9. Balance the following equations and indicate the type of chemical reaction taking place:
   a) $Zn + HCl \rightarrow ZnCl_2 + H_2$
   b) $Mg + CO_2 \rightarrow MgO + C$
   c) $Al_2O_3 + H_2 \rightarrow Al + H_2O$
   d) $Cu(NO_3)_2 + H_2S \rightarrow CuS + HNO_3$
   e) $CaO + HNO_3 \rightarrow Ca(NO_3)_2 + H_2O$

10. Draw a diagram of a cell that can be used to obtain energy from the spontaneous reaction

$$Zn(s) + Pb(NO_3)_2(aq) \rightarrow Zn(NO_3)_2(aq) + Pb(s)$$

Label the anode and the cathode. Indicate the directions of the electron flow in the external circuit and of the ion movements in the internal circuit. Write the equation for the reactions occurring at each electrode.

11. Describe schematically an electrolytic cell which uses molten potassium chloride as the electrolyte. Write the equations for the reactions which occur at each electrode and for the overall reaction. Indicate the direction of motion of particles in the external and internal circuits.

12. Why is a fuel cell more efficient for producing electricity than is the burning of coal?

13. What is conserved in a chemical reaction?

14. What is meant by chemical energy? Why is it released during an exothermic chemical reaction?

15. What two things must happen if a molecule is to react with another molecule? Why?

16. Balance the following equations:

a) $Ca(AlO_2)_2 + HCl \rightarrow AlCl_3 + CaCl_2 + H_2O$

b) $O_2 + Sb_2S_3 \rightarrow Sb_2O_4 + SO_2$

c) $Cr + O_2 \rightarrow Cr_2O_3$

d) $C_2H_6 + O_2 \rightarrow CO_2 + H_2O$

e) $F_2 + NaOH \rightarrow O_2 + NaF + H_2O$

f) $NH_3 + O_2 \rightarrow H_2O + NO$

g) $Cl_2 + CrBr_3 \rightarrow Br_2 + CrCl_3$

h) $Sr(IO_3)_2 \rightarrow SrI_2 + O_2$

i) $Al_2(SO_4)_3 + NH_3 + H_2O \rightarrow Al(OH)_3 + (NH_4)_2SO_4$

j) $SiO_2 + Al \rightarrow Si + Al_2O_3$

17. What is the relationship between the average kinetic energy of a collection of molecules and temperature?

18. Why does the pathway for a chemical reaction generally consist of a number of simple reactions involving the collision of two atoms or molecules?

19. List three ways in which the rate of a chemical reaction may be increased.

20. In the chemical equation

$$Mg(s) + 2\,HCl(aq) \rightarrow MgCl_2(aq) + H_2(g) + heat$$

what evidence is there that a chemical reaction has taken place?

21. In which chemical family would you expect to find the most readily oxidized elements? The most readily reduced elements? Explain your answer.

22. Describe how an electrolytic cell might be used to electroplate silver onto a teaspoon.

23. Why must an initial source of energy be provided even if a reaction is exothermic?

24. A good rule of thumb for many reactions is that the rate of a reaction doubles for every 10°C rise in temperature. If a reaction takes 80 min at 20°C, how long will it take at 50°C?

25. Explain the following:

a) When an iron nail is placed in a blue solution of copper(II) sulfate, the colour of the solution becomes less intense.

b) A bonfire will burn faster when there is a strong wind.

26. Is the following one of the four major reaction types that we studied? If so, which type is it?

$$3\,NO_2 + H_2O \rightarrow 2\,HNO_3 + NO$$

27. For the reaction

$$KClO_3 + 3\,Na_2SnO_2 \rightarrow KCl + 3\,Na_2SnO_3$$

indicate the oxidizing agent, the reducing agent, the substance oxidized, the substance reduced, and the total number of electrons lost.

28. Balance the equation

$$C_7H_5N_3O_6(s) + O_2(g) \rightarrow CO_2(g) + N_2(g) + H_2O(g)$$

11 Two Elements and a Compound: Hydrogen, Oxygen, and Water

In this chapter, we describe the physical and chemical properties of two elements and a compound. The two elements are hydrogen and oxygen. The compound is water. Why do these three substances deserve their own chapter? What makes them so special?

Hydrogen appears to be the most abundant element in the universe. It is the third most common element in the earth's crust and atmosphere in terms of the total number of atoms; it follows oxygen and silicon. On the earth, hydrogen generally exists in compounds rather than by itself. It is found in water, in some minerals, in petroleum products, and in nearly all plant and animal tissues.

Oxygen is an impressive element. It is the most common element in the earth's crust and atmosphere in terms of both mass and number of atoms. In the earth's atmosphere, oxygen can exist by itself, uncombined with other elements. Uncombined oxygen is essential for the support of plant and animal life. Oxygen forms compounds with all of the elements except helium, neon, and argon. Oxygen is the second most electronegative element (after fluorine).

Water is quite possibly the most important of all compounds. It is the most abundant liquid; it makes up the oceans, lakes, and rivers that cover about three-fourths of the earth's surface. Water is found in all living things and is essential for life. About two-thirds of the human body is water. Water is able to dissolve many substances; thus, many chemical reactions occur in it. Of course, water itself is the product of the chemical reaction of hydrogen and oxygen.

Key Objectives

When you have completed studying this chapter, you should be able to
1. describe the occurrence of hydrogen, oxygen, and water.
2. describe the various methods of preparation of hydrogen and oxygen, giving a chemical equation for each method.
3. describe the physical properties of hydrogen, oxygen, and water.
4. describe the chemical properties of hydrogen, oxygen, and water, using chemical equations as examples.
5. list the uses of hydrogen, oxygen, and water.
6. name and describe the types of water pollution.

11-1 Discovery of Hydrogen

In 1766, Sir Henry Cavendish (Fig. 11-3) found that "inflammable air" could be prepared by the reaction of metals such as iron, zinc, and tin with dilute acid solutions. When this combustible gas was burned in air, water was formed. Antoine Lavoisier concluded that Cavendish's combustible gas was a new element that combined with oxygen during combustion to form water. Lavoisier named this element hydrogen, from the Greek *hydro genes*—water former.

11-2 Occurrence of Hydrogen

Hydrogen is a reactive element, and thus we would expect to find it in the free state (uncombined) in only very small quantities. It is found free in small amounts in the atmosphere, in natural gas, in the gases of active volcanoes, and in the gases present in some coal mines. It is believed that the atmosphere of the sun and other stars is composed mainly of hydrogen. For example, approximately 90% of the sun's mass is hydrogen. Hydrogen is the most abundant element in the universe.

Fig. 11-2 The solar corona and prominences shown here were photographed during the February, 1979 total eclipse. The corona is the 'atmosphere' of the sun. Its composition is approximately 73% hydrogen, 25% helium, and about 2% other elements. (Photo courtesy of David Dunlap Observatory)

11-3 Physical Properties of Hydrogen

Hydrogen consists of diatomic molecules, H_2, and is a colourless, odourless, and tasteless gas at ordinary temperatures. It is virtually insoluble in water. Hydrogen is the least dense known substance, with a density of 0.089 87 g/L at $0°C$ and standard atmospheric pressure (101.3 kPa). If hydrogen is compressed and cooled sufficiently, it changes to a liquid which boils at $-252.7°C$. Hydrogen freezes to a transparent solid at $-259.14°C$. The low boiling and melting temperatures of hydrogen reflect the weakness of the forces between hydrogen molecules. However, the covalent bond holding two hydrogen atoms together in a hydrogen molecule is very strong. At temperatures as high as $2400°C$, only about one per cent of the H_2 molecules is dissociated into atoms.

11-4 Isotopes of Hydrogen

Atoms which have the same number of protons but different numbers of neutrons are called isotopes. There are three isotopes of hydrogen: ^1_1H (protium), ^2_1H (deuterium, D), and ^3_1H (tritium, T). The protium nucleus consists of a lone proton. The deuterium nucleus has one proton and one neutron, and the tritium nucleus has one proton and two neutrons. Naturally occurring hydrogen contains 0.0156% ^2_1H. This means that there are 156 deuterium atoms for every one million hydrogen atoms. Tritium, which is formed continuously in the upper atmosphere in nuclear reactions, occurs naturally in only minute quantities (one tritium for every 10^{17} hydrogen atoms). Thus, about 99.98% of all natural hydrogen atoms are ^1_1H.

The different isotopic forms of hydrogen have the same electronic structures, and thus their chemical properties are essentially identical. Since the isotopes have different atomic masses, however, their physical properties differ. For example, H_2 freezes at $-259.1°C$ and boils at $-252.7°C$, while D_2 freezes at $-254.4°C$ and boils at $-249.6°C$.

The ^1_1H and ^2_1H nuclei are both stable, but the ^3_1H nucleus is not stable. It is radioactive, and half of any sample of ^3_1H changes to ^3_2He in 12.5 years.

Henry Cavendish was born in France of a noble English family. Educated at Cambridge University, he lived as a recluse and devoted almost all of his time to research. Although he inherited a fortune in middle life, he continued his frugal habits.

Cavendish was a magnificent experimenter, with a mathematical turn of mind. Thus, most of his researches were quantitative. He studied the various "airs" (gases), such as CO_2, H_2, and CO, that had been discovered. He was the first to study "inflammable air" (H_2). He showed that different airs had different specific gravities.

He demonstrated the composition of water by passing a spark through a mixture of "inflammable air" and "dephlogisticated air" (O_2). Although he didn't realize it, he showed that ordinary air contains not only "dephlogisticated air" and "phlogisticated air" (N_2), but also another "air" amounting to about $\frac{1}{120}$ of the total. This work led Lord Rayleigh to the discovery of argon a century later. Cavendish also showed that ordinary air has a constant composition.

Cavendish was interested in many areas of physics also. He published a paper on electricity, and showed that the effects of the torpedo (a Mediterranean fish) on the human body are electrical in nature. He determined the melting point of mercury and derived an extremely accurate value for the average density of the earth.

Fig. 11-3 Henry Cavendish (1731-1812) (Photo courtesy of The Bettman Archive, Inc.)

11-5 Preparation of Hydrogen

Hydrogen may be prepared by a number of different methods. We shall show several of these, including a laboratory method and two commercial methods. It is most important that a laboratory method be convenient. The preparation of hydrogen by reacting an acid with a metal such as zinc is one convenient method. For commercial methods, the most important consideration is cost. The purest, but most expensive, hydrogen is made by the electrolysis of water. Commercial hydrogen is also made by reacting methane and steam at high temperatures.

Preparation by the Electrolysis of Water

Hydrogen gas may be prepared by the electrolysis of water in the apparatus shown in Fig. 11-4, overleaf. When a direct electric current is passed through water containing a small amount of an electrolyte such as H_2SO_4, bubbles of hydrogen are formed at the cathode (negative electrode), and oxygen is produced at the anode (positive electrode). The reaction may be written

$$2H_2O(\ell) \xrightarrow{\text{electrical energy}} 2H_2(g) + O_2(g)$$

Fig. 11-4 Electrolysis of Water

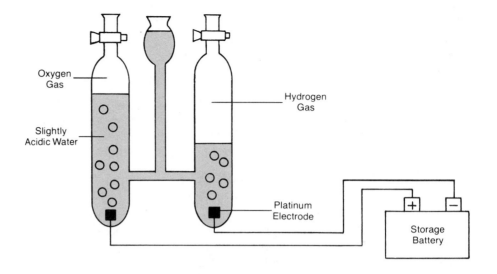

Preparation from Acids

Hydrogen is usually prepared in the laboratory by the reaction of certain metals with an acid. Most often pieces of zinc and iron are reacted with dilute solutions of hydrochloric or sulfuric acid at room temperature (Fig. 11-5).

$$Zn(s) + 2HCl(aq) \rightarrow ZnCl_2(aq) + H_2(g)$$
$$Zn(s) + H_2SO_4(aq) \rightarrow ZnSO_4(aq) + H_2(g)$$
$$Fe(s) + 2HCl(aq) \rightarrow FeCl_2(aq) + H_2(g)$$
$$Fe(s) + H_2SO_4(aq) \rightarrow FeSO_4(aq) + H_2(g)$$
$$2Al(s) + 3H_2SO_4(aq) \rightarrow Al_2(SO_4)_3(aq) + 3H_2(g)$$

Fig. 11-5 Laboratory Apparatus for the Preparation of Hydrogen by the Action of an Acid on a Metal

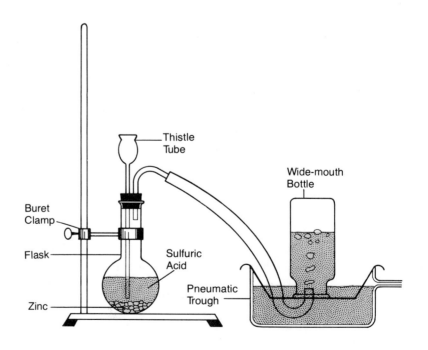

Preparation by the Action of Active Metals on Water

Very reactive metals such as sodium, potassium, and calcium react with water at room temperature to produce hydrogen:

$$2Na(s) + 2H_2O(l) \rightarrow 2NaOH(aq) + H_2(g)$$
$$2K(s) + 2H_2O(l) \rightarrow 2KOH(aq) + H_2(g)$$
$$Ca(s) + 2H_2O(l) \rightarrow Ca(OH)_2(aq) + H_2(g)$$

The reactions involving Na and K are so vigorous that the hydrogen frequently bursts into flames. Thus, the reactions of sodium or potassium with water are too dangerous to be good laboratory methods for preparing hydrogen.

Preparation by the Action of Certain Elements on Reactive Bases

Certain elements, such as zinc, aluminum, and silicon, react with concentrated aqueous solutions of sodium hydroxide or potassium hydroxide to produce hydrogen gas:

$$Zn(s) + 2NaOH(aq) + 2H_2O(l) \rightarrow Na_2Zn(OH)_4(aq) + H_2(g)$$
$$2Al(s) + 2NaOH(aq) + 6H_2O(l) \rightarrow 2NaAl(OH)_4(aq) + 3H_2(g)$$
$$Si(s) + 2NaOH(aq) + H_2O(l) \rightarrow Na_2SiO_3(aq) + 2H_2(g)$$

Drain cleaners such as Drāno® make use of the reaction of aluminum and sodium hydroxide. These drain cleaners contain over 50% sodium hydroxide and about 4% aluminum particles. When the drain cleaner is poured into a blocked drain, the sodium hydroxide dissolves, and heat is produced. This vigorous process heats up the water near the blockage, and the obstruction begins to melt away. At the same time, the dissolved sodium hydroxide reacts with the aluminum particles to generate hydrogen gas. The bubbling of the hydrogen gas helps to dislodge the blockage in the drain.

Commercial Preparation of Hydrogen

Industrially, hydrogen is obtained when a mixture of methane and steam is heated to a high temperature ($750°C$) in the presence of a catalyst such as nickel:

$$CH_4(g) + H_2O(g) \xrightarrow[\text{catalyst}]{\triangle} CO(g) + 3H_2(g)$$

$$CO(g) + H_2O(g) \xrightarrow[\text{catalyst}]{\triangle} CO_2(g) + H_2(g)$$

11-6 Chemical Properties of Hydrogen

At ordinary temperatures hydrogen is not very reactive. However, when it is heated, it takes part in many chemical reactions. Hydrogen is able to form H^-, the hydride ion, when reacting with very reactive metals such as Li, Na, and

Ca. Hydrogen forms H^+, as in H_3O^+. Hydrogen is able to form single covalent bonds with nonmetals and many metals.

Reaction With Metals

Hydrogen reacts with very reactive metals to form crystalline ionic hydrides. The best method of preparation is by the direct reaction of the metal with hydrogen gas at temperatures up to about 700°C:

$$2Li(s) + H_2(g) \rightarrow 2LiH(s)$$
$$2Na(s) + H_2(g) \rightarrow 2NaH(s)$$
$$Ca(s) + H_2(g) \rightarrow CaH_2(s)$$

The hydrogen in these metallic hydrides exists as H^- ions.

Reaction With Oxygen

Hydrogen reacts vigorously with oxygen to form water when a mixture of the two is ignited by a spark or a flame:

$$2H_2(g) + O_2(g) \rightarrow 2H_2O(g) + heat$$

This reaction often results in an explosion, but it is possible for hydrogen to burn without explosion if the amounts of hydrogen and oxygen are carefully controlled. The large amount of heat that is released when hydrogen burns has a practical application in the oxyhydrogen blowtorch. The very hot flame of this torch is capable of cutting through thick sheets of many metals, as it produces temperatures up to 2800°C.

Reaction With Other Nonmetals

Hydrogen gas will react with all the nonmetals except the noble gases to form covalent compounds:

$$8H_2(g) + S_8(s) \rightarrow 8H_2S(g)$$
$$3H_2(g) + N_2(g) \rightarrow 2NH_3(g)$$
$$H_2(g) + F_2(g) \rightarrow 2HF(g)$$
$$H_2(g) + Cl_2(g) \rightarrow 2HCl(g)$$
$$H_2(g) + Br_2(\ell) \rightarrow 2HBr(g)$$
$$H_2(g) + I_2(s) \rightarrow 2HI(g)$$

Reaction With Compounds

Hydrogen reacts with the oxides of many metals to form the free metal and water:

$$HgO(s) + H_2(g) \rightarrow Hg(\ell) + H_2O(g)$$
$$FeO(s) + H_2(g) \rightarrow Fe(s) + H_2O(g)$$
$$CuO(s) + H_2(g) \rightarrow Cu(s) + H_2O(g)$$

Hydrogen gas reacts with carbon monoxide at high temperatures and pressures in the presence of a catalyst to produce methyl alcohol, CH_3OH:

$$CO(g) + 2H_2(g) \xrightarrow[\text{catalyst}]{\triangle} CH_3OH(g)$$

Hydrogen has a tendency to add to a double or triple bond between two carbon atoms. This reaction is called hydrogenation and is used in the production of solid cooking fats from liquid oils:

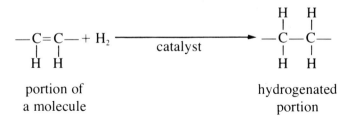

portion of
a molecule

hydrogenated
portion

11-7 Compounds of Hydrogen

Many of the compounds of hydrogen are found in living materials and in compounds derived from living materials, such as natural gas and petroleum. Hydrogen is also found in water—the most abundant compound of hydrogen on earth. All common acids such as H_2SO_4 (sulfuric acid) and HNO_3 (nitric acid) contain hydrogen.

11-8 Uses of Hydrogen

Hydrogen is an important raw material in many manufacturing processes. Large quantities of hydrogen gas, mixed with other gases, are used as an industrial fuel. Hydrogen is used in the synthesis of ammonia, methyl alcohol, and hydrogenated vegetable oils. It is used in the manufacture of gasoline and hydrochloric acid.

If two light nuclei combine to form a heavier, more stable nucleus, the process is called a nuclear fusion reaction. A deuteron, ^2_1H, and a triton, ^3_1H, which are the nuclei of two isotopes of hydrogen, will undergo a nuclear fusion reaction at extremely high temperatures to form a helium nucleus and a neutron:

$$^2_1H + {}^3_1H \rightarrow {}^4_2He + {}^1_0n$$

This reaction is accompanied by the release of a large amount of energy and is the nuclear reaction of the hydrogen bomb. If current research on the development of nuclear fusion reactors (in which the fusion of hydrogen nuclei is controlled) is successful, the world will possess an inexhaustable energy source.

Because hydrogen has such a low density, it has good lifting power and is used to inflate weather balloons. However, hydrogen is not used in passenger balloons because it burns so readily (Fig. 11-6, overleaf). Hot air or helium gas is used in passenger balloons.

Fig. 11-6 The Hindenberg disaster
illustrates the danger of using
hydrogen gas in passenger balloons.
(Photo courtesy of Canapress)

11-9 Discovery of Oxygen

Oxygen was first recognized as an active part of air by the Swedish chemist, Carl Wilhelm Scheele, while he was studying the chemical nature of air. An English philosopher, Joseph Priestley (Fig. 11-7), discovered oxygen when he prepared it by focusing the sun's rays on mercury(II) oxide. He noticed that a candle burned more brightly in this gas than in air. Antoine Lavoisier first proposed the name oxygen, which means ''acid former'', because he thought that all acids contained oxygen.

11-10 Occurrence of Oxygen

Oxygen is the most abundant and widely distributed element found on earth. Oxygen occurs as three isotopes, $^{16}_{8}O$ (99.759%), $^{17}_{8}O$ (0.0374%), and $^{18}_{8}O$ (0.2039%). It occurs in both the free state as O_2 and in the combined state in many chemical compounds.

In the free state, it makes up about 21% of the atmosphere by volume. In the combined state, it forms 89% of water by mass and 50% of the earth's crust by mass. In the earth's crust, it is principally combined with silicon. Silica, SiO_2, is the main component of sand. Oxygen also makes up a large part of the mass of plants and animals.

Halides

Sodium chloride and potassium chloride are so readily available in nature that they serve as raw materials for the preparation of other metals and of chlorine. They are mined directly, and, during the purification of the crude materials, small amounts of the other alkali metal halides are also recovered.

Sodium chloride (salt) is one of the most important minerals. Tens of millions of tonnes of sodium chloride are used each year. Most of it is used in the manufacture of sodium hydroxide and chlorine by electrolysis. Much is used in the manufacture of sodium hydrogen carbonate and sodium carbonate. Canadians are well aware of the large amounts of salt that are used for de-icing highways. Salt is also used in the home, in the dairy industry, in the treatment of animal hides, and in the regeneration of the resins in home water softeners.

Salt is obtained from underground mines and by evaporation of water from the brines pumped to the surface from deep wells. Occasionally water is pumped underground to salt deposits, and the brine solution is then forced back to the surface for evaporation. Salt is also obtained by evaporation of sea water. We should note, however, that all brines contain in addition to sodium chloride smaller amounts of potassium, calcium, and magnesium chlorides, bromides, and iodides.

Many tonnes of potassium chloride are used in the manufacture of fertilizers. This is one example in which the alkali metals are not interchangeable in use. Growing plants need potassium for growth, and the potassium cannot be replaced by sodium.

Carbonates

Of all of the alkali metal compounds, sodium carbonate, Na_2CO_3, also called washing soda or soda ash, is second only to sodium chloride in the number of tonnes used annually. About half of it is used in the manufacture of glass. The rest is used in the preparation of other chemicals, in the pulp and paper industry, and in the preparation of soaps and detergents.

At one time, most sodium carbonate was produced in a process discovered in 1863 by the Belgian chemist, Ernest Solvay. In this process carbon dioxide is bubbled through a cold concentrated brine solution that is saturated with ammonia, and a precipitate of sodium hydrogen carbonate is formed. The reaction may be viewed as occurring in three stages:

a) The carbon dioxide dissolves in the water to form carbonic acid:

$$CO_2(g) + H_2O(\ell) \rightarrow H_2CO_3(aq)$$

b) The basic ammonia neutralizes the acidic carbonic acid to form a solution of ammonium hydrogen carbonate:

$$NH_3(aq) + H_2CO_3(aq) \rightarrow NH_4^+(aq) + HCO_3^-(aq)$$

c) The hydrogen carbonate ions are precipitated by the sodium ions from the sodium chloride:

$$Na^+(aq) + Cl^-(aq) + HCO_3^-(aq) \rightarrow NaHCO_3(s) + Cl^-(aq)$$

The overall result obtained by adding the three equations is

$$CO_2(g) + H_2O(\ell) + NH_3(aq) + Na^+(aq) + Cl^-(aq) \rightarrow$$
$$NaHCO_3(s) + NH_4^+(aq) + Cl^-(aq)$$

The sodium hydrogen carbonate is then converted to sodium carbonate by heating to 300°C:

$$2NaHCO_3(s) \xrightarrow{\triangle} Na_2CO_3(s) + CO_2(g) + H_2O(g)$$

The economic success of the Solvay process depends on the use of cheap, readily available starting materials such as sodium chloride and calcium carbonate (limestone), and on the efficient recycling of the by-products of the above reaction. For example, the carbon dioxide produced in the roasting of sodium hydrogen carbonate was reused in Step (a). Other carbon dioxide was prepared by heating the limestone:

$$CaCO_3(s) \xrightarrow{\triangle} CaO(s) + CO_2(g)$$

The calcium oxide formed above could be reacted with water to form calcium hydroxide:

$$CaO(s) + H_2O(\ell) \rightarrow Ca(OH)_2(s)$$

And the calcium hydroxide was used to recover the expensive ammonia from the ammonium ions remaining in solution at the end of Step (c):

$$Ca(OH)_2(s) + 2NH_4^+(aq) + 2Cl^-(aq) \xrightarrow{\triangle}$$
$$2NH_3(g) + 2H_2O(\ell) + Ca^{2+}(aq) + 2Cl^-(aq)$$

Thus, every by-product formed in the Solvay process was recycled for further use, with one exception—the calcium chloride formed in the last reaction. Although a small amount could be used on highways, most of it could not be sold and was simply dumped in nearby streams. Environmental concerns have sharply limited the amount of such dumping that can now occur, and, until some chemist finds a use for large quantities of calcium chloride, the Solvay process will remain in disfavour.

Fortunately, there are localized deposits of an almost pure mineral called *trona*, $Na_2CO_3 \cdot NaHCO_3 \cdot 2H_2O$, from which sodium carbonate is obtained by heating:

$$2Na_2CO_3 \cdot NaHCO_3 \cdot 2H_2O \ (s) \xrightarrow{\triangle} 3Na_2CO_3(s) + CO_2(g) + 5H_2O(g)$$

An increasing amount is produced by this more expensive process.

Sodium hydrogen carbonate is also known as baking soda. Although most of it is used in the preparation of sodium carbonate, some is used in medicine, and some is used in baking ingredients (e.g., baking powder). Both uses depend on the fact that hydrogen carbonates react with acids to form carbon dioxide:

$$HCO_3^-(aq) + H_3O^+(aq) \rightarrow 2H_2O(\ell) + CO_2(g)$$

In medicinal uses, the acid is either in gastric juice or is mixed with the sodium hydrogen carbonate in the solid state (e.g., citric or tartaric acid). In baking soda, the solid acid is often potassium hydrogen tartrate. The two solids do not react with each other in the dry state. In the presence of water, as in a cake batter, the two solids dissolve and react with each other to produce bubbles of carbon dioxide gas which cause the cake to rise as it is baked.

Finely divided potassium hydrogen carbonate is used in "dry chemical" fire extinguishers, because it decomposes readily to form carbon dioxide which smothers the fire:

$$2KHCO_3(s) \xrightarrow{\triangle} K_2CO_3(s) + H_2O(g) + CO_2(g)$$

Sulfates

Sodium sulfate was formerly obtained by reacting sodium chloride with sulfuric acid:

$$H_2SO_4(\ell) + 2NaCl(s) \rightarrow Na_2SO_4(s) + 2HCl(g)$$

Many industrial processes use sulfuric acid, which is eventually neutralized with sodium hydroxide:

$$H_2SO_4(aq) + 2NaOH(aq) \rightarrow Na_2SO_4(aq) + 2H_2O(\ell)$$

Thus, much of the sodium sulfate is now obtained as an industrial by-product, especially from the manufacture of rayon. The bulk of the sodium sulfate is used in the paper industry. In the kraft process for making paper, wood chips are cooked with a hot solution of NaOH and Na_2SO_4. This dissolves the lignin which holds the wood together and releases the cellulose from which the paper is made. About 50 kg of sodium sulfate are required for every tonne of paper produced.

12-8 Uses of Sodium

The alkali metals other than sodium are not used to any great extent. Sodium is used because of its abundance, and because of its typical metallic properties. Despite the sensitivity of sodium to water and air, a way has been found to encase sodium wires in polyethylene, and such wires make excellent underground high-voltage conductors. Because it is an excellent conductor of heat, it is used in certain nuclear reactors as a heat transfer medium. Because of the ease with which it gives up electrons, it is used as a reducing agent, as in the preparation of other metals from their chlorides. We have already seen the preparation of potassium by the sodium reduction of potassium chloride. Chromium is prepared by a similar reaction:

$$3Na(\ell) + CrCl_3(s) \rightarrow 3NaCl(s) + Cr(s)$$

12-9 Less Widely Known Alkali Metals

Lithium is found in practically all rocks, but the amounts are usually small. The major source is lepidolite, a complex mica mineral with a lithium content of only 1.5%. The isolation of the pure metal is a difficult process involving the precipitation of lithium carbonate and its conversion to lithium chloride, followed by electrolysis of the fused chloride.

Lithium is used in certain batteries and in the manufacture of certain alloys. Although lithium fluoride is nearly insoluble, its other halides are among the most soluble salts known. Lithium aluminium hydride, $LiAlH_4$, is an important reducing agent in organic chemistry, because of its high reactivity and its solubility in solvents such as ether. The reaction proceeds more rapidly when both reactants are in solution. Rubidium and cesium are scarcer than lithium and are quite expensive. Usually sodium or potassium can serve equally well where rubidium and cesium might be used. However, rubidium has its own uses, mainly as an ingredient in sleep inducers and sedatives, in the treatment of epilepsy and goiter, and in the preparation of light-sensitive photocells. Cesium also finds special use in photocells, and in research on the development of ion-propulsion rockets.

12-10 History of the Halogens

The earliest halogen to be prepared was chlorine. In 1774, the Swedish chemist Carl Wilhelm Scheele prepared chlorine by the action of manganese dioxide on hydrochloric acid:

$$MnO_2(s) + 4HCl(aq) \rightarrow MnCl_2(aq) + Cl_2(g) + 2H_2O(\ell)$$

Chlorine was believed to be a compound, however, not an element. It was not until 1810 that the British chemist Sir Humphry Davy convincingly demonstrated that it was an element. Davy named it for its greenish-yellow colour (Greek *chloros*, green).

Iodine was first observed in 1811 by a French manufacturer of saltpeter, Bernard Courtois. He had been burning certain seaweeds, the ashes of which were valued in his day for their sodium and potassium compounds. He used water to dissolve all the soluble materials in the ash. Then he began to evaporate the water. At one point he added sulfuric acid, whereupon clouds of a beautiful violet vapour with an irritating odour filled the room. The vapours condensed on cold objects to form dark lustrous crystals. The name of the element is derived from its colour (Greek *ioeides*, violet-coloured). Iodine was thus the first element to be isolated from the sea.

Bromine was discovered in 1826 by the French chemist Antoine-Jérome Balard. Balard had treated a concentrated solution of salts (obtained from brines at Montpellier) with chlorine, and distilled it to obtain a dark red liquid. He obtained the same liquid by treating the liquid extract from seaweed ashes with chlorine. The liquid had a bad odour, which resulted in its name (Greek *bromos*, stench).

In 1886, after nearly 74 years of effort by scientists, the French chemist Henri Moissan finally succeeded in preparing elemental fluorine. After many attempts and interruptions caused by serious poisonings, Moissan tried passing an electric current through a solution of dry potassium hydrogen fluoride (KHF_2) in anhydrous hydrogen fluoride. A highly reactive gas appeared at the anode; he demonstrated it to be elemental fluorine (named for the mineral fluorite, CaF_2).

Astatine, a radioactive element, was first prepared in 1940 by D.R. Corson, K.R. MacKenzie, and E. Segrè at the University of California. They bombarded bismuth with alpha particles and obtained traces of the highly radioactive element astatine (Greek *astatos*, unstable).

12-11 Occurrence of the Halogens

Each member of the halogen family requires only one electron to complete its valence shell. The tendency to acquire this additional electron is so strong that the halogens are not normally found in nature in the free state. They are usually found as the halide ions, F^-, Cl^-, Br^-, I^-, combined with metal ions.

Fluorine is the second most abundant of the halogens. It constitutes 0.03% of the earth's crust. Since it is the most reactive of all elements, it is always found in combination with other elements. The two most common fluorine-containing minerals are fluorspar (CaF_2) and cryolite (Na_3AlF_6).

Chlorine is the most abundant halogen. It comprises about 0.19% of the earth's crust. It exists as the chloride ion in sea water, in brine wells, and in salt beds, where it is combined with sodium, potassium, calcium, and magnesium ions.

Bromine is much less abundant than chlorine, constituting only about 0.0002% of the earth's crust. It occurs as the bromide ion in NaBr, KBr, and $CaBr_2$, in small quantities in sea water, and in brine wells.

Iodine constitutes about 0.0001% of the earth's crust. It occurs as the iodide ion in small quantities in sea water, brine wells, and salt beds. Certain seaweeds concentrate the iodine from sea water. These plants can be burned and the iodine extracted from their ashes. Iodine is also obtained as $NaIO_3$ from huge deposits of saltpeter in Chile.

Astatine occurs only in minute quantities as a radioactive decay product of thorium and uranium.

12-12 Preparation and Production of the Halogens

The halogens may be prepared by passing an electric current through a molten halide (electrolysis). For fluorine this is the only method available. Since fluorine is the most electronegative of all the elements, no other substance is capable of oxidizing (removing the electrons from) fluoride ions to form fluorine atoms.

The Preparation of Fluorine

Fluorine is prepared commercially by electrolysis. Two major problems arise. First, the high reactivity of fluorine makes it difficult to find suitable materials from which to construct the electrodes and the cell. Second, molten fluorides are poor conductors of electricity. However, a mixture of three parts of potassium hydrogen fluoride (KHF_2) and two parts of anhydrous hydrogen fluoride is a good conductor. Since the mixture melts at $72°C$ it can be kept in a molten state by heating the cell with a steam jacket.

An electrolytic cell for the preparation of fluorine is shown in Fig. 12-8. The cell is constructed of copper, which reacts with fluorine to form an inert coating of copper fluoride protecting the copper from further attack. At the anode, fluoride ions give up electrons to form fluorine atoms which combine to form fluorine molecules:

$$\text{Oxidation: } 2F^- \rightarrow F_2(g) + 2e^-$$

At the cathode, hydrogen ions accept electrons and become reduced to hydrogen molecules:

$$\text{Reduction: } 2H^+ + 2e^- \rightarrow H_2(g)$$

Thus the overall reaction is

$$2H^+ + 2F^- \rightarrow H_2(g) + F_2(g)$$

Hydrogen is a by-product, and since it reacts explosively with fluorine, a screen made of Monel metal (a corrosion-resistant alloy of nickel, copper, and a little iron) must be used to keep the gases separate. As the hydrofluoric

Fig. 12-8 Electrolysis Cell for the Preparation of Fluorine

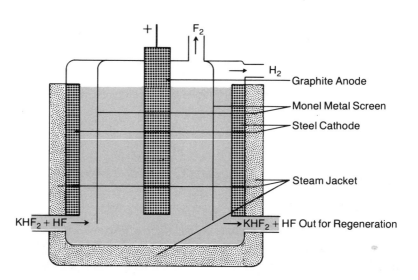

acid is decomposed, more KHF_2 and HF mixture is added so that the cell can be operated continuously.

The Preparation of Chlorine

Chlorine is usually prepared commercially by the electrolysis of an aqueous sodium chloride solution in a diaphragm cell (Fig. 12-7). The chemical equation for the reaction is

$$2NaCl(aq) + 2H_2O(\ell) \xrightarrow{\text{electrolysis}} Cl_2(g) + H_2(g) + 2NaOH(aq)$$

The chlorine is liberated at the anode (positive electrode), and the other products (the hydrogen gas and the sodium hydroxide solution) are used in other industrial chemical processes.

Chlorine is also obtained as a by-product when sodium is prepared by the electrolysis of sodium in a Downs cell (Fig. 12-5):

$$2NaCl(\ell) \xrightarrow{\text{electrolysis}} 2Na(\ell) + Cl_2(g)$$

The preparation of calcium and magnesium metals by the electrolysis of calcium chloride and magnesium chloride also yields commercial quantities of chlorine gas as a by-product.

Chlorine is prepared in the laboratory by oxidizing hydrochloric acid with manganese(IV) oxide:

$$\overset{+4}{Mn}O_2 + 4\overset{-1}{H}Cl \longrightarrow \overset{+2}{Mn}Cl_2 + \overset{0}{Cl_2} + 2H_2O$$

gain of electrons

loss of electrons

In aqueous solution the hydrochloric acid and manganese(II) chloride are almost completely ionized. The reaction is better represented by the equation

$$MnO_2(s) + 4H_3O^+(aq) + 4Cl^-(aq) \rightarrow$$
$$Mn^{2+}(aq) + 2Cl^-(aq) + Cl_2(g) + 6H_2O(\ell)$$

It is apparent that two of the chloride ions are simply spectator ions. They take no part in the reaction and can be omitted from the equation:

$$MnO_2(s) + 4H_3O^+(aq) + 2Cl^-(aq) \rightarrow Mn^{2+}(aq) + Cl_2(g) + 6H_2O(\ell)$$

The equation shows that the preparation of chlorine requires only chloride ions (Cl^-), acid (H_3O^+), and an oxidizing agent (e.g., MnO_2). Thus, it is also possible to prepare chlorine by the action of MnO_2 on a mixture of sodium chloride (source of chloride ions) and sulfuric acid (source of acid). Somewhat more heat is required when using sodium chloride and sulfuric acid than when using hydrochloric acid, so that the latter method is usually used. The apparatus is usually arranged as in Fig 12-9, overleaf. The solid MnO_2 is covered with the concentrated hydrochloric acid, and the mixture is warmed gently. The chlorine, which is 2.5 times as dense as air, is collected by the upward displacement of air. The experiment is carried out in a well-ventilated area because of the poisonous nature of chlorine.

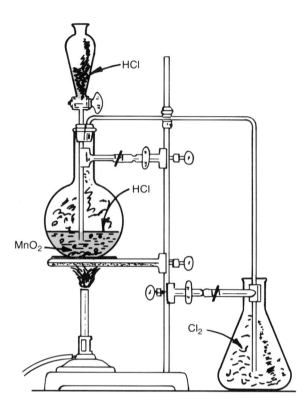

Fig. 12-9 Laboratory Preparation of Cl$_2$

HCl

HCl

MnO$_2$

Cl$_2$

The Preparation of Bromine

Bromine is obtained commercially from the bromides present in certain brine wells and from seawater. The process is based on the fact that chlorine has a greater tendency to accept electrons than does bromine. Hence chlorine gas is a cheap oxidizing agent for obtaining bromine from its salts:

$$Cl_2(aq) + 2Br^-(aq) \rightarrow 2Cl^-(aq) + Br_2(aq)$$

Bromine is quite volatile, and the small quantities of bromine released from the seawater are removed from it by a current of air and concentrated in a solution of sodium carbonate:

$$3Br_2(g) + 6CO_3^{2-}(aq) + 3H_2O(\ell) \rightarrow 5Br^-(aq) + BrO_3^-(aq) + 6HCO_3^-(aq)$$

The solution is next acidified to release the bromine:

$$5Br^-(aq) + BrO_3^-(aq) + 6HCO_3^-(aq) + 12H_3O^+(aq) \rightarrow$$
$$3Br_2(aq) + 6CO_2(g) + 21H_2O(\ell)$$

The bromine can then be distilled from the more concentrated solution.

Bromine is made in the laboratory by oxidation of either hydrobromic acid or a mixture of sodium bromide and sulfuric acid with manganese(IV) oxide. The reaction is analogous to the preparation of chlorine:

$$MnO_2(s) + 4H_3O^+(aq) + 2Br^-(aq) \rightarrow Mn^{2+}(aq) + Br_2(g) + 6H_2O(\ell)$$

The Preparation of Iodine

Iodine is the most easily oxidized of the halide ions. Much iodine is obtained commercially by chlorine oxidation of the iodide ions in brine wells:

$$Cl_2(g) + 2I^-(aq) \rightarrow 2Cl^-(aq) + I_2(aq)$$

Some iodine is obtained commercially by treating the sodium iodate impurity in Chile saltpeter with controlled amounts of sodium hydrogen sulfite. The reaction is

$$2IO_3^-(aq) + 5HSO_3^-(aq) + 2H_2O(\ell) \rightarrow I_2(aq) + 5SO_4^{2-}(aq) + 3H_3O^+(aq)$$

Iodine is made in the laboratory by oxidation of a mixture of sodium iodide and sulfuric acid with manganese(IV) oxide:

$$MnO_2(s) + 4H_3O^+(aq) + 2I^-(aq) \rightarrow I_2(g) + Mn^{2+}(aq) + 6H_2O(\ell)$$

The apparatus is shown in Fig. 12-10. The mixture of NaI, MnO_2, and H_2SO_4 is heated gently. Beautiful violet-coloured clouds of iodine vapour rise within the beaker to condense as lustrous black crystals on the bottom of a cold evaporating dish. The reaction must be carried out with good ventilation, because some of the sulfuric acid is reduced to poisonous hydrogen sulfide gas during the process:

$$8I^-(aq) + SO_4^{2-}(aq) + 10H_3O^+(aq) \rightarrow 4I_2(g) + H_2S(g) + 14H_2O(\ell)$$

The formation of H_2S can be avoided by replacing the H_2SO_4 with H_3PO_4.

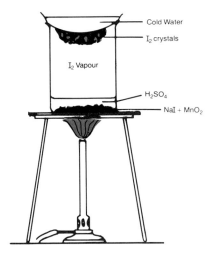

Fig. 12-10 Laboratory Preparation of Iodine

12-13 Properties of the Halogens

The elements fluorine, chlorine, bromine, iodine, and astatine are found in Group VII of the periodic table. They are known as the **halogens**, from two Greek words meaning "salt former." The name arises from the fact that in combination with metals such as sodium, potassium, calcium, and magnesium, they form salts, similar to ordinary table salt. These salts are among the most abundant soluble salts found in nature (especially in seawater).

The halogens are considered as a family because they all have similar electronic configurations, with a total of seven electrons in their valence shells. Thus one atom of any halogen can add one electron to form an ion with a single negative charge:

$$:\overset{..}{\underset{..}{Br}}\cdot \quad + \quad e^- \quad \rightarrow \quad :\overset{..}{\underset{..}{Br}}:^-$$

bromine   electron   bromide
atom   ion

This negative ion can then pair up with a positive ion such as a potassium ion, K^+, by electrostatic attraction, to form a typical salt such as potassium bromide, KBr.

Some properties of the halogens are summarized in Table 12-3. The specific values are not as noteworthy as the regular variation in a given property as one goes from the top to the bottom of the periodic table within the halogen family. The boiling points and melting points, for example, increase regularly as atomic mass increases. At the same time, the colour changes from a very pale yellow to a deep violet-black. The halogens are all diatomic elements. They are all reactive, since their atoms can gain a stable octet simply by acquiring one more valence electron.

TABLE 12-3 Physical Properties of the Halogens

HALOGEN	FLUORINE	CHLORINE	BROMINE	IODINE
Formula	F_2	Cl_2	Br_2	I_2
Appearance at 25°C	pale yellow gas	yellow-green gas	red-brown liquid	purple-black solid
Melting point (°C)	−223	−102	−7	114
Boiling point (°C)	−187	−34	59	183
Solubility in H_2O at 20°C (mol/L)	(reacts)	0.090	0.021	0.0013
Atomic radius (pm)	72	99	114	133
Ionic radius (pm)	136	181	195	216
Electronegativity	4.0	3.0	2.8	2.5
Electron affinity (kJ/mol)	333	349	324	295
1st Ionization Potential (V)	17.34	12.95	11.80	10.6

12-14 Chemical Properties of the Halogens

The halogens have great chemical reactivity because of the tendency to acquire an additional valence electron. There is a regular decrease in chemical reactivity from fluorine to iodine. In fact, fluorine is the most reactive element known.

Reaction of Halogens with Hydrogen

Fluorine is so reactive that solid fluorine reacts violently with liquid hydrogen to produce hydrogen fluoride:

$$F_2(s) + H_2(\ell) \rightarrow 2HF(g)$$

At room temperature the reaction is explosive.
Chlorine combines with hydrogen in the dark:

$$Cl_2(g) + H_2(g) \rightarrow 2HCl(g)$$

In bright sunlight or at temperatures above 250°C the reaction becomes explosive. Both fluorine and chlorine support combustion in the same manner that oxygen does. A jet of hydrogen burning in air will continue to burn when lowered into a jar of fluorine or chlorine.

Hydrogen reacts with bromine at high temperatures, or at lower temperatures (250°C) in the presence of a catalyst (Pt):

$$Br_2(g) + H_2(g) \xrightarrow[Pt]{\triangle} 2HBr(g)$$

Hydrogen reacts with iodine only under carefully controlled conditions:

$$I_2(g) + H_2(g) \xrightarrow{\triangle} 2HI(g)$$

The product, HI, is sufficiently unstable that most of it decomposes.

Reaction of Halogens with Other Elements

Active metals such as the alkali metals burn in an atmosphere of either fluorine or chlorine, liberating both heat and light. For example,

$$2Na(s) + Cl_2(g) \rightarrow 2NaCl(s)$$

The greater reactivity of fluorine is shown by the fact that ordinary materials such as wood or plastic burn in fluorine. Even asbestos burns in fluorine! And even more unbelievably, a stream of fluorine gas flowing onto the surface of water actually causes the water to burn! Fluorine is so reactive that it reacts with xenon, radon, and krypton (the noble gases!) to form fluorides. The reaction with xenon occurs at room temperature in the presence of ultraviolet light:

$$Xe(g) + F_2(g) \xrightarrow[\text{light}]{\text{ultraviolet}} XeF_2(s)$$

XeF_2 is a colourless, crystalline compound which melts at 140°C and decomposes in water:

$$2XeF_2(s) + 2H_2O(\ell) \rightarrow 2Xe(g) + 4HF(g) + O_2(g)$$

Chlorine is capable of reacting with other elements such as sulfur and phosphorus:

$$S_8(s) + 4Cl_2(g) \rightarrow 4S_2Cl_2(\ell)$$
$$P_4(s) + 6Cl_2(g) \rightarrow 4PCl_3(\ell)$$
$$P_4(s) + 10Cl_2(g) \rightarrow 4PCl_5(s)$$

Reaction of Halogens with Compounds

The halogens, generally speaking, behave as oxidizing agents in their reactions with various compounds. Fluorine is the strongest oxidizing agent, and the oxidizing ability of the halogens decreases with increasing atomic number. Nevertheless, even the poorest oxidizing halogen, I_2, is able to oxidize hydrogen sulfide to sulfur:

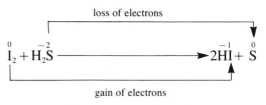

The relative order of oxidizing ability means that one halogen can oxidize another halogen which is below it in the periodic table (i.e., has less oxidizing ability). Thus, an aqueous solution of chlorine is able to liberate bromine from an aqueous solution of sodium bromide:

$$Cl_2(aq) + 2Br^-(aq) \rightarrow 2Cl^-(aq) + Br_2(aq)$$

The occurrence of the reaction is easily noticed, because the liberated bromine causes the aqueous solution to turn brown.

As one might expect, chlorine water (an aqueous solution of chlorine) converts the even more easily oxidized iodide ion to free iodine:

$$Cl_2(aq) + 2I^-(aq) \rightarrow 2Cl^-(aq) + I_2(aq)$$

Again, the appearance of a brown colour in the solution shows that a reaction has occurred. The aqueous iodine solution can be distinguished from an aqueous bromine solution by shaking it with carbon tetrachloride. The carbon tetrachloride does not mix with the water, and the iodine dissolves preferentially in the carbon tetrachloride layer to form a beautiful violet-coloured solution. Bromine would dissolve in the carbon tetrachloride layer to form a brown-coloured solution. Trichlorotrifluoroethane (TTE) is usually substituted for carbon tetrachloride in school laboratories because carbon tetrachloride vapours are toxic.

Bromine is a stronger oxidizing agent than iodine, and can liberate iodine from an aqueous solution of its iodide salts:

$$Br_2(aq) + 2I^-(aq) \rightarrow 2Br^-(aq) + I_2(aq)$$

Again, the iodine can be identified by the violet colour obtained when the aqueous solution is shaken with carbon tetrachloride.

Another useful property of iodine which can be used for identification purposes is its ability to react with starch molecules to produce a deep blue colour. The iodine molecules enter channels in the starch molecules, where they are subjected to rather strong intermolecular forces. Electrons are actually transferred from the starch to the iodine molecules, and a highly coloured substance called a *charge transfer complex* is formed. The interaction between iodine and oxygen-containing solvents such as water and ethanol also leads to the formation of charge transfer complexes. Thus, an aqueous solution of iodine has a brown colour rather than the "normal" violet colour which is found in solutions when such complexes cannot be formed.

In general, halogens react with hydrogen compounds of nonmetals to form the hydrogen halide and the free nonmetal:

$$8Cl_2(g) + 8H_2S(g) \rightarrow 16HCl(g) + S_8(s)$$

All hydrocarbons burn in chlorine to produce hydrogen chloride and free carbon:

$$C_6H_6(\ell) + 3Cl_2(g) \rightarrow 6C(s) + 6HCl(g)$$
benzene

A piece of filter paper moistened with turpentine (which consists mainly of $C_{10}H_{16}$ molecules) bursts into flame spontaneously when immersed in a bottle of chlorine:

$$C_{10}H_{16}(\ell) + 8Cl_2(g) \rightarrow 10C(s) + 16HCl(g)$$
(turpentine)

12-15 Compounds of the Halogens

Metal Halides

Perhaps the best-known compounds of the halogens are the halides, most of which are made by direct combination between the halogen and another element. For example,

$$2Na(s) + Cl_2(g) \rightarrow 2NaCl(s)$$
$$H_2(g) + Cl_2(g) \rightarrow 2HCl(g)$$

The metal halides are also formed by reaction between active metals and hydrohalic acids. For example,

$$Ca(s) + 2HCl(aq) \rightarrow CaCl_2(aq) + H_2(g)$$

The metal halides tend to be ionic compounds with high melting points (e.g., NaCl, m.p. 801°C). Halides of nonmetals are covalent compounds with lower melting points and boiling points (e.g., PCl_3, m.p. −110°C, b.p. 76°C). Molecular halides have a tendency to hydrolyze (react with water), some more readily than others:

$$BCl_3(\ell) + 3H_2O(\ell) \rightarrow H_3BO_3(aq) + 3HCl(aq)$$
$$SiCl_4(\ell) + 3H_2O(\ell) \rightarrow H_2SiO_3(s) + 4HCl(aq)$$

Hydrogen Halides

The most important halides, however, are the halides of hydrogen. They are all colourless gases with pungent, disagreeable odours.

Hydrogen fluoride, HF, is formed by direct reaction between hydrogen and fluorine, but the reaction is so violent that an explosion occurs:

$$H_2(g) + F_2(g) \rightarrow 2HF(g) \text{ (explosive)}$$

A more convenient way of preparing hydrogen fluoride is by the action of sulfuric acid on calcium fluoride:

$$CaF_2(s) + H_2SO_4(\ell) \rightarrow CaSO_4(s) + 2HF(g)$$

Hydrogen fluoride is extremely corrosive. It slowly dissolves glass:

$$SiO_2(s) + 4HF(g) \rightarrow SiF_4(g) + 2H_2O(\ell)$$

A design scratched into a thin wax covering on a glass surface and exposed to hydrogen fluoride appears as a frosted area on the glass when the wax is removed. Hydrogen fluoride gas can be stored in copper containers only because the inner surface of the copper is converted to copper(II) fluoride which is then inert to further attack.

Hydrogen chloride, bromide, and iodide can be prepared by direct combination of hydrogen and halogen:

$$H_2(g) + Cl_2(g) \rightarrow 2HCl(g)$$
$$H_2(g) + Br_2(g) \rightarrow 2HBr(g)$$

The reaction with iodine is not particularly useful, because only small quantities of HI are produced. A more convenient preparation of all three hydrogen halides involves gentle warming of the corresponding sodium halide with a strong acid:

$$NaCl(s) + H_2SO_4(\ell) \rightarrow HCl(g) + NaHSO_4(s)$$
$$NaBr(s) + H_3PO_4(\ell) \rightarrow HBr(g) + NaH_2PO_4(s)$$
$$NaI(s) + H_3PO_4(\ell) \rightarrow HI(g) + NaH_2PO_4(s)$$

All of the hydrogen halides dissolve readily in water to form solutions which are acidic. The aqueous solutions are called *hydrohalic acids*. Thus, an aqueous solution of HF is called hydrofluoric acid; an aqueous solution of HCl is hydrochloric acid; aqueous HBr is hydrobromic acid; and aqueous HI is called hydriodic acid (one "o" is eliminated for ease of pronunciation).

Hydrofluoric acid is a weak acid. Only a few of the HF molecules ionize in water to form H_3O^+ ions. A further complication is that F^- ions are strongly hydrogen bonded to neutral HF molecules to form HF_2^- ions:

$$HF(aq) + H_2O(\ell) \rightarrow H_3O^+(aq) + F^-(aq)$$
$$\underline{F^-(aq) + HF(aq) \rightarrow HF_2^-(aq)}$$
$$2HF(aq) + H_2O(\ell) \rightarrow H_3O^+(aq) + HF_2^-(aq)$$

Even though hydrofluoric acid is a weak acid, it must still be handled with extreme care because of its corrosive nature. It must be stored in wax or Teflon® bottles, and it must not be allowed to contact the skin, because it causes painful sores which are slow to heal.

Aqueous solutions of HCl, HBr, and HI are strong acids. Molecules of these substances are completely ionized in aqueous solution:

$$HCl(g) + H_2O(\ell) \rightarrow H_3O^+(aq) + Cl^-(aq)$$

These solutions have a sour taste, turn blue litmus red, and release hydrogen when treated with an active metal:

$$Mg(s) + 2HBr(aq) \rightarrow MgBr_2(aq) + H_2(g)$$

Both metallic and hydrogen halides have one property in common — their aqueous solutions all contain halide ions. A simple test for the presence of halide ions involves the addition of a silver nitrate solution. A precipitate indicates the presence of a halide.

$$Cl^-(aq) + Ag^+(aq) \rightarrow AgCl(s)$$
$$\text{curdy white precipitate}$$

$$Br^-(aq) + Ag^+(aq) \rightarrow AgBr(s)$$
$$\text{pale yellow precipitate}$$

$$I^-(aq) + Ag^+(aq) \rightarrow AgI(s)$$
$$\text{light yellow precipitate}$$

Silver chloride is further distinguished by its solubility in a dilute solution of ammonia:

$$AgCl(s) + 2NH_3(aq) \rightarrow Ag(NH_3)_2^+(aq) + Cl^-(aq)$$

The silver ions form a soluble complex salt with the ammonia molecules. Removal of ammonia by neutralization with an acid such as nitric acid causes the curdy white precipitate to reappear:

$$Ag(NH_3)_2^+(aq) + Cl^-(aq) + 2H_3O^+(aq) \rightarrow AgCl(s) + 2NH_4^+(aq) + 2H_2O(\ell)$$

Compounds with Oxygen

The halogens also form compounds with oxygen. Among these are oxygen difluoride, OF_2. This is a pale yellow gas which has been studied for use in rocket fuels. It is formed by passing fluorine gas through a dilute aqueous solution of sodium hydroxide:

$$2F_2(g) + 2NaOH(aq) \rightarrow OF_2(g) + 2NaF(aq) + H_2O(\ell)$$

An important halogen oxide is chlorine dioxide, ClO_2. This is a reactive, unstable, reddish-yellow gas which is a powerful oxidizing agent and reacts violently with many substances. In the paper industry, it is generated as needed and diluted with air for the bleaching of wood pulp. The equation for the preparation of ClO_2 is

$$2NaClO_3(aq) + SO_2(g) + H_2SO_4(aq) \rightarrow 2ClO_2(g) + 2NaHSO_4(aq)$$

Oxygenated Halogen Acids

Many important halogen acids contain oxygen. The simplest among these are the hypohalous acids, HXO. Aqueous solutions of chlorine, bromine, and iodine always contain small amounts of hydrohalic and hypohalous acids because of the reaction

$$X_2(aq) + H_2O(\ell) \rightleftharpoons HX(aq) + HXO(aq)$$
$$X = Cl, Br, I$$

The reaction occurs to the greatest extent when X=Cl, and to the smallest extent when X=I. The hypohalous acids are weak acids. They cannot be isolated in the pure state because they decompose readily. They are mild oxidizing agents, and a solution of chlorine in water is an oxidizing agent because of the formation of hypochlorous acid.

Sodium salts of the hypohalous acids are formed by reaction of the halogen with sodium hydroxide solution:

$$Cl_2(g) + 2NaOH(aq) \rightarrow NaCl(aq) + NaClO(aq) + H_2O(\ell)$$

Solutions of sodium hypochlorite are stable at room temperature and are sold commercially as bleach solution.

The *halous acids*, HXO_2, are weak acids. The only one of importance is chlorous acid, $HClO_2$. It is obtained by treating barium chlorite with sulfuric acid and filtering off the precipitate of barium sulfate:

$$Ba(ClO_2)_2(aq) + H_2SO_4(aq) \rightarrow 2HClO_2(aq) + BaSO_4(s)$$

Chlorous acid is a weak acid. It cannot be isolated in the pure state because it decomposes.

The *halic acids*, HXO_3, form aqueous solutions which are strong acids and powerful oxidizing agents. Chloric and bromic acids ($HClO_3$ and $HBrO_3$) are formed by the action of sulfuric acid on the corresponding barium salt:

$$Ba(ClO_3)_2(aq) + H_2SO_4(aq) \rightarrow 2HClO_3(aq) + BaSO_4(s)$$

Iodic acid, HIO_3, can be obtained as a stable, white solid by the action of concentrated nitric acid on iodine:

$$I_2(s) + 10HNO_3(\ell) \rightarrow 2HIO_3(s) + 10NO_2(g) + 4H_2O(\ell)$$

The *perhalic acids* have the general formula HXO_4. Perchloric acid, $HClO_4$, is a strong acid and a powerful oxidizing agent. Periodic acid, HIO_4, is a colourless solid with strong oxidizing power. It reacts smoothly and rapidly in many oxidation reactions.

12-16 Uses of Halogens

The halogens and their compounds are used widely. Fluorine is used industrially in the preparation of organic fluorocarbons such as Freon® and Teflon®. Freon-12® (CCl_2F_2) is a volatile, inert liquid which is widely used as a refrigerant fluid (replacing formerly used toxic gases such as SO_2 and NH_3). It has also been used as a propellant in aerosol cans, but its use in this application is diminishing because of fears that widespread use of Freon® aerosols will damage the earth's atmospheric ozone layer, allowing harmful amounts of ultraviolet radiation to reach the earth's surface. Teflon® is a heat- and corrosion-resistant polymer that finds widespread use in bearings, pipes, and various containers. Its resistance to heat and its slippery surface make it an ideal coating for kitchenware such as frying pans. Many toothpastes also contain fluorine, in the form of fluoride ions.

Chlorine is highly poisonous when inhaled, yet it is routinely used in purification of drinking water, to kill bacteria and remove undesirable tastes and odours. Its use in this area has been questioned, however, since it is now suspected that chlorine reacts with some of the substances in polluted water to produce carcinogenic (cancer-causing) compounds. Chlorine is used in enormous quantities in the bleaching of paper and textiles, where the unwanted coloured substances are oxidized to colourless compounds. Huge quantities of chlorine are used in the preparation of useful plastics (e.g., polyvinyl chloride and Saran®) and insecticides (e.g., DDT, dieldrin, aldrin, lindane).

Bromine is used mainly to make bromine compounds. Some of these are medicinal compounds. Much bromine has been used in making ethylene dibromide, $C_2H_4Br_2$, a gasoline additive, and in making silver bromide, the light-sensitive compound present in most photographic films and papers.

Iodine is used medicinally as an antiseptic. A solution of iodine in alcohol is called tincture of iodine. A small amount of iodine (0.023%) in the form of potassium iodide is added to table salt; the product is called iodized salt. The body needs to synthesize small amounts of an iodine-containing substance called thyroxin. If the diet does not provide sufficient iodine, a condition known as goiter develops, in which the thyroid gland in the neck enlarges greatly in an attempt to provide more of the necessary thyroxin.

A Final Word

In this chapter we have learned that the alkali metals and the halogens are among the most important of the elements. The chemical and physical properties of the elements in a family vary in a regular fashion from the top to the bottom of the periodic table.

The alkali metals are among the most active of all the metals. They react readily with the halogens and with oxygen, sulfur, water, nitrogen, hydrogen, and acids. Among their important compounds are their halides, oxides, hydroxides, carbonates, and sulfates.

Just as alkali metals are the most active metals, the halogen family contains the most active nonmetals. They react with hydrogen and with many other elements and compounds. Their most important compounds are the metal halides, the hydrogen halides, and aqueous solutions of the halogen acids.

Now that you have finished studying this chapter, you should reread the Key Objectives to make sure that you have learned the most important points of the chapter.

Questions

1. From what substances were the following elements first prepared: potassium, sodium, lithium? What method was used in each case?
2. What new invention enabled Bunsen and Kirchoff to discover cesium and rubidium? What property of these two elements made their discovery possible?

3. Why do the melting points and boiling points of the alkali metals decrease with increasing atomic mass?

4. Why do the alkali metals not exist as free elements in nature?

5. Why are the alkali metals powerful reducing agents?

6. Complete and balance the following equations:
   a) $K + Br_2 \rightarrow$
   b) $Rb + O_2 \rightarrow$
   c) $Cs + Se \rightarrow$
   d) $K + H_2O \rightarrow$
   e) $Na + H_2 \rightarrow$
   f) $Li + HCl \rightarrow$

7. For what reason will lithium continue to burn in air even after the oxygen has been used up?

8. Describe the preparation of sodium by the Downs process. Why is a mixture of NaCl and $CaCl_2$ used instead of NaCl in the Downs cell?

9. Why can we not make potassium by a process similar to the Downs process?

10. Complete and balance the following equations:
    a) $K_2O + H_2O \rightarrow$
    b) $K_2O_2 + H_2SO_4 \rightarrow$
    c) $Na_2O + CO_2 \rightarrow$
    d) $K_2CO_3(aq) + Ca(OH)_2(aq) \rightarrow$

11. Describe the production of sodium hydroxide solution in the Nelson cell.

12. Sodium salts are often used in place of the corresponding potassium salts. Why? There is one instance in which potassium salts must be used. What is it?

13. What are the two most widely used alkali metal compounds?

14. Describe the preparation of sodium carbonate by the Solvay process. Why has the Solvay process come into some disfavour?

15. Why is potassium hydrogen carbonate suitable for use in dry chemical fire extinguishers?

16. Why are the halogens not normally found in nature in the free state?

17. Describe the preparation of fluorine. Why is it that fluorine can be prepared only by electrolysis?

18. Describe a laboratory procedure for the preparation of chlorine gas.

19. From what source is bromine prepared commercially?

20. Describe a laboratory procedure for the preparation of iodine.

21. Which of the halogens is the most reactive?

22. Which of the hydrogen halides forms most readily? Which is the most unstable?

23. What would you expect to see when the following aqueous solutions are mixed and shaken with carbon tetrachloride: Cl_2 and I^-; Br_2 and I^-; Br_2 and Cl^-; Cl_2 and Br^-? Write equations for any reactions that take place.

24. Complete and balance the following:
    a) $Cl_2 + H_2S \rightarrow$
    b) $K + Br_2 \rightarrow$
    c) $C_2H_6 + Cl_2 \rightarrow$
    d) $Mg + HBr \rightarrow$
    e) $BBr_3 + H_2O \rightarrow$
    f) $KBr + H_3PO_4 \rightarrow$

25. What are the hydrohalic acids? Which is the weakest hydrohalic acid? Write the equation for the ionization of HBr.
26. Write the three sequential reactions which form a test for chloride ion.
27. What type of bonding would you predict to exist in compounds formed by reactions of the halogens with the alkali metals?
28. Write general formulas for hypohalous acids, halous acids, halic acids, and perhalic acids.
29. Complete and balance the following:
   a) $I_2 + H_2O \rightarrow$
   b) $Br_2 + NaOH \rightarrow$
   c) $BaBrO_2 + H_2SO_4 \rightarrow$
   d) $I_2 + HNO_3 \rightarrow$
30. What are the main uses of each of the halogens?
31. Write the formulas of three oxides of cesium.
32. Why is NaCl the only product formed when sodium is reacted with chlorine?
33. Aqueous silver nitrate was added to a solution suspected of containing a halide. A pale yellow precipitate resulted. What halide was present?
34. Why is the element fluorine so difficult to prepare?
35. Do you think that astatine is capable of oxidizing bromide ions to form bromine? Explain.
36. Why should you never pick up metallic sodium with your bare hands?

13

The Mole and Its Use

Chemists spend much of their time studying compounds and chemical reactions. When they discover a new compound, one of the things they want to know is, What is the formula of this compound? When they study a chemical reaction, one of the things they need to know is, How much of each substance is required for this reaction? In this chapter, we learn the calculations that can be used to answer these questions.

Chemists use the mole concept to determine mass relationships in chemical formulas and chemical equations. Since so many chemical calculations are based on the mole, the mole concept is one of the most important concepts in chemistry.

For example, sulfur-containing coal is burned at some thermal electric generating stations, and sulfur dioxide is one of the exhaust gases. Since sulfur dioxide is a major cause of acid rain, procedures have been developed to remove sulfur dioxide from exhaust gases. One of the procedures is to react the sulfur dioxide with calcium oxide, forming particles of calcium sulfite:

$$CaO(s) + SO_2(g) \rightarrow CaSO_3(s)$$

The calcium sulfite particles can be removed as the exhaust gases move up the smokestack. If you were the manager of such a thermal electric generating station, you might ask, ''How much calcium oxide do we need to remove the sulfur dioxide from our exhaust gases this year?'' The answer to your question would involve calculations based on the mole concept.

Key Objectives

When you have finished studying this chapter, you should be able to
1. given the formula of a substance, calculate its molecular mass (or formula mass), molar mass, and percentage composition.
2. use the molar mass of a substance to convert from grams to moles or from moles to grams.
3. given the percentage composition of a compound, calculate its empirical formula.
4. given the molecular mass and either the empirical formula or the percentage composition of a compound, calculate its molecular formula.

5. given a balanced equation and the number of grams or moles of one or two substances involved in the reaction, calculate the corresponding number of grams or moles of any other substance appearing in the equation.
6. given any two of mass of solute, volume of solution, and concentration of solution in moles per litre, calculate the third quantity.

Fig. 13-1 The coal-fired thermal electric generating station at Lingan, Nova Scotia produces 300 MW of power. (Photo courtesy of Nova Scotia Power Corporation)

13-1 Avogadro's Number and the Mole

One of the most important concepts to follow from the theory of the atom is that of atomic mass. Actually, the mass of an atom is extremely small. For example, the absolute mass of an atom of the most common isotope of oxygen is 2.66×10^{-23} g. This small number indicates that the gram is too large a mass unit to be used for determining the mass of an oxygen atom. In fact, the gram is much too large a mass unit to be used for determining the mass of any atom.

As we have learned, the atomic mass unit (u) is the unit of mass we use when obtaining the mass of any atom. One atomic mass unit is $\frac{1}{12}$ the mass of a carbon-12 atom. The carbon-12 atom has been assigned a mass of 12 u.

Fig. 13-2 Amedeo Avogadro (1776-1856) (Photo courtesy of The Bettman Archive Inc.)

Amedeo Avogadro was born in Turin, Italy, where he obtained the licentiate in philosophy at the age of 13, the baccalaureate in jurisprudence at 16, and the doctorate in ecclesiastical law four years later. He practiced law for about three years, but then tired of the petty squabbles in the courts and began a serious study of mathematics and physics.

In 1809 Avogadro became professor of physics at the Royal College at Vercelli. Two years later he published the famous hypothesis which bears his name. Not a single scientist in the world commented on it! It was partly because of his quiet, unassuming nature that his hypothesis was not immediately accepted and adopted.

Despite the lack of attention paid to his hypothesis, Avogadro continued to lead a busy life. He persisted with his studies in physics, especially of capillary action and thermal expansion of liquids. He filled many public offices, especially those connected with public education, national statistics, meteorology, and weights and measures. He did not care for prominent positions or public honours. Rather, he led the life of an old-time philosopher, wholly occupied in his studies but not forgetting his duties as a citizen and as a father.

In 1820 Avogadro was appointed professor of mathematical physics at the University of Turin, where he worked quietly until his retirement. He died peacefully in his 80th year.

The mass of the most common oxygen isotope is about $\frac{4}{3}$ as great as the mass of carbon-12. Therefore, the mass of an atom of oxygen is about 16 u ($12 \times \frac{4}{3} = 16$). A more accurate value is 15.994 91 u. This is an extremely small amount of mass. No balance is capable of measuring such a small quantity of matter.

Thus, it is not possible to measure the masses of individual atoms. However, an important aspect of chemistry is calculating mass relationships involved in chemical reactions. Chemists frequently carry out chemical reactions between measured quantities of substances. They must be able to calculate the amount of one substance needed to react with or to produce a required quantity of another substance.

Let us consider a simple chemical reaction. Iron and sulfur react to form iron(II) sulfide. If we wanted to use just enough sulfur to react with a measured amount of iron, it would be useful to know the relationship between the mass of iron and the mass of sulfur involved in the reaction. That is, how much iron reacts with how much sulfur? The chemical equation for this reaction is

$$Fe(s) + S(s) \rightarrow FeS(s)$$

Since the iron atoms and the sulfur atoms react on a one-to-one basis to form iron(II) sulfide, a mass relationship in this reaction can be determined by looking up the atomic masses of iron and sulfur in a set of tables. Thus, 56 u of iron reacts with 32 u of sulfur to produce iron(II) sulfide. However, it is not possible to measure 56 u of iron or 32 u of sulfur, and this mass relationship is not particularly useful.

Since it is impossible to react one iron atom with one sulfur atom, a large number of iron atoms must be reacted with an *equal* number of sulfur atoms. The large number which is convenient to use is Avogadro's number (N). In Section 3-16, it was established that Avogadro's number of atoms of any element has a mass in grams numerically equal to the element's atomic mass. The atomic masses of iron and sulfur are 56 u and 32 u respectively. Therefore, Avogadro's number of iron atoms has a mass of 56 g, and Avogadro's number of sulfur atoms has a mass of 32 g. The mass relationship is that 56 g of iron (Avogadro's number of iron atoms) reacts with 32 g of sulfur (Avogadro's number of sulfur atoms) to produce iron(II) sulfide.

The Mole Concept

The quantity of a substance which is useful for determining mass relationships in chemical reactions is called the mole. The definition of the atomic mass unit is based on the carbon-12 atom, and so is the definition of the mole. A **mole** of a substance is the quantity of that substance which contains the same number of chemical units (atoms, molecules, formula units, or ions) as there are atoms in exactly 12 g of carbon-12. Of course, 12 g is the mass of carbon which is numerically equal to the atomic mass of carbon, and therefore 12 g of carbon contains Avogadro's number of carbon atoms. A mole can thus be considered to be the mass of any substance which contains Avogadro's number of chemical units of the substance.

The **molar mass** of a substance is the mass of one mole of the substance. In the case of an element, the molar mass is the atomic mass of the element expressed in grams. We shall discuss the molar masses of compounds in Section 13-5. The molar mass of carbon is 12 g, and this mass of carbon consists of Avogadro's number of carbon atoms. The molar mass of iron is 56 g, and this mass of iron consists of Avogadro's number of iron atoms. The molar mass of sulfur is 32 g, and this mass of sulfur consists of Avogadro's number of sulfur atoms.

13-2 Determining Avogadro's Number

How large is Avogadro's number? One method for determining Avogadro's number makes use of radioactive substances which emit alpha particles. Alpha particles are helium nuclei (He^{2+}). Chemists have learned that one mole of any gas will occupy 22.4 L at $0°C$ and a pressure of 101.3 kPa. Therefore, one mole of helium will occupy 22.4 L at $0°C$ and 101.3 kPa. If a radioactive element emits alpha particles, it is possible to design the experiment so that the charges of the alpha particles are neutralized and helium atoms are produced:

$$He^{2+} + 2e^- \rightarrow He$$

One can then count the number of alpha particles emitted with a Geiger counter, measure the volume of helium gas produced, correct this volume to

0°C and 101.3 kPa, and calculate Avogadro's number (N).

$$N = \frac{\text{alpha particles counted}}{\text{litres of He produced}} \times \frac{22.4 \text{ L}}{1 \text{ mol}}$$

Experiments like this have shown that Avogadro's number is 6.02×10^{23}. Therefore, if the atomic mass of iron is 55.8 u, then the mass of 6.02×10^{23} iron atoms is 55.8 g. If the atomic mass of sulfur is 32.1 u, the mass of 6.02×10^{23} sulfur atoms is 32.1 g. If the atomic mass of any element is x u, the mass of 6.02×10^{23} atoms of that element is x g. One mole of an element consists of 6.02×10^{23} atoms of the element. The mass of one mole of the element is the atomic mass of the element expressed in grams.

Practice Problem 13-1

In an actual experiment, 1.82×10^{17} alpha particles were counted. The helium gas which was produced occupied a volume of 0.006 73 mL at 0°C and 101.3 kPa. Show that this experiment gives a value of 6.06×10^{23} for Avogadro's number.

13-3 The Number of Atoms in a Given Mass of an Element

One mole (1 mol) of atoms of an element consists of 6.02×10^{23} atoms. One mole of sulfur has a mass of 32 g. That is, 6.02×10^{23} atoms of sulfur have a total mass of 32 g. Suppose 8.0 g of sulfur were measured. How many atoms of sulfur would be present? If 32 g of sulfur is the mass of 1 mol, then 8.0 g of sulfur is $\frac{8.0}{32} = 0.25$ mol. Now 1 mol of sulfur contains 6.02×10^{23} atoms, and 0.25 mol of sulfur contains $0.25 \times 6.02 \times 10^{23} = 1.5 \times 10^{23}$ atoms. There would be 1.5×10^{23} sulfur atoms present in an 8.0 g sample of sulfur.

Sample Problem 13-1

How many iron atoms are present in a 167.4 g sample of iron?

SOLUTION
1 mol Fe = 55.8 g Fe

x mol Fe = 167.4 g Fe $\times \dfrac{1 \text{ mol Fe}}{55.8 \text{ g Fe}}$ = 3.00 mol Fe

1 mol Fe contains 6.02×10^{23} atoms Fe

x atoms Fe = 3.00 mol Fe $\times \dfrac{6.02 \times 10^{23}}{1.00 \text{ mol Fe}}$ atoms Fe

$\qquad = 1.81 \times 10^{24}$ atoms Fe

Practice Problem 13-2

How many argon atoms are present in a 10.0 g sample of argon? (*Answer:* 1.51×10^{23})

13-4 Molecular Mass and Formula Mass

When atoms combine to form molecules, mass is neither created nor destroyed. Thus the mass of a molecule such as carbon dioxide (CO_2) can be obtained by adding the masses of each atom in the molecule. In the case of carbon dioxide there is one carbon atom (12 u) and two oxygen atoms (16 u each) in every molecule. Therefore the *molecular mass* of carbon dioxide is $12+16+16=44$ u.

In the case of a crystal of ionically-bonded material like NaCl, CaF_2, or AlF_3 the formulas do not describe molecules. The formula NaCl should suggest to you that a crystal of sodium chloride is made up of positive sodium ions attracted to negative chloride ions and that there is one sodium ion for every one chloride ion in the crystal. The formula CaF_2 should suggest that there are two fluoride ions for every one calcium ion in a crystal of calcium fluoride; and the formula $Al(NO_3)_3$ should suggest that there are three nitrate ions for every one aluminum ion in a crystal of aluminum nitrate. Thus, in solid ionic materials like sodium chloride there are no molecules—only arrangements of ions. Therefore, we do not speak of the molecular mass of NaCl. We speak of the *formula mass*. However, there is no problem in obtaining the formula mass of sodium chloride. One merely adds the mass of sodium (23.0 u) to the mass of chlorine (35.5 u) and obtains a formula mass of 58.5 u for NaCl.

Sample Problem 13-2

Alanine, $C_3H_7NO_2$, is a compound which is one of the building blocks of protein. What is the molecular mass of alanine?

SOLUTION

$$
\begin{aligned}
3\,C &= 3 \times 12.0\ u = 36.0\ u \\
7\,H &= 7 \times 1.0\ u = 7.0\ u \\
1\,N &= 1 \times 14.0\ u = 14.0\ u \\
2\,O &= 2 \times 16.0\ u = \underline{32.0\ u}
\end{aligned}
$$

The molecular mass of alanine = 89.0 u

Sample Problem 13-3

What is the formula mass of aluminum nitrate, $Al(NO_3)_3$?

SOLUTION

$$
\begin{aligned}
1\,Al &= 1 \times 27.0\ u = 27.0\ u \\
3\,N &= 3 \times 14.0\ u = 42.0\ u \\
9\,O &= 9 \times 16.0\ u = 144.0\ u
\end{aligned}
$$

The formula mass of aluminum nitrate = 213.0 u

Practice Problem 13-3

What is the molecular mass of H_2SO_4? What is the formula mass of $Ca(HSO_4)_2$?
(*Answers:* 98.1 u; 234.3 u)

13-5 Expanding the Mole Concept

We have learned that Avogadro's number of atoms of any element has a mass in grams numerically equal to the atomic mass of the element. We have also learned that a mole is the quantity of any substance which contains Avogadro's number of chemical units of the substance. We can expand the mole concept to include compounds.

A sample of formaldehyde consists of CH_2O molecules:

$$1\,C = 1 \times 12.0\,u = 12.0\,u$$
$$2\,H = 2 \times 1.0\,u = 2.0\,u$$
$$1\,O = 1 \times 16.0\,u = \underline{16.0\,u}$$
$$\text{molecular mass} = 30.0\,u$$

One mole of formaldehyde is the quantity which contains Avogadro's number (N) of formaldehyde molecules. Each formaldehyde molecule contains one carbon atom, two hydrogen atoms, and one oxygen atom. Therefore, Avogadro's number of formaldehyde molecules contains N carbon atoms, $2\,N$ hydrogen atoms, and N oxygen atoms:

$$1\,N\,C = 1 \times 12.0\,g = 12.0\,g$$
$$2\,N\,H = 2 \times 1.0\,g = 2.0\,g$$
$$1\,N\,O = 1 \times 16.0\,g = \underline{16.0\,g}$$
$$\text{molar mass} = 30.0\,g$$

The molar mass of formaldehyde is its molecular mass expressed in grams.

The molar mass of a molecular compound is its molecular mass expressed in grams. Similarly, the molar mass of an ionic compound is its formula mass expressed in grams, and the molar mass of an ion is its ionic mass expressed in grams. For example, the molar mass of NaCl is 58.5 g, and the molar mass of OH^- is 17.0 g.

Practice Problem 13-4

What is the molar mass of each of the following: $C_3H_7NO_2$, $Al(NO_3)_3$, H_2SO_4, $Ca(HSO_4)_2$, and PO_4^{3-}? (*Answers:* 89.0 g; 213.0 g; 98.1 g; 234.3 g; 95.0 g)

Sample Problem 13-4

a) How many molecules are present in 5.00 mol of CH_2O?
b) How many atoms are present in 5.00 mol of CH_2O?

SOLUTION
a)   1 mol CH_2O = 6.02 × 10^{23} molecules CH_2O

$$x \text{ molecules } CH_2O = 5.00\,\cancel{\text{mol } CH_2O} \times \frac{6.02 \times 10^{23} \text{ molecules } CH_2O}{1.00\,\cancel{\text{mol } CH_2O}}$$
$$= 3.01 \times 10^{24} \text{ molecules } CH_2O$$

b)   1 molecule CH_2O contains 4 atoms

$$1 \text{ mol } CH_2O = 6.02 \times 10^{23} \text{ molecules } CH_2O \times \frac{4 \text{ atoms}}{1 \text{ molecule } CH_2O}$$

$$= 2.41 \times 10^{24} \text{ atoms}$$

$$x \text{ atoms} = 5.00 \text{ mol } CH_2O \times \frac{2.41 \times 10^{24} \text{ atoms}}{1.00 \text{ mol } CH_2O}$$

$$= 1.20 \times 10^{25} \text{ atoms}$$

Practice Problem 13-5

How many molecules are present in 7.50 mol of H_2SO_4? How many atoms are present in 0.45 mol of H_2SO_4? (*Answers:* 4.52×10^{24} molecules; 1.9×10^{24} atoms)

Sample Problem 13-5

How many moles are present in 23.1 g of $Al(NO_3)_3$?

SOLUTION

$$1.00 \text{ mol } Al(NO_3)_3 = 213 \text{ g } Al(NO_3)_3$$

$$x \text{ mol } Al(NO_3)_3 = 23.1 \text{ g } Al(NO_3)_3 \times \frac{1.00 \text{ mol } Al(NO_3)_3}{213 \text{ g } Al(NO_3)_3}$$

$$= 0.108 \text{ mol } Al(NO_3)_3$$

Practice Problem 13-6

How many moles are present in 139 g of $HC_2H_3O_2$? (*Answer:* 2.32 mol)

Sample Problem 13-6

What is the mass of 0.763 mol of HNO_3?

SOLUTION

$$1.00 \text{ mol } HNO_3 = 63.0 \text{ g } HNO_3$$

$$x \text{ g } HNO_3 = 0.763 \text{ mol } HNO_3 \times \frac{63.0 \text{ g } HNO_3}{1.00 \text{ mol } HNO_3}$$

$$= 48.1 \text{ g } HNO_3$$

Practice Problem 13-7

What is the mass of 2.40 mol of NaCl? (*Answer:* 140 g)

Sample Problem 13-7

How many atoms are present in 15.0 g of CH_2O?

SOLUTION
From Sample Problem 13-4,

$$1 \text{ mol } CH_2O = 2.41 \times 10^{24} \text{ atoms}$$
$$\text{also } 1 \text{ mol } CH_2O = 30.0 \text{ g } CH_2O$$
$$\therefore 2.41 \times 10^{24} \text{ atoms} = 30.0 \text{ g } CH_2O$$
$$x \text{ atoms} = 15.0 \text{ g } CH_2O \times \frac{2.41 \times 10^{24} \text{ atoms}}{30.0 \text{ g } CH_2O}$$
$$= 1.20 \times 10^{24} \text{ atoms}$$

Practice Problem 13-8

How many atoms are present in 27 g of H_2SO_4? In 16 g of Br_2? (*Answers:* 1.2×10^{24} atoms; 1.2×10^{23} atoms)

Sample Problem 13-8

Formula units

What is the mass of 1.71×10^{24} ~~molecules~~ of H_2SO_4?

SOLUTION

$$1 \text{ mol } H_2SO_4 = 6.02 \times 10^{23} \text{ molecules } H_2SO_4$$
$$\text{also } 1 \text{ mol } H_2SO_4 = 98.1 \text{ g } H_2SO_4$$
$$\therefore 6.02 \times 10^{23} \text{ molecules } H_2SO_4 = 98.1 \text{ g } H_2SO_4$$
$$x \text{ g } H_2SO_4 = 1.71 \times 10^{24} \text{ molecules } H_2SO_4 \times \frac{98.1 \text{ g } H_2SO_4}{6.02 \times 10^{23} \text{ molecules } H_2SO_4}$$
$$= 279 \text{ g } H_2SO_4$$

Practice Problem 13-9

What is the mass of 2.50×10^{22} molecules of $C_3H_7NO_2$? (*Answer:* 3.70 g)

13-6 Percentage Composition

In Sample Problem 13-2 the molecular mass of alanine was calculated to be 89.0 u. How much of this mass was contributed by the 3 carbon atoms, by the 7 hydrogen atoms, by the nitrogen atom, and by the 2 oxygen atoms? In other words, what is the *percentage composition* of alanine? The percentage composition by mass of a substance can be calculated as shown in Sample Problems 13-9, 13-10, and 13-11.

Sample Problem 13-9

What is the percentage composition of hydrogen peroxide, H_2O_2?

SOLUTION

The total atomic mass of hydrogen in H_2O_2 is $2 \times 1.0\ u = 2.0\ u$

The total atomic mass of oxygen in H_2O_2 is $2 \times 16.0\ u = \underline{32.0\ u}$

The total molecular mass of $H_2O_2 = 34.0\ u$

$$\% H = \frac{\text{mass of H in 1 molecule}}{\text{mass of molecule}} \times 100\%$$

$$= \frac{2.0\ u}{34.0\ u} \times 100\% = 5.9\%$$

$$\% O = \frac{\text{mass of O in 1 molecule}}{\text{mass of molecule}} \times 100\%$$

$$= \frac{32.0\ u}{34.0\ u} \times 100\% = 94.1\%$$

Sample Problem 13-10

What is the percentage composition of nitric acid, HNO_3?

SOLUTION

The total atomic mass of hydrogen in HNO_3 is $1 \times 1.0\ u = 1.0\ u$

The total atomic mass of nitrogen in HNO_3 is $1 \times 14.0\ u = 14.0\ u$

The total atomic mass of oxygen in HNO_3 is $3 \times 16.0\ u = \underline{48.0\ u}$

The total molecular mass of $HNO_3 = 63.0\ u$

$$\% H = \frac{\text{mass of H in 1 molecule}}{\text{mass of molecule}} \times 100\%$$

$$= \frac{1.0\ u}{63.0\ u} \times 100\% = 1.6\%$$

$$\% N = \frac{\text{mass of N in 1 molecule}}{\text{mass of molecule}} \times 100\%$$

$$= \frac{14.0\ u}{63.0\ u} \times 100\% = 22.2\%$$

$$\% O = \frac{\text{mass of O in 1 molecule}}{\text{mass of molecule}} \times 100\%$$

$$= \frac{48.0\ u}{63.0\ u} \times 100\% = 76.2\%$$

Sample Problem 13-11

What is the percentage composition of alanine, $C_3H_7NO_2$?

SOLUTION

The total atomic mass of carbon in alanine is $3 \times 12.0\ u = 36.0\ u$

The total atomic mass of hydrogen in alanine is $7 \times 1.0\ u = 7.0\ u$

The total atomic mass of nitrogen in alanine is $1 \times 14.0\ u = 14.0\ u$

The total atomic mass of oxygen in alanine is $2 \times 16.0\ u = \underline{32.0\ u}$

The total molecular mass of alanine $= 89.0\ u$

$$\% \text{ C} = \frac{\text{mass of C in 1 molecule}}{\text{mass of molecule}} \times 100\%$$

$$= \frac{36.0 \text{ u}}{89.0 \text{ u}} \times 100\% = 40.4\%$$

$$\% \text{ H} = \frac{\text{mass of H in 1 molecule}}{\text{mass of molecule}} \times 100\%$$

$$= \frac{7.0 \text{ u}}{89.0 \text{ u}} \times 100\% = 7.9\%$$

$$\% \text{ N} = \frac{\text{mass of N in 1 molecule}}{\text{mass of molecule}} \times 100\%$$

$$= \frac{14.0 \text{ u}}{89.0 \text{ u}} \times 100\% = 15.7\%$$

$$\% \text{ O} = \frac{\text{mass of O in 1 molecule}}{\text{mass of molecule}} \times 100\%$$

$$= \frac{32.0 \text{ u}}{89.0 \text{ u}} \times 100\% = 36.0\%$$

Practice Problem 13-10

What is the percentage composition of barium peroxide, BaO_2? (*Answer:* 81.1% Ba; 18.9% O)

Practice Problem 13-11

What is the percentage composition of sulfuric acid, H_2SO_4? (*Answer:* 2.0% H; 32.7% S; 65.2% O)

Practice Problem 13-12

What is the percentage composition of potassium hydrogen oxalate, KHC_2O_4? (*Answer:* 30.5% K; 0.8% H; 18.7% C; 50.0% O)

13-7 Empirical Formula Determination

When a new compound is prepared, chemists are interested in determining its formula. They do this by analyzing the molecule to find out its percentage composition. The percentage composition information is then used to determine the empirical formula.

The **empirical formula** is the simplest formula. It gives a bare minimum of information about the compound because it shows only the relative numbers of moles of each type of atom in the compound. In writing the empirical formula, we write the symbols of the elements with subscripts to designate the relative numbers of moles of these elements. The empirical formula CH_2O represents a compound in which there is 1 mol of carbon atoms and 2 mol of hydrogen atoms for every 1 mol of oxygen atoms. However, 1 mol of atoms of

Robert Boyle was the seventh son and fourteenth child of fifteen born to the Earl of Cork. He was sent to Eton at age 8 and to Geneva three years later for completion of his studies. He returned to England in 1644 to reside in Dorset. Here he was admitted to the *invisible college*, the forerunner of the Royal Institution. In the same year he moved to Oxford, where young Robert Hooke assisted him in his investigation of "The Spring of the Air."

By 1659 he had constructed a new and superior air pump, which he used to prove that air pressure supports the column of a mercury barometer and to demonstrate the connection between pressure and the boiling point of water. Criticism led him to conduct further experiments, which resulted in the publication of his famous law two years later.

In addition to the formulation of his Law, Boyle taught the value of experimentation. In his book *The Sceptical Chymist*, he examined the pretensions of the chemists of his time and exposed the mixture of error and imposture in most of their writings. He was the first to use the term "chemical analysis" in its modern sense. He showed that not only fire is to be used in the analysis of compounds, but other substances may also be necessary. He laid the foundations of modern analytical chemistry.

In 1669, Boyle moved to London and lived as an invalid, the victim of a lifelong kidney disorder which led to his death in 1691.

Fig. 14-3 Robert Boyle (1627-1691) (Photo courtesy of The Bettman Archive, Inc.)

theorized that the atmosphere should balance a much shorter column of mercury than water. Mercury is 13.6 times as dense as water, so the column ought to be only $\frac{1}{13.6}$ as high as 10.3 m, or about 0.8 m. Torricelli tried the experiment in 1643 using a closed tube and found that the mercury column stayed at a level of about 760 mm (0.76 m). This experiment led him to the invention of the mercury barometer, a device which measures the small variations in atmospheric pressure (Fig. 14-2(b)).

14-2 Robert Boyle

Robert Boyle (Fig. 14-3) was a dedicated scientist who remained single throughout his life and devoted all his effort to the study of science and religion. With his new, more efficient air pump he conducted many experiments. In one experiment he placed a barometer inside a container from which he could pump the air. He found that the mercury level fell as the air was removed from the container (Fig. 14-4, overleaf). Boyle felt this proved conclusively that it was the pressure of the air on the surface of the mercury which supported the column, thus confirming Torricelli's findings.

Boyle published his results the following year. His conclusions were immediately attacked by Franciscus Linus, a Jesuit priest. Linus explained the action of a barometer by supposing that the mercury column was held up by an invisible internal cord. Boyle naturally felt this was a poor hypothesis and immediately began a series of experiments to support his own. In this process he formulated Boyle's Law, which stated the mathematical relationship between the pressure of a gas and its volume.

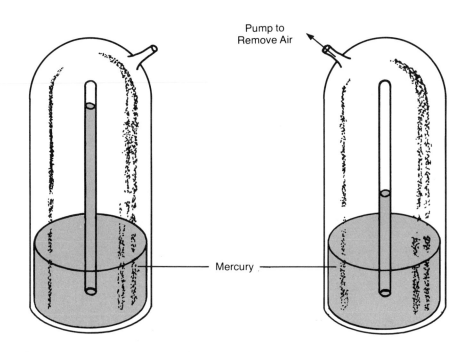

Pump to Remove Air

Mercury

14-3 Boyle's Law

With a J-shaped tube similar to that shown in Fig. 14-5, Boyle used a column of mercury to trap a sample of air in the short closed end. When he added more mercury to the longer open end, the air was compressed to a smaller volume. When he decreased the pressure by removing mercury, the air expanded to a greater volume. When he measured the air volumes corresponding to varying pressures, he noticed a simple relationship. Some of his data are given in Table 14-1.

TABLE 14-1 Some of Robert Boyle's Data

VOLUME OF AIR V(m)*	PRESSURE P(m)†	PV PRODUCT
0.305	0.74	0.226
0.254	0.90	0.229
0.203	1.12	0.227
0.152	1.49	0.226
0.102	2.23	0.227

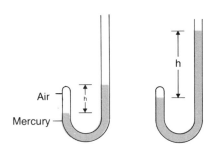

Air

Mercury

Fig. 14-5 Boyle's Apparatus. The longer the column of mercury, h, the more the air is compressed.

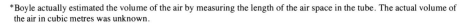

*Boyle actually estimated the volume of the air by measuring the length of the air space in the tube. The actual volume of the air in cubic metres was unknown.

†Boyle expressed the pressure as the height (h) in metres of the mercury column plus the pressure of the atmosphere above the open end, which he estimated at 0.74 m. The metre is not an SI unit of pressure and will not be used as such in this book again. It is used here for historical reasons only.

Boyle noticed that the product of the volume of air times the pressure exerted on it was very nearly a constant (in this case 0.227), or PV = constant. This can be rearranged as

$$P = \frac{\text{constant}}{V} \quad \text{or} \quad V = \frac{\text{constant}}{P}$$

Note that if V increases, P decreases proportionately, and vice versa. Such relations are called inverse relations or inverse proportions. These expressions are simply the mathematical expression of **Boyle's Law** which states that *the volume of a fixed mass of a gas varies inversely with the pressure, provided the temperature remains constant*. Actually, Boyle was not really concerned about the effects of temperature. Luckily for him the temperature stayed roughly constant during his experiments.

Since gases tend to resist being squeezed into a smaller volume, Boyle thought in terms of the "spring" of gases. He thought that gases were made up of very small particles similar to extremely minute coiled springs. Gases exerted a pressure because the "ether" (a mysterious "something" that was thought to fill the spaces between the gas particles) whirled the particles so violently that each particle tried to prevent all others from coming into its own neighbourhood.

14-4 Charles' Law

Boyle had investigated the relationship between the volume and the pressure of a gas in 1659. However, it was not until 1787, over a century later, that the French physicist J. A. Charles discovered the relationship between the volume and the temperature of a gas at constant pressure.

We are all familiar with the fact that gases expand when heated and contract on cooling. A balloon becomes larger when held over a hot stove and smaller when the balloon is removed from the heat. Many motorists release air from their tires to relieve the pressure caused by heat buildup from sustained high-speed driving. The problem is that they may forget to replace this when tire temperatures return to normal, and the tire may wear excessively because of under-inflation.

Charles' experiments were rather crude and were later performed more accurately in 1801 by John Dalton and in 1802 by the French chemist Joseph Louis Gay-Lussac. Nevertheless Charles deserves the credit for the early investigations.

We can repeat Charles' early observations by using a mercury "piston," made by trapping a quantity of air in a piece of narrow-bore glass tubing with a small plug of mercury (Fig. 14-6). Since the tube is open to the atmosphere and the mercury is free to move up and down the tube, the pressure exerted on the trapped air remains constant. If the tube is immersed in hot water, the air expands and the mercury plug moves up the tube. Typical data for a Charles' law experiment are shown on Table 14-2, overleaf.

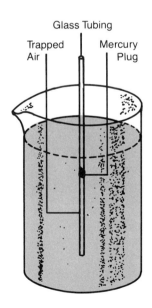

Fig. 14-6 Charles' Law Experiment

TABLE 14-2 Typical Data for Charles' Law Experiment

TEMPERATURE, T (°C)	GAS VOLUME V (mm³)
0	648
25	714
50	766
75	817
100	885

It is obvious that the volume increases as the Celsius temperature increases. The relationship is not a direct proportionality, however, because doubling the temperature from 50°C to 100°C results in a volume increase of only $\frac{885}{766}$ or 1.16 times. A graph of volume versus temperature is a straight line, showing that the increase in volume is regular and uniform (Fig. 14-7).

Fig. 14-7 Graph of Charles' Law Data

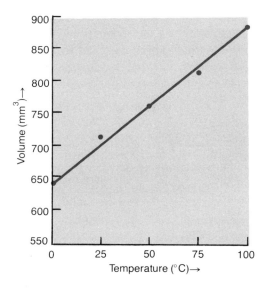

What is the relationship? We notice that at 100°C the volume is $\frac{885}{648}$ or 1.366 times the volume at 0°C. An increase in temperature of 100°C causes a volume increase of 0.366 times the volume at 0°C. So an increase in temperature of 1°C causes an increase in volume of $\frac{0.366}{100}$ or 0.003 66 times its volume at 0°C. The decimal fraction 0.003 66 is equivalent to the proper fraction $\frac{1}{273}$. So another way of stating the results of the experiment is that the volume of a sample of gas at 0°C increases by $\frac{1}{273}$ of its original volume for each degree it is warmed above 0°C. We can check this statement: at 75°C the volume should be $1\frac{75}{273}$ or 1.275 times the volume at 0°C. The predicted volume is 1.275×648 mm³ $= 826$ mm³. The experimental value is 817 mm³. The difference can be attributed to the difficulty of making sufficiently precise measurements (experimental error!).

The Kelvin Scale

If the results of the experiment are valid, we should be able to state the results in a different way: the volume of a gas at 0°C decreases by $\frac{1}{273}$ of its original volume for each degree it is cooled below 0°C. At some temperature, the volume of the gas should become zero. What is this temperature? It is −273°C. In practice, this zero volume has never been observed because all gases liquefy and the majority solidify before reaching −273°C. Nevertheless, −273°C is a theoretically important temperature. The *Kelvin scale* is based on it. In this scale, −273°C becomes zero kelvins (0 K). This is called *absolute zero*. Other temperatures are obtained simply by adding 273 to the corresponding Celsius temperature. Thus, the freezing point of water is 273 K and the boiling point of water is 373 K. (Notice that the degree symbol is omitted when writing Kelvin temperatures.)

Let us now reexamine the data of Table 14-2, expressing the temperatures in the Kelvin scale shown in Table 14-3. Now we see that increasing the temperature from 273 K to 373 K (a factor of $\frac{373}{273} = 1.366$) causes the volume to increase from 648 mm³ to 885 mm³, also a factor of $\frac{885}{648} = 1.366$. There is now a direct proportionality. We can now state **Charles' Law** in modern terms: *the volume of a fixed mass of gas varies directly with the Kelvin temperature, provided the pressure remains constant.*

$$V = \text{constant} \times T$$

TABLE 14-3 Data for Charles' Law Experiment

TEMPERATURE		VOLUME
°C	K	mm³
0	273	648
25	298	714
50	323	766
75	348	817
100	373	885

14-5 Application of Boyle's and Charles' Laws

If we know the volume and the pressure of a fixed mass of gas at a given temperature, then we can use Boyle's Law to calculate the volume at any other pressure, or the pressure at any other volume. For example, a 2.00 L sample of a gas at a pressure of 1000 kPa is allowed to expand until its pressure drops to 300 kPa. If the temperature remains constant, what will be the new volume?

To solve this problem, let us first list the quantities we know and those we are to find:

$$P_{old} = 1000 \text{ kPa}^* \qquad P_{new} = 300 \text{ kPa}$$
$$V_{old} = 2.00 \text{ L} \qquad V_{new} = ?$$

We know that since volume depends on the pressure, the new volume should equal the old volume multiplied by a quantity which we shall call a pressure factor:

$$V_{new} = V_{old} \times (\text{pressure factor})$$

The pressure factor is the ratio of the two pressures. It is either 1000 kPa/300 kPa or 300 kPa/1000 kPa. The first of these is a number greater than one. The second is a number smaller than one. Since a gas expands as the pressure decreases, the new volume must be larger than the old volume, and the pressure factor must be a number greater than one:

$$V_{new} = 2.00 \text{ L} \times \frac{1000 \text{ kPa}}{300 \text{ kPa}} = 6.67 \text{ L}$$

If the 6.67 L of gas in the previous example was orginally at a temperature of 300 K and is now cooled to 150 K, what will be its new volume?

In this case the new volume is the old volume multiplied by a temperature factor:

$$V_{new} = V_{old} \times (\text{temperature factor})$$

The temperature factor is either 150 K/300 K or 300 K/150 K. Since Charles' Law tells us that gases contract on cooling, the temperature factor is a number less than one, and we can write

$$V_{new} = 6.67 \text{ L} \times \frac{150 \text{ K}}{300 \text{ K}} = 3.33 \text{ L}$$

It is possible to combine the two laws into one mathematical operation. The question might have been worded like this: A certain mass of a gas occupies a volume of 2.00 L at a pressure of 1000 kPa and a temperature of 300 K. What will be its volume at a pressure of 300 kPa and a temperature of 150 K?

We could then write

$$V_{new} = V_{old} \times (\text{pressure factor}) \times (\text{temperature factor})$$

Using the same arguments as before we would find

$$V_{new} = 2.00 \text{ L} \times \frac{1000 \text{ kPa}}{300 \text{ kPa}} \times \frac{150 \text{ K}}{300 \text{ K}} = 3.33 \text{ L}$$

---

*Note: The symbol for the SI unit of pressure called the kilopascal is kPa. The normal atmospheric pressure at sea level is about 101 kPa. Laboratory barometers are usually calibrated to measure atmospheric pressure in millimetres of mercury. One millimetre of mercury exerts a pressure of 133 Pa or 0.133 kPa.

Practice Problem 14-1

If a given mass of a gas occupies a volume of 8.4 L at a pressure of 101 kPa, what is its volume at a pressure of 112 kPa and the same temperature? (*Answer*: 7.6 L)

Practice Problem 14-2

If a given mass of a gas occupies a volume of 4.2 L at a temperature of 0°C, what is its volume at a temperature of 91°C, if the pressure remains constant? (*Answer*: 5.6 L)

Practice Problem 14-3

If a given mass of a gas occupies a volume of 6.3 L at a pressure of 101 kPa and 0°C, what volume will it occupy at a pressure of 143 kPa and a temperature of 113°C? (*Answer*: 6.3 L)

14-6 Standard Temperature and Pressure

Since the volume of a gas varies with temperature and pressure, it is customary to choose some standard conditions of temperature and pressure so that the properties of different gases can be compared on a uniform basis. The choice is rather arbitrary, but usually the pressure of the atmosphere at sea level (101.3 kPa) is chosen as **standard pressure**. The freezing point of water (0°C or 273 K) is chosen as **standard temperature**. These two conditions together are usually referred to as **standard temperature and pressure**, or **STP**. Scientists do not usually measure gas volumes at STP, but they usually use Boyle's and Charles' Laws to ''correct'' their experimental values to standard conditions.

For example, a chemist may find that a sample of a gas occupies a volume of 43.4 mL at a pressure of 97.3 kPa and a temperature of 27°C. What is its volume at STP?

We can summarize the data as

$$V_{old} = 43.4 \text{ mL} \qquad V_{new} = ?$$
$$P_{old} = 97.3 \text{ kPa} \qquad P_{new} = 101.3 \text{ kPa}$$
$$T_{old} = 27°C = 300 \text{ K} \qquad T_{new} = 0°C = 273 \text{ K}$$

$$V_{new} = V_{old} \times \text{(pressure factor)} \times \text{(temperature factor)}$$

Since pressure increases, volume decreases, and the pressure factor <1. Since temperature decreases, volume decreases, and the temperature factor <1.

$$\therefore V_{new} = 43.4 \text{ mL} \times \frac{97.3 \text{ kPa}}{101.3 \text{ kPa}} \times \frac{273 \text{ K}}{300 \text{ K}} = 37.9 \text{ mL}$$

Practice Problem 14-4

What is the STP volume of a sample of gas which occupies 500 mL at a temperature of 100°C and a pressure of 200 kPa? (*Answer*: 723 mL)

14-7 Dalton's Law of Partial Pressures

We have already noted that John Dalton performed experiments with gases. He had a keen interest in the weather, and his early experiments dealt with measuring the water content of the air. In Dalton's time air was generally thought to be a compound of oxygen, nitrogen, and water. Dalton showed that air always contained 21 parts of oxygen for every 79 parts of nitrogen, but the amount of water vapour in the air varied. He concluded that air was a mixture. He demonstrated that if he added water vapour to a sample of dry air, the pressure exerted by the air increased. The increase in pressure was just equal to that exerted by the water vapour alone at the same temperature. As a result of these observations and his experiments with other gas mixtures as well, Dalton formulated the law which is now called **Dalton's Law of Partial Pressures**. The total pressure exerted by a mixture of gases is the sum of the pressures of each gas when measured alone:

$$P_{total} = P_1 + P_2 + P_3 + \cdots$$

For example, let us add 1.00 L of nitrogen with a pressure of 100 kPa to 1.00 L of oxygen with a pressure of 200 kPa. If the temperature is constant and the volume remains at 1.00 L, the new pressure will be 300 kPa:

$$P_{total} = P_{nitrogen} + P_{oxygen} = 100 \text{ kPa} + 200 \text{ kPa} = 300 \text{ kPa}$$

Dalton's studies led him to believe that a gas consisted of particles which could move throughout a volume already occupied by the particles of another gas, without being affected by the gas particles already there, provided the gases did not react. This was a reasonable assumption provided that gas particles were extremely small compared to the distances between them.

Oxygen is usually prepared in the laboratory by heating potassium chlorate and collecting the gas over water (Fig. 14-8). The gas collected is not pure oxygen. It is a mixture of oxygen and water vapour. We must correct for (allow for) the presence of this water vapour whenever we wish to make calculations involving the pressure or volume of a gas collected over water. Say, for example, that we have collected 400 mL of oxygen over water at a temperature of 27°C (300 K) and at an atmospheric pressure of 100.0 kPa. According to Dalton's Law,

$$P_{total} = P_{oxygen} + P_{water\ vapour}$$

or

$$P_{oxygen} = P_{total} - P_{water\ vapour}$$

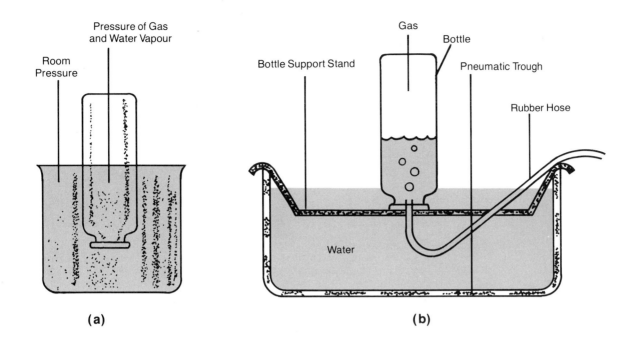

(a)

(b)

At 27°C the vapour pressure of the water is 3.57 kPa. (See Appendix D for a table for water vapour pressures at various temperatures.)

$$\therefore P_{\text{oxygen}} = 100.0 \text{ kPa} - 3.57 \text{ kPa} = 96.4 \text{ kPa}$$

What would be the volume of the dry oxygen at 27°C and 100.0 kPa? If the water vapour were removed, the pressure exerted by 400 mL of dry oxygen would be 96.4 kPa. However, since the pressure exerted on the dry oxygen must be 100.0 kPa, the volume of the dry oxygen must decrease so that its pressure will increase from 96.4 kPa to 100.0 kPa. According to Boyle's Law,

$$V_{\text{new}} = V_{\text{old}} \times (\text{pressure factor})$$

$$V_{\text{new}} = 400 \text{ mL} \times \frac{96.4 \text{ kPa}}{100.0 \text{ kPa}} = 386 \text{ mL}$$

Dalton's Law of Partial Pressure is thus a valuable tool for calculations involving mixtures of gases. If the partial pressures of the individual gases are known, the total pressure of the mixture can be calculated. If the total pressure and the partial pressure of all but one of the gases are known, the partial pressure of the remaining gas can be calculated.

Practice Problem 14-5

A volume of 110 mL of hydrogen is collected over water at a temperature of 17°C and an atmospheric pressure of 95.0 kPa. What is the volume of the dry hydrogen at STP? (*Answer*: 95.2 mL)

(c)

Fig. 14-8(a) Collecting a Gas Over Water. The pressure exerted by the wet gas (gas + water vapour) is equal to the atmospheric pressure when the water level is the same inside and outside the bottle.
(b) A Diagram of How a Pneumatic Trough is Set Up
(c) A Pneumatic Trough

14-8 A Model for Gases—The Kinetic Molecular Theory

If a bottle of concentrated ammonia is opened in a room, the odour of the ammonia will soon be detected throughout the room. This suggests that the particles of a gas can move or diffuse through another gas. A Scottish botanist, Robert Brown, discovered in 1827 that small particles suspended in a gas or a liquid are in constant zigzag motion. This so-called **Brownian motion** was assumed to be due to collisions of the gas particles with the suspended material.

We can now make assumptions concerning the nature of gases. That is, we will now develop a model by making the simplest possible assumptions.

Building on the results of Boyle, Charles, and others, as well as the results of his own experiments, John Dalton in 1801 proposed a kinetic molecular model for gases. This was refined and developed by J. C. Maxwell, a British physicist, in 1859. The basic assumptions of the model are

1. Gases consist of extremely small particles called molecules. These molecules are so small that their volume is negligible in comparison with the volume of the container.
2. The molecules of a gas are in rapid, random, straight-line motion. They collide with each other and with the walls of the container.
3. All collisions are perfectly elastic; that is, there are no energy losses due to friction.
4. There are no attractive forces between the molecules.
5. At constant temperature, the average velocity of the molecules of all gases is constant. If the temperature increases, the average velocity increases; if the temperature decreases, the average velocity decreases.

The last postulate was added to Dalton's theory by Maxwell. These few postulates are sufficient to explain all the observations about gases that we have discussed.

Postulate 1 explains the compressibility of gases. Since the volume of a gas is mostly empty space, it should be fairly easy to force the molecules into a smaller volume.

Postulate 3 is necessary because, if molecules lost energy during nonelastic collisions, they would gradually slow down and come to rest at the bottom of the container. This has never been observed for any gas.

The first four postulates together explain Dalton's Law of Partial Pressures. Since the distance between molecules is relatively large, it is always possible to add more gas molecules; and since there are no intermolecular forces, the gases will act independently in their collisions with the walls of the container. Thus the total pressure is equal to the sum of the individual partial pressures.

The kinetic molecular theory of gases explains Boyle's Law. Pressure must be due to the collisions of the gas molecules with the walls of the container. What would happen if the volume of the container were decreased? The gas molecules would hit the walls of the container more often, and therefore the pressure on the container walls would be increased. If the volume of the container were increased, the gas molecules would collide with the walls less frequently because they have further to travel. Therefore the pressure would be decreased.

The kinetic molecular theory also explains Charles' Law. Consider a container which can easily expand, such as a balloon. If the balloon is heated, Postulate 5 states that the gas molecules will speed up. They will strike the wall of the balloon more often and with more force, and therefore the balloon will expand. Thus the volume of a gas increases as its temperature increases.

Gay-Lussac's Law

The kinetic molecular theory of gases predicts a relationship we have not yet mentioned, that is, the relation between pressure and temperature. Consider a gas-filled container, such as a scuba tank, that cannot easily expand. If the container is heated, the gas molecules will speed up. They will strike the walls of the container more frequently and with more force. Therefore the pressure will increase. The pressure of a gas increases as its temperature increases, and decreases with a decrease in temperature. The pressure exerted by a gas is directly proportional to its Kelvin temperature, provided the volume remains constant. This holds true experimentally and is called **Gay-Lussac's Law**. Stated mathematically, Gay-Lussac's Law can be written

$$P = (\text{constant}) \times T$$

Fig. 14-9 This radiosonde weather balloon is filled with hydrogen gas. Radiosonde balloons are sent up twice daily at 36 Canadian radiosonde stations to measure temperature, air pressure, and humidity. (Photo courtesy of Environment Canada)

14-9 Further Applications of the Gas Laws

We have been using Boyle's and Charles' Laws to calculate new volumes. It is possible to use these Laws in conjunction with Gay-Lussac's Law to solve problems involving the pressure, volume, and temperature relationships of a gas.

For example, a certain mass of a gas occupies a volume of 400 mL at a pressure of 150 kPa and a temperature of 280 K. What will be its pressure when its volume is 380 mL and its temperature is 300 K?

We could write

$$P_{\text{new}} = P_{\text{old}} \times (\text{volume factor}) \times (\text{temperature factor})$$

The volume factor is the ratio of the two volumes. It is either 400 mL/380 mL or 380 mL/400 mL. The first of these is a number greater than 1. The second is a number smaller than 1. Since the prssure increases as the volume decreases, the new pressure must be larger than the old one, and the volume factor must be a number greater than 1:

$$P_{\text{new}} = 150 \text{ kPa} \times \frac{400 \text{ mL}}{380 \text{ mL}} \times (\text{temperature factor})$$

The temperature factor is either 280 K/300 K or 300 K/280 K. Since Gay-Lussac's Law tells us that the pressure increases as the Kelvin temperature increases, the temperature factor is a number greater than 1:

$$P_{new} = 150 \text{ kPa} \times \frac{400 \text{ mL}}{380 \text{ mL}} \times \frac{300 \text{ K}}{280 \text{ K}} = 169 \text{ kPa}$$

Practice Problem 14-6

If a given mass of a gas occupies a volume of 175 mL at a pressure of 95.0 kPa and a temperature of 100°C, what will be its pressure when its volume is 200 mL and its temperature is 50°C? (*Answer*: 72.0 kPa)

A certain mass of a gas occupies a volume of 7.50 L at a pressure of 101.0 kPa and a temperature of 27° C. What will be its Celsius temperature when its volume is 7.15 L and its pressure is 85.0 kPa?

We could write

$$T_{new} = T_{old} \times (\text{pressure factor}) \times (\text{volume factor})$$

The pressure factor is either 85.0 kPa/101.0 kPa or 101.0 kPa/85.0 kPa. Since Gay-Lussac's Law tells us that the pressure decreases as the temperature decreases, the pressure factor is a number less than 1, and we can write

$$T_{new} = (273 + 27) \text{ K} \times \frac{85.0 \text{ kPa}}{101.0 \text{ kPa}} \times (\text{volume factor})$$

The volume factor is either 7.15 L/7.50 L or 7.50 L/7.15 L. Since Charles' Law tells us that gases contract on cooling, the volume factor is a number less than 1, and we can write

$$T_{new} = 300 \text{ K} \times \frac{85.0 \text{ kPa}}{101.0 \text{ kPa}} \times \frac{7.15 \text{ L}}{7.50 \text{ L}} = 241 \text{ K}$$

$$241 \text{ K} = (241 - 273)°\text{C} = -32°\text{C}$$

Practice Problem 14-7

If a given mass of a gas occupies a volume of 125.0 mL at a pressure of 110.0 kPa and a temperature of 30°C, what will be its Celsius temperature when its volume is 148.0 mL and its pressure is 127.0 kPa? (*Answer*: 141°C)

14-10 Behaviour of Real Gases

A gas which obeys Boyle's Law, Charles' Law, and Gay-Lussac's Law is called an ideal gas and is said to behave ideally. At ordinary temperatures and pressures, most real gases, such as hydrogen, nitrogen, and carbon dioxide do obey the gas laws reasonably well. Thus, they behave ideally. However, at low temperatures and high pressures, real gases deviate from ideal behaviour.

Assume, for example, that you have one litre of carbon dioxide gas at 25°C and at a pressure of 100 kPa. What happens to the volume at 25°C as the pressure on the gas is increased to 10 000 kPa? The volume decreases. The data are given in Table 14-4. According to Boyle's Law, the product of the pressure and the volume of a gas at a given temperature should remain constant at all pressures. We see from the third column of Table 14-4 that the PV product is not constant. It decreases steadily to about one-third of its original value, then starts to increase again. Carbon dioxide does not obey Boyle's Law at high pressures and does not behave ideally.

TABLE **14-4** **Pressure-Volume Measurements for Carbon Dioxide at 25°C**

PRESSURE (kPa)	VOLUME (mL)	$P \times V$ (kPa·mL)
100	1000	100 000
2 000	46	92 000
4 000	20	80 000
6 000	10	60 000
8 000	4	32 000
10 000	4	40 000

Reasons for the Behaviour of Real Gases

How can we explain this deviation from ideal behaviour? Recall two postulates of the kinetic molecular theory. The kinetic molecular theory assumes that the volume of the gas molecules is negligible and that there are no attractive forces between molecules.

When a high pressure is used to force molecules into a small volume, the average distances between molecules become small. Attractive forces between molecules (van der Waals forces) are greater when the molecules are close together. These attractive forces cause the volume of the gas to be smaller than it would be if there were no attractions. Because the volume is less than it would be if there were no attractive forces, the PV product decreases as the pressure on the gas increases.

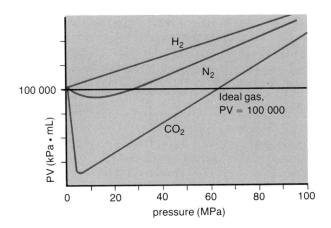

Fig. 14-10 Non-ideal Behaviour of Real Gases

Another point to notice in Table 14-4 is that it appears difficult to reduce the volume of the gas to less than 4 mL. When high pressures are used to force molecules into a small volume, the volume of the molecules themselves becomes a significant portion of the total volume. Thus, increasing the pressure on the carbon dioxide does not decrease its volume much below 4 mL. Since V remains constant as P increases above 80 000 kPa, the PV product increases.

All real gases show deviations from ideal behaviour. Fig. 14-10 (on previous page) is a plot of PV vs P for hydrogen, nitrogen, and carbon dioxide. If Boyle's Law were followed, PV for each gas would always lie on the horizontal line. We see, however, that both nitrogen and carbon dioxide have PV products which are less than predicted, because van der Waals forces reduce the volumes. At higher pressures, the N_2 and CO_2 molecules occupy enough volume themselves to prevent theoretical compression, and the PV product is larger than expected. In contrast, the PV product of hydrogen does not decrease at all, but starts to increase almost immediately. This means that, although the H_2 molecules are closer together at higher pressures, the van der Waals forces between them still remain negligible.

The Behaviour of Real Gases at Low Temperatures

At lower temperatures, the molecules move more slowly and spend more time at closer distances to each other. Thus, as long as the pressure is not large enough to have forced the molecules as close together as they can get, the van der Waals forces of attraction increase at lower temperatures. The increased van der Waals forces reduce the volume of the gas below the volume that would be predicted by Charles' Law.

14-11 Liquefaction of Gases

At high pressures, the molecules of a gas are closest to each other, and the attractive forces are most important. As the temperature increases, the molecules move more rapidly, and this motion tends to keep the molecules apart. As the temperature decreases, the molecules slow down and are less able to overcome the attractive forces. When the temperature is low enough, the attractive forces can draw the molecules together to form a liquid. The temperature at which the gas molecules come together to form a liquid is called the *liquefaction temperature*. It is easier to liquefy a gas at higher pressures, because the molecules are close to each other, and the intermolecular forces are more effective. Thus, the higher the pressure, the higher the liquefaction temperature of a gas.

Critical Temperature

For each gas there is some temperature, called the **critical temperature**, above which it is impossible to liquefy the gas, no matter how much pressure is applied. Above the critical temperature, the substance can exist only as a gas. The motion of the molecules is so vigorous that the attractive forces can no longer overcome the motions of the molecules, no matter how high the pressure.

The critical temperature depends on the strength of the intermolecular forces. A polar substance has strong attractive forces which aid in overcoming molecular motion. Thus, a polar substance may be liquefied at relatively high temperatures. A nonpolar substance has weak attractive forces. It has a low critical temperature. At higher temperatures the molecular motions are able to overcome the weak attractive forces. Table 14-5 lists the critical temperatures for some common substances. We see that water, which is highly polar and has strong attractive forces, can be liquefied at temperatures as high as 647 K. Helium, on the other hand, has such weak attractive forces that it cannot be liquefied above 5.2 K.

TABLE **14-5** **Critical Temperatures and Pressures for Some Common Substances**

SUBSTANCE	CRITICAL TEMPERATURE (K)	CRITICAL PRESSURE (MPa)
H_2O	647	22.1
NH_3	406	11.3
HCl	324	8.27
CO_2	304	7.40
O_2	153	5.04
N_2	126	3.39
H_2	33	1.30
He	5.2	0.229

Critical Pressure

The minimum pressure required to liquefy a gas at its critical temperature is called the **critical pressure** of the gas. Critical pressures are listed along with critical temperatures in Table 14-5.

14-12 Cooling of Gases by Expansion

The Joule-Thomson Effect

You may have noticed that air cools as it escapes rapidly through the valve of a bicycle tire. The cooling of a gas as it expands rapidly is called the *Joule-Thomson effect*. As the gas expands, the average distance beween molecules increases, in spite of the intermolecular forces of attraction. Energy is required to overcome the attractive forces and separate the molecules. Since no outside energy is available, the molecules must use up some of their kinetic energy. The average kinetic energy drops. Because the Kelvin temperature is directly proportional to the average kinetic energy of the molecules, the temperature also drops.

Liquid Air

The Joule-Thomson effect is used commercially in the preparation of liquid air. Before the air can be liquefied, the water vapour and carbon dioxide must be removed because both of these substances solidify on cooling and clog the pipes of the liquid air machine (Fig. 14-11). The dry air is first compressed to about 20 MPa. It is then pumped through pipes leading through a cooling bath containing a coolant such as liquid ammonia (normal boiling point $-33°C$). The cold compressed air is then passed through other cooling coils in the liquefier, where it escapes through an expansion valve and expands to a pressure of 2 MPa. The air cools upon expansion, because it uses up kinetic energy to overcome the intermolecular forces of attraction. The cold, expanded air is passed over the cooling coils to further cool the incoming air. As the process continues, each quantity of air that escapes from the expansion valve is colder than that which preceded it. Finally, part of the air condenses to a liquid, which is drawn off at the bottom of the expansion chamber.

Fig. 14-11 Liquefaction of Air

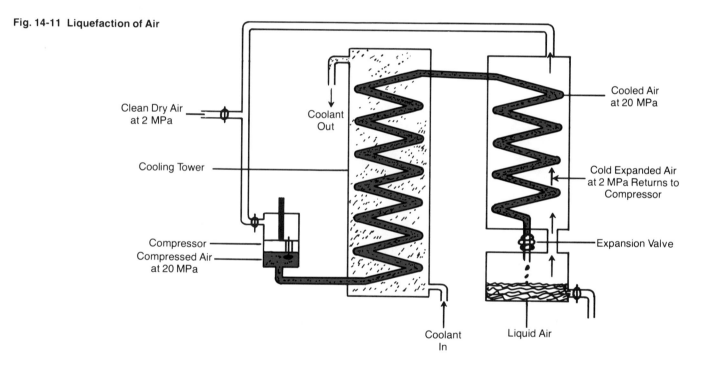

Liquid air is a mobile liquid with a pale blue colour. It consists of about 78% nitrogen, 21% oxygen, 1% argon, and smaller amounts of the noble gases, ozone, and hydrogen. Oxygen boils at $-183.0°C$, argon at $-185.7°C$, and nitrogen at $-195.8°C$. Liquid air has no definite boiling point, because it is a mixture. It finds much use as a low temperature coolant. Liquid oxygen, liquid nitrogen, and liquid argon are obtained commercially by fractional distillation of liquid air. Liquid oxygen is used in rockets and missiles.

14-13 Heating of Gases by Compression

We have seen that if a gas in a container is allowed to expand rapidly, the temperature of the gas will be lowered. In the same way, when a gas in a container is compressed very rapidly, the temperature of the gas will be increased. This happens because the energy from the piston of the compressor is transferred to the gas molecules which collide with it. These molecules rebound with greater kinetic energy, and therefore the temperature of the gas increases.

The Diesel Engine

The heating of a gas by rapid compression is used in the diesel engine (Fig. 14-12). At the beginning of the compression stroke, a blower fills the cylinder with air. As the piston rises, the exhaust valves close, and the air is rapidly compressed to one-sixteenth of its original volume. The temperature of the compressed air rises above the ignition temperature of diesel fuel. At this point, fuel is injected into the cylinder, and it ignites immediately. The expanding gaseous reaction products drive the piston down in a power stroke. When the piston reaches its lowest point, the exhaust gases are blown out, and the sequence begins again.

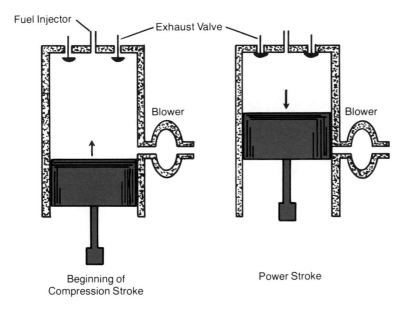

Fuel Injector

Exhaust Valve

Blower

Blower

Beginning of
Compression Stroke

Power Stroke

Fig. 14-12 A Diesel Engine

Diesel engines need no spark plugs—the hot air causes self-ignition of the fuel. Because it uses an excess of air, a diesel engine emits less carbon monoxide than an ordinary gasoline engine. If it is poorly maintained, a diesel engine has special smoke and odour problems. Anyone who has driven in the dark fumes behind some trucks and cars knows this.

Fig. 14-13 Air Pollution over Toronto, Ontario. (Photo courtesy of Ontario Ministry of the Environment)

14-14 Chemistry and the Gaseous Environment

In the 1970s, people became more aware of their effect on the environment and of the interrelatedness of all living things as they exist in nature. During the centuries that human beings have occupied this earth, the human population and technological advances have increased together. This has been especially true during the last several decades. To many people, technology seems to be the main factor responsible for our problems with pollution. Some may regard technology and progress as demons responsible for the destruction of the environment. However, we should recall that technology is merely the application of scientific knowledge by people. People have misused technology to despoil the environment. Therefore, people must use technology to clean up the environment.

One other point should be made. We cannot lay all the blame for our environmental problems at the feet of technologists. We should also consider the effect of the increasing human population. Living things have always had an effect on nature. Because of the sheer size of the global environment, nature has been able to adjust its balance. However, the disruptive effect of a highly concentrated population in a particular area may so alter the environment of that area that the balance of nature can never be achieved. The concentration of humanity in large cities means the concentration of humanity's effects on the environment in those areas. This is true regardless of the state of the technology. Would Toronto be more habitable if horses were used instead of automobiles? Even if there were room for the horses, the accumulated animal refuse would probably make the streets of Toronto unacceptable.

In the remainder of this chapter, we shall consider some of the information dealing with air pollution.

14-15 Changes in the Air Environment

Air is a mixture of gases such as oxygen, nitrogen, argon, carbon dioxide, and others. The atmosphere consists of air plus droplets of liquid, mainly water, and finely divided solid particles. The gaseous part of the atmospheric mixture is quite uniform near the earth's surface. The gas molecules are constantly in random motion and tend to mix evenly. Wind aids this mixing process. Thus, the atmosphere is a dynamic system in which the molecules are in continuous random motion. Chemical reactions occur among the substances present in the atmospheric mixture, and physical changes also take place. These physical changes include the settling out of solid and liquid particles. Water vapour condenses on dust particles to form water droplets (clouds and fog). The water droplets in clouds may become large enough to fall to earth as rain, or the drops may freeze and fall as hail or snow.

Most scientists believe that the earth has been in a stable orbit for eons and that, over the period of the earth's history, natural balances have slowly been established in the atmosphere and a wide variety of equilibria have been reached. What is an equilibrium? To learn about equilibria in general, we shall consider the cycles by which the amount of carbon dioxide in the atmosphere has been limited to a concentration of about 0.03 percent.

Carbon Dioxide and the Atmosphere

Natural events such as forest fires, animal respiration, and volcanic eruptions pour carbon dioxide into the atmosphere. Some of this carbon dioxide is used by plants for photosynthesis. When animals eat the plants and breathe, the carbon dioxide returns to the atmosphere to complete the cycle. Other carbon dioxide dissolves in the water present in the atmosphere:

$$CO_2(g) + H_2O(\ell) \rightarrow H_2CO_3(aq)$$
carbonic acid

The carbonic acid reacts with minerals to form limestone, $CaCO_3$. Carbon dioxide also dissolves in the oceans and some of it ends up as $CaCO_3$ in the shells of ocean creatures.

Thus, carbon dioxide is involved in an equilibrium process. The amount of carbon dioxide entering the atmosphere from forest fires, volcanic activity, and animal and plant respiration is equal to the amount of carbon dioxide leaving the atmosphere through photosynthesis and carbonic acid formation. An equilibrium like this takes years to be reached and can be destroyed if another factor enters the picture.

The other factor is our need for heat. People have increased the carbon dioxide content of the atmosphere by the massive burning of fossil fuels such as coal and petroleum. The natural processes by which carbon dioxide is removed from the atmosphere cannot keep pace with this increase in carbon dioxide content. Thus, we have destroyed nature's carbon dioxide balance. It now appears that the carbon dioxide content of the atmosphere is increasing.

Other Gases and the Atmosphere

Other gases such as carbon monoxide (CO), sulfur oxides (SO_2 and SO_3), nitrogen oxides (NO and NO_2), and hydrocarbons have always been present in the atmosphere. Volcanic action has produced sulfur oxides, and lightning produces nitrogen oxides from nitrogen and oxygen. However, we have added to the concentration of these noxious gases. In some areas of the world, people have died because of high concentrations of these pollutants.

A **pollutant** is a substance that is present in high enough concentration to produce adverse effects on the things that human beings value. These must include not only their own health, safety, and property, but also acceptable

Fig. 14-14 This paper mill in Thunder Bay, Ontario, emits both SO_2 and CO_2 into the atmosphere. (Photo courtesy of Ontario Ministry of the Environment)

conditions for all plants and animals. We cannot control the amount of pollutants injected into the atmosphere by natural processes. However, the balancing mechanisms of nature normally act to prevent these quantities of pollutant molecules from rising to dangerous levels. What we *must* control is the quantity of pollutant molecules that enter the atmosphere as a result of our actions. In the next sections, a number of substances that are known air pollutants will be discussed.

14-16 The Effects of Solid Particles in the Atmosphere

The presence of particles of dust and smoke has a great effect on the ability of the atmosphere to transmit radiation from the sun. The earth is warmed by infrared radiation from the sun. Any change in the amount of infrared radiation reaching the earth would change the temperature of the earth. Most atmospheric particles have a size ranging from 0.1 μm to 10 μm in diameter. Larger particles are too heavy to remain in the atmosphere. The smaller particles are bounced about by collisions with gas molecules and tend to remain airborne for long times. These particles create a hazy atmosphere which allows less infrared light to reach the surface of the earth. Evidence actually exists that the average global temperature has fallen 0.2°C between 1940 and 1967. This may be due to a larger number of particles in the air. Continued temperature decreases would change the climate of portions of the globe.

Some solid particles, such as those in the smoke of metal smelters, contain poisons which are harmful to animals. The harmful effects of filling the lungs with soot, silica, arsenic oxides, or lead are well known. Studies suggest that respiratory diseases can be caused by breathing air which contains large quantities of particles.

Nature removes particles from the atmosphere by gravitational settling, rain, and snow. We already have the technology which can aid nature in removing particles from the atmosphere. Taller smoke stacks are not the answer since they merely disperse the particles higher into the atmosphere. Filter bags made of glass fiber, cotton, nylon, wool, or felt can be used to filter particles from gases. Centrifugal separators whirl gases and throw particles to the walls of the apparatus where they can be collected.

Electrostatic Precipitators

Electrostatic precipitators (Fig. 14-15) can remove dust particles from plant exhaust gases. The dust particles pass through a strong electric field (about 50 kV). If the particles are not already charged, they become charged. The charged particles are quickly attracted to oppositely charged plates where they are neutralized and fall to the bottom of the precipitator to be collected.

Equipment like electrostatic precipitators can remove more than 99 percent of the dust particles from exhaust gases.

Another control consists of better regulation of the combustion process. If

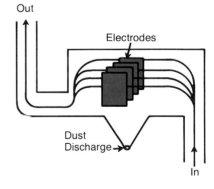
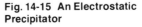

Fig. 14-15 An Electrostatic Precipitator

enough air is used to burn carbon-containing compounds, more carbon dioxide and less carbon soot is produced.

14-17 Carbon Dioxide and The Greenhouse Effect

The carbon dioxide content of the atmosphere is increasing. Carbon dioxide is not a poisonous gas, nor is it very corrosive; however, it is interesting to observe that even carbon dioxide can cause environmental problems if its concentration in the atmosphere becomes too great.

Light from the visible and ultraviolet regions of the spectrum passes through carbon dioxide molecules without being absorbed. However, infrared light (heat energy) causes the CO_2 molecules to vibrate more vigorously. Thus, the carbon dioxide molecules absorb and later emit infrared light.

The Greenhouse Effect

When the surface of the earth cools at night or under a cloud layer, the infrared energy which the earth gives off is trapped by the carbon dioxide in the atmosphere, and part of this infrared energy is emitted back to the earth. This leads to what is called the **greenhouse effect**. The glass roof of a greenhouse allows light and heat in, but it reflects back into the greenhouse some of the heat that tries to escape. The temperature inside a greenhouse is higher than the temperature outside it.

The atmospheric CO_2 content was constant until the start of the Industrial Revolution. The burning of fuels to power machines caused the CO_2 level to increase until, by 1975, it was 13% higher than originally. It is estimated that doubling the CO_2 level would raise the average surface temperature of the earth by 2 to 3°C, but the warming effect would be greatest (8 to 10°C) in the polar regions. This could cause a melting of the polar ice caps and result in the flooding of many coastal cities. If we continue to burn all available fossil fuels at the same accelerating rate as we did between 1960 and 1970, the CO_2 level will be doubled by 2020.

Nobody knows the maximum permissible level of atmospheric CO_2 (the level above which the greenhouse effect would become too dangerous). A level 50% above pre-industrial values would cause a temperature increase of 1 to 2°C, and this might be tolerable. In that case, our production of CO_2 could continue to increase until 2000. However, it would then have to level off rapidly between 2030 and 2080 to pre-1970 values, in order to prevent the CO_2 level from increasing to more than 50% above pre-industrial values. Clearly, we cannot continue to burn fossil fuels at the present growth rate for much longer. We have more than enough fossil fuel to supply our needs for several hundred years, but by the turn of the century we will have to find new technologies for the world-wide production of energy. If we do not find these new technologies, the time may come when CO_2 will have to be regarded as a dangerous pollutant.

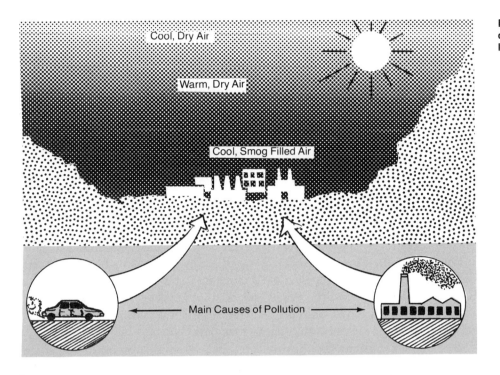

Cool, Dry Air

Warm, Dry Air

Cool, Smog Filled Air

← Main Causes of Pollution →

14-18 Photochemical or Los Angeles-Type Smog

There are two general types of smog. We have already studied the London type, which is largely caused by the combustion of coal and oil (Section 9-23). This type of smog contains sulfur dioxide mixed with soot, fly ash, smoke, and some organic compounds. The second type of smog is photochemical smog, or Los Angeles-type smog. It is called photochemical smog because light from the sun is important in starting the chemical process. This second type of smog is practically free of sulfur dioxide, but it contains large amounts of nitrogen oxides, ozone, ozonated hydrocarbons, organic peroxides, and hydrocarbons of varying complexities. As we shall see, the smog for which Los Angeles is so famous (and which most cities have in varying degrees) is caused primarily by automobiles.

Los Angeles had almost no air pollution problem until around 1940, when population growth and industrial expansion in the area suddenly accelerated. It was at this time that the air pollution problem began to appear. The previously clean atmosphere frequently became transformed into smog—a brown haze of smoke and offensive odours. Several factors were responsible for this: the sudden increase in the number of automobiles in Southern California and the peculiar natural climatic conditions in and around Los Angeles (including the legendary California sunshine) combined with the fact that the city lies in a mountain-rimmed depression.

Before the anti-pollution laws controlling automobile emissions were enacted, the thousands of cars around Los Angeles daily poured out enormous quantities of pollutants consisting mainly of nitrogen oxides and hydrocarbons (crankcase oil vapours and unburnt gasoline). These were the starting materials in the smog formation process.

Thermal Inversion

Because of its unusual geography, the city often experiences an abnormal meteorological phenomenon known as **thermal inversion** which prevents any pollutants from moving to the upper atmosphere where they can be dispersed. Normally, a layer of warmer, less dense air first forms near the earth and then rises, carrying with it pollutants such as smoke, gases, dust, and others. The colder, more dense air from the upper atmosphere moves downward to replace it and the cycle is repeated. When thermal inversion occurs, a layer of warm air is *already* resting on top of a layer of cooler, more dense air near the earth. This lower layer cannot move upward; nor can it move sideways because of the mountains ringing Los Angeles. So a stagnant layer of polluted air remains trapped in and over the city. The abundant solar radiation acts on the trapped nitrogen oxides and hydrocarbons and the resultant photochemical reactions produce the smog (Fig. 14-16, on previous page).

Thus, when nature supplies sunshine and a thermal inversion, and people supply the killing ingredients through gasoline combustion and evaporation in automobiles, a photochemical smog results. Nature supplies the reaction vessel—the energy in the form of sunlight—and people supply the chemicals. When suitable meteorological conditions prevail, the concentrations of contaminants in Los Angeles are enough to produce an objectionable smog during a one- or two-hour exposure to bright sunlight.

The Chemistry of Smog

Research into the series of photochemical reactions that produce smog has added to our understanding of the process. Nitrogen(II) oxide (NO) arises from a direct combination of nitrogen and oxygen which is produced by the high temperature inside the automobile engine cylinders during the ignition stroke:

$$N_2 + O_2 + heat \rightarrow 2\ NO$$

This nitrogen(II) oxide immediately reacts with oxygen to form nitrogen dioxide:

$$2\ NO + O_2 \rightarrow 2\ NO_2$$

At this point, the photochemical process is thought to begin. Ultraviolet light from the sun breaks up the nitrogen dioxide molecule:

$$NO_2 + UV\ light \rightarrow NO + O$$

The oxygen atom has only six outer electrons, and it is a highly reactive species. It can react with oxygen to form ozone:

$$O + O_2 \rightarrow O_3$$

Ozone is a form of oxygen which has three atoms of oxygen per molecule. Ozone is called an allotrope of oxygen, and it is toxic and corrosive to tissue. Even at low concentrations ozone can kill plants.

Some ozone reacts with nitrogen(II) oxide to re-form nitrogen dioxide:

$$NO + O_3 \rightarrow NO_2 + O_2$$

Some of the reactive oxygen atoms follow another path. They can react with hydrocarbon molecules in the atmosphere to produce organic free radicals. Free radicals are organic fragments in which unpaired electrons impart a great reactivity to the species. These free radicals can react with molecular oxygen to produce even more reactive free radicals, which can then react to form secondary pollutants such as aldehydes (formaldehyde, acetaldehyde, acrolein), ketones, and peroxyacyl nitrates (PAN):

$$CH_2{=}CH{-}\overset{\overset{\displaystyle O}{\|}}{C}{-}H \qquad CH_3{-}\overset{\overset{\displaystyle O}{\|}}{C}{-}O{-}O{-}NO_2$$

acrolein   *a peroxyacyl nitrate*

It is known that formaldehyde, acrolein, and PAN are all lachrymators (tear producers). These three substances cause most of the physical discomfort produced by smog. Smog, however, contains hundreds of different molecules as a result of these free radical reactions.

14-19 Effects of Photochemical Smog

What is it like to be in Los Angeles when a combination of thermal inversion, low winds, bright sunlight, and hundreds of thousands of automobiles bring on the smog? Consider the possibilities.

The day begins clear and sunny. As traffic increases, the air begins gradually to become a yellow-brown haze. The odour is sharp and pungent. The shroud of pollution obscures prominent landmarks and limits visibility. The intensity of the smog increases during the day. Around noon the pollution becomes intense. People complain of eye irritation, and many find it difficult to breathe.

At street level, the carbon monoxide emitted from automobile exhausts reaches 50 mg/kg, and traffic police complain of headaches. The carbon monoxide is combining with hemoglobin in their blood and is starving their bodies of oxygen.

The smog worsens, and school children are not allowed to have outdoor recreation classes. The ozone level has exceeded 0.35 mg/kg, and at that level fifteen minutes in the outdoors can cause respiratory irritation accompanied by choking, coughing, and severe fatigue.

The smog grows thicker. The air mass is still held stationary by the thermal inversion and by the mountains. There is no wind—not even a breeze. The people of Los Angeles live in an atmospheric sewer, each person breathing

25 m³ of this polluted air every day, three hundred days a year. The air contains more than 50 pollutants. More than 2 million Californians (one person in eight) have some kind of respiratory problem such as emphysema, bronchitis, or asthma. There is more lung disease in California than in any other part of North America.

Through this sewage drives John Citizen. He wonders if he should have his wife's car tuned up. He wishes that the emission control devices did not mean such low gasoline mileage. He wonders if his daughter's car has been safety-checked this year. He wonders what kind of automobile he will get for his 17-year-old son. Above all, he wonders when someone is going to do something about all this smog.

Although Los Angeles remains the chief center for photochemical smog, this phenomenon has been detected in varying degrees in most major metropolitan areas. Unless pollutant emissions are controlled, the sun, which has made life on this planet possible, could make city life unbearable.

14-20 What Can Be Done About Air Pollution?

The previous sections have included discussions concerning some (but not all) of the possible air pollutants. The question is, what should be done about air pollution?

The first step is to pass laws to regulate the introduction of pollutants into the atmosphere. One city has banned the use of soft coal for heating purposes. Soft coal has a high sulfur content, and when it burns, it releases large quantities of sulfur dioxide into the air. Other cities have forbidden the burning of rubbish and the construction of private incinerators. Use of atomic energy would cut down air pollution. Smokestacks should have electrostatic precipitators to cut down on the amount of particles they produce. Eventually we will require national and international air standards. As the world population grows, we will need tougher air standards. However, with a combination of common sense, necessity, and research, there is no reason to believe that we will not be successful.

For example, because we know that the automobile produces hydrocarbons, nitrogen(II) oxide, and carbon monoxide, we will try to cut down the emission of these pollutants from automobile exhaust. Hydrocarbons and carbon monoxide will perhaps be burned more efficiently to produce carbon dioxide. A direct flame afterburner (Fig. 14-18(a)) would mix unburned pollutants from the engine exhaust with additional fresh air, and then ignite the mixture with a spark or a flame. A catalytic device (Fig. 14-18(b)) would consume these same pollutants by passing them together with additional air over a bed of mixed catalysts. We will also require catalysts capable of converting nitrogen(II) oxide to nitrogen and oxygen. This will be done while the gases are still in the engine or in the exhaust system. Tetraethyllead has to

Fig. 14-17 An air sampling device traps particulate matter and rainwater to allow environmentalists to study air pollution. (Photo courtesy of Ontario Ministry of the Environment)

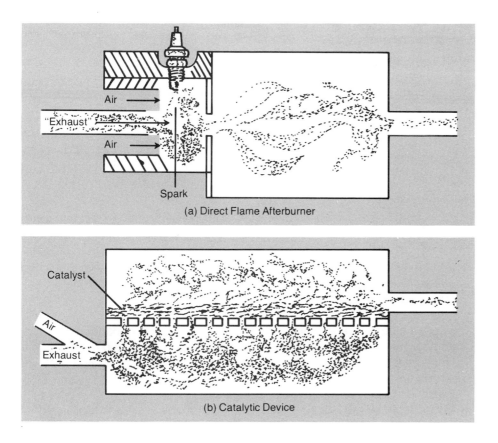

Fig. 14-18 Devices for Controlling
Automobile Exhaust Pollution

(a) Direct Flame Afterburner

(b) Catalytic Device

be left out of gasoline used in automobiles equipped with catalytic devices because the lead renders the catalyst ineffective.

A Final Word

In this chapter, we have studied the laws that describe the behaviour of gases when they undergo changes of pressure, volume, or temperature. We used these laws to predict quantitatively the effect that a change in any two of these variables would have on the third.

We studied a model of gases, the kinetic molecular theory, which explained the laws and led to new predictions. We saw, however, that real gases do not fit this model exactly. Their behaviour shows deviations from what is predicted by the kinetic molecular theory.

Finally, we described some of the effects of the pollution of the atmosphere by both solid and gaseous pollutants and some of the steps that can be taken to ease the problem of air pollution.

Now that you have finished reading this chapter, you should reread the Key Objectives to make sure that you have learned the most important points of the chapter. In addition, you should learn the meaning of each important term found in the chapter.

Key Terms

What is the meaning of each of the following terms?

Boyle's Law
Charles' Law
standard pressure
standard temperature
STP
Dalton's Law of
   Partial Pressures

Brownian motion
Gay-Lussac's Law
critical temperature
critical pressure
pollutant
greenhouse effect
thermal inversion

Questions

1. The pressure on 220 mL of a gas is 110 kPa. What will be the volume if the pressure is changed to 55.0 kPa, keeping the temperature constant?
2. The pressure on 6.00 L of a gas is 200 kPa. What will be the volume if the pressure is doubled, keeping the temperature constant?
3. A gas initially at a pressure of 300 kPa is allowed to expand at constant temperature until its volume has increased from 100 to 225 mL. What is the final pressure?
4. The initial pressure of a gas is 150 kPa. What will be the final pressure if the gas is compressed to one half its original volume?
5. A gas is contained in a spherical vessel of 450 mL volume at a pressure of 101 kPa. When a stopcock connecting the vessel to an adjacent evacuated chamber is opened to allow the gas to flow into the chamber, the pressure stabilizes to 6.50 kPa. What is the volume of the adjacent chamber?
6. In a McLeod gauge a large volume of a gas at an unknown low pressure is compressed to a much smaller volume, and the new pressure is measured. In one experiment a sample of nitrogen at 20°C was compressed from 300 mL to 0.360 mL, and its new pressure was found to be 400 Pa. What was the original pressure of the nitrogen?
7. Convert the following Celsius temperatures to Kelvin temperatures: 27°C; 273°C; −162°C; 727°C.
8. Convert the following Kelvin temperatures to Celsius temperatures: 0 K; 273 K; 1000 K; 328 K; 225 K.
9. Convert **a)** 400 K to °C; **b)** −150°C to K; **c)** 298 K to °C; **d)** 1 MK to °C; **e)** 1×10^6°C to K.
10. If a sample of a gas measures 2.00 L at 25°C, what is its volume at 50°C if the pressure remains constant?
11. If a sample of gas measures 500 mL at STP, what is its volume at 101.3 kPa and 34°C?
12. On a day when the temperature is 20°C, an automobile tire has a pressure of 200 kPa. After several hours of high speed driving the tire temperature has risen to 30°C. Assuming that the volume of the tire does not change, what is the tire pressure?
13. The scientists of the remote oil-rich island of Salamia use units of potlins (*P*) for pressure, vurniks (*V*) for volume, and kelvins (K) for temperature. If a

sample of methane gas has a volume of 13.0 V at a pressure of 4.00 P and a temperature of 150 K, what is its volume when the temperature has increased to 298 K at a pressure of 4.00 P?

14. A gas storage tank is designed to hold a fixed volume of a gas at 175 kPa and 30°C. In order to prevent excessive pressure build-up by overheating, the tank is fitted with a relief valve that opens at 200 kPa. At what temperature will the relief valve open?

15. The gaseous contents of an "empty" aerosol spray can are at a pressure of 110 kPa at room temperature (20°C). What pressure is generated inside the can if it is thrown into a fire where the temperature is 750°C?

16. A sample of a gas whose volume at 27°C is 127 mL is heated at constant pressure until its volume becomes 317 mL. What is the final Celsius temperature of the gas?

17. Correct the following volumes to STP:
    a) 24.5 L at 25°C and 104 kPa
    b) 1000 mm^3 at 100°C and 75.0 kPa
    c) 45.0 mL at −40°C and 140 kPa

18. A 200 mL sample of gas is collected at 50.0 kPa and a temperature of 271°C. What volume would this gas occupy at 100 kPa and a temperature of −1°C?

19. Natural gas is usually stored in large underground reservoirs or in above-ground tanks. Suppose that a supply of natural gas is stored in an underground reservoir of volume 8.0 × 10^5 m^3 at a pressure of 360 kPa and 16°C. How many above-ground tanks of volume 2.7 × 10^4 m^3 at a temperature of 6°C could be filled with the gas at a pressure of 120 kPa?

20. The volume of a certain mass of a gas is doubled at 22°C. In order to restore the gas to its original pressure, what should be the new Celsius temperature of the gas?

21. Air is a mixture of many gases. The partial pressure of nitrogen is 80.0 kPa. The partial pressure of oxygen is 20.3 kPa. Atmospheric pressure is 101.3 kPa. What is the partial pressure due to all the other gases present in air?

22. The total pressure of a mixture of hydrogen, helium, and argon is 99.3 kPa. If the partial pressure of helium is 42.7 kPa and the partial pressure of argon is 54.7 kPa, what is the partial pressure of hydrogen?

23. If oxygen is collected over water at 18°C and standard pressure, what is the partial pressure of the oxygen when the water level inside the flask equals the water level outside the flask?

24. A student collects 45.0 mL of hydrogen over water at 19°C and 104.2 kPa. What would be the volume of the dry hydrogen at STP?

25. If 80.0 mL of oxygen are collected over water at 20°C and 95.0 kPa, what volume would the dry oxygen occupy at STP?

26. In an experiment a student collects 107 mL of hydrogen over water at a pressure of 104.8 kPa and a temperature of 31°C. What volume would this hydrogen occupy when dry at STP?

27. A student collects 100 mL of oxygen over water at 100.7 kPa and 21°C. What is the partial pressure of the oxygen?

28. A sample of argon gas having a volume of 200 mL at 98.0 kPa and 26°C is collected over water at the same temperature. What is the new volume of the dry gas if the atmospheric pressure is 98.0 kPa?

29. One litre of a gas at 100 kPa and $-20°C$ is compressed to half a litre at $40°C$. What is its final pressure?

30. A sample of a gas occupies a volume of 119 mL at STP. To what temperature must the sample be heated to occupy a volume of 92 mL at 225 kPa?

31. A gas mixture consists of 60.0% argon, 30.0% neon, and 10.0% krypton by volume. If the pressure of this gas mixture is 80.0 kPa, what is the partial pressure of each of the gases?

32. If 2.00 L of dry nitrogen at STP are collected over water at $20°C$ and 95.0 kPa, what volume will be occupied by the wet gas?

33. What volume would 250 mL of pure, dry oxygen at STP occupy if collected over water at $20°C$ and at an atmospheric pressure of 98.0 kPa?

34. If 450 mL of hydrogen at STP occupy 511 mL when collected over water at $18°C$, what is the atmospheric pressure?

35. What are two main causes of the increase in pollution in recent years?

36. The carbon dioxide content in the atmosphere at one time was kept constant because the amount of carbon dioxide entering the atmosphere was equal to the amount of carbon dioxide leaving the atmosphere. What process injected carbon dioxide into the atmosphere, and what processes removed carbon dioxide from the atmosphere? What fairly recent factor has disturbed this carbon dioxide balance?

37. What is a good definition of a pollutant?

38. Evidence exists that the average global temperature has fallen $0.2°C$ between 1940 and 1967. To what do we attribute this temperature decrease?

39. What is the main effect of an increasing amount of carbon dioxide in the atmosphere?

40. What is a thermal inversion?

41. What is the main cause of photochemical smog?

42. Describe the factors that operate to give Los Angeles such a severe photochemical smog problem.

43. Free radicals are involved in the production of photochemical smog. What feature of the structure of free radicals makes them so reactive?

44. What are the major sources of the following air pollutants?
   a) oxides of nitrogen
   b) ozone
   c) carbon monoxide

45. Suppose you are disturbed by the odour of some small animals you keep in a cage in your room. Comment on each of the possible solutions to your problem:
   a) Place a fan in the window to blow out the bad air.
   b) Spray a pleasant scent into the room to make it smell better.
   c) Clean the cage every day.
   d) Spray a disinfectant into the room to kill the germs.
   e) Install a device to pass the room air through activated charcoal.
   f) Install an air conditioner to cool and recirculate the room air.

46. Use the postulates of the kinetic molecular theory to explain why the pressure of a gas decreases when the volume of the gas increases.

47. Use the postulates of the kinetic molecular theory to explain why the volume of a gas increases when the temperature of the gas increases.

48. Complete the following table:

P_{OLD}(kPa)	V_{OLD}(L)	T_{OLD}(K)	P_{NEW} (kPa)	V_{NEW}(L)	T_{NEW}(K)
100	200	300	200	?	300
100	200	300	?	800	300
200	300	400	200	?	200
200	300	400	200	600	?
300	100	200	300	100	?
300	100	200	?	100	400

49. When a bottle of ammonia is opened, the odour is eventually detected across the room. Explain this in terms of the kinetic molecular theory. If molecules have the velocities of rifle bullets, why don't you smell the ammonia immediately after the bottle is opened?

50. You partially fill a balloon with helium and release the balloon to the atmosphere. As the balloon ascends, will it expand, contract, or remain the same size? Explain.

51. The barrel of a bicycle pump usually becomes warm when it is used to inflate a tire. Explain this observation in terms of kinetic molecular theory.

52. Fig.1-9 shows a model in which ball bearings illustrate the movement of gas molecules. In what ways does the behaviour of this model differ from that of a real gas?

53. A concentration of 1 μg/kg of ethylene (C_2H_4) in the air cannot be smelled. It has no effect on people, animals, or materials, but it injures growing orchids and makes them unfit for sale. Is ethylene a pollutant? Should its level in the atmosphere be controlled? What factors would you consider in formulating your answers?

54. If most of the world's population suddenly turned to the burning of coal as a source of energy, what would be the effect on the air environment? Would using coal to produce energy be a change for the better or for the worse?

55. It is frequently difficult to force an industry that is polluting the atmosphere to comply with clean air standards. What arguments might a company executive make to justify continuing air pollution by the company? What arguments might a pollution control board make to justify allowing the pollution to continue?

56. Can the speed of a given molecule in a gas double at constant temperature? Explain your answer.